Clifford's
Family

To Shane Stalling

ISBN 978-0-545-21585-5

20 19   15 16 17

Printed in the U.S.A. 40
This edition first printing, September 2010

Clifford's
Family

Norman Bridwell

SCHOLASTIC INC.

New York   Toronto   London   Auckland
Sydney   Mexico City   New Delhi   Hong Kong

I'm Emily Elizabeth, and this is my dog.
His name is Clifford.

We live in a small town now, but we were both born in the city.

One day we went back to visit
our old home in the city.

CITY
10 MI

Clifford hadn't seen his mother since he was a tiny puppy.
She hardly knew him.

She still treated him like a puppy.
She checked his teeth.

And she looked at his ears to see if he had been washing them.

The man told us where Clifford's brother and sisters lived. We went to find them.

Clifford's sister, Claudia, lived nearby.
She was taking her owner for a walk.

We went to the park with them. A taxi was blocking the crosswalk.

Clifford took care of that.

Next we found his brother, Nero.
Nero was a rescue dog at a fire station.

While we were there, the alarm rang. We followed the fire truck. Nero rushed into the building.

Clifford helped him.

Nero was very brave.

Then we set off to the country. Clifford's other sister, Bonnie, was a farm dog.

One of Bonnie's jobs was to herd sheep into their pen.

Clifford wanted to do some farm work too.

He started to drive the cows toward the barn.

One of the cows was a bull, and
bulls don't like the color red.

Clifford wasn't scared—he was smart.
He didn't want to hurt the bull,
so he jumped out of the way.
When Clifford jumps, he really jumps!

We had one more place to visit. It was
Clifford's father's home in a town nearby.

The house was small, and there were
a lot of kids playing in the yard.

Clifford's father didn't have a collar, or a dog
dish, or a doghouse. But he seemed very happy.

I guess it was the kids. He sure loved kids.
He was a lot like Clifford, just a little smaller.

Clifford wished his family could come and live with us. But they all had people who needed them...

...just as I need Clifford, the best dog of all.

www.wadsworth.com

wadsworth.com is the World Wide Web site for Wadsworth and is your direct source to dozens of online resources.

At *wadsworth.com* you can find out about supplements, demonstration software, and student resources. You can also send e-mail to many of our authors and preview new publications and exciting new technologies.

wadsworth.com
Changing the way the world learns®

FROM THE WADSWORTH SERIES IN PRODUCTION

Albarran, Alan B., *Management of Electronic Media*

Alten, Stanley, *Audio in Media*, 5th Ed.

Armer, Alan A., *Writing the Screenplay*, 2d Ed.

Eastman, Susan Tyler, and Douglas A. Ferguson, *Broadcast/Cable Programming: Strategies and Practices*, 5th Ed.

Gross, Lynne S., and Larry W. Ward, *Electronic Moviemaking*, 4th Ed.

Hausman, Carl, Lewis B. O'Donnell, and Philip Benoit, *Announcing: Broadcast Communicating Today*, 4th Ed.

Hausman, Carl, Philip Benoit, and Lewis B. O'Donnell, *Modern Radio Production*, 5th Ed.

Hilliard, Robert L., *Writing for Television and Radio*, 7th Ed.

Mamer, Bruce, *Film Production Technique: Creating the Accomplished Image*, 2d Ed.

Meeske, Milan D., *Copywriting for the Electronic Media*, 3d Ed.

Morley, John, *Scriptwriting for High-Impact Videos: Imaginative Approaches to Delivering Factual Information*

Viera, Dave, *Lighting for Film and Electronic Cinematography*

Zettl, Herbert, *Sight Sound Motion*, 3d Ed.

Zettl, Herbert, *Television Production Handbook*, 7th Ed.

Zettl, Herbert, *Television Production Workbook*, 7th Ed.

Zettl, Herbert, *Video Basics*, 3d Ed.

Zettl, Herbert, *Video Basics Workbook*, 3d Ed.

Zettl, Herbert, *Zettl's VideoLab 2.1* CD-ROM

Video Basics 3

Herbert Zettl

San Francisco State University

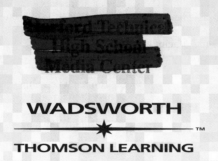
WADSWORTH
™
THOMSON LEARNING

Australia ■ Canada ■ Mexico ■ Singapore
Spain ■ United Kingdom ■ United States

Radio-TV-Film Editor: Karen Austin
Executive Editor: Deirdre Cavanaugh
Editorial Assitant: Aimee Lilles
Publisher: Clark Baxter
Executive Marketing Manager: Stacey Purviance
Project Editor: Cathy Linberg
Print Buyer: Mary Noel
Permissions Editor: Joohee Lee
Production Service: Gary Palmatier, Ideas to Images
Photo Researcher: Roberta Broyer
Copy Editor: Elizabeth von Radics
Illustrator: Robaire Ream, Ideas to Images
Cover Designer: Gary Palmatier
Cover Images: Poleng Hong, Kevin Jun, and Sean Phillips
Cover Printer: Phoenix Color
Compositor: Ideas to Images
Printer: Courier, Kendallville

The audio signature used on the cover and title page of this book represents the spoken words *Video Basics* as they are digitally represented in Adobe Premiere, a nonlinear video-editing program.

The photo credits shown on page 414 of this book are an extension of this copyright page.

The company Image and Imagination, Inc., or Triple-I, is entirely fictitious, and any resemblance to an actual video studio is unintended.

ExamView® and *ExamView Pro*® are registered trademarks of FSCreations, Inc. Windows is a registered trademark of Microsoft Corporation used herein under license. Macintosh and Power Macintosh are registered trademarks of Apple Computer, Inc., used herein under license.

Library of Congress Cataloging-in-Publication Data
Zettl, Herbert.
    Video basics 3 / Herbert Zettl. — 3rd ed.
       p.   cm.
    Includes bibliographical references and index.
    ISBN 0-534-52624-1
    1. Television cameras. 2. Cinematography. 3. Television—Production and direction. I. Title: Video basics three.
II. Title.

TR882.5. Z483 2000
778.59—dc21   00-026332

For more information, contact
Wadsworth/Thomson Learning
10 Davis Drive
Belmont, CA 94002-3098
USA

For information about our products, contact us:
Thomson Learning Academic Resource Center
1-800-423-0563
http://www.wadsworth.com

International Headquarters
Thomson Learning
International Division
290 Harbor Drive, 2nd Floor
Stamford, CT 06902-7477
USA

UK/Europe/Middle East/South Africa
Thomson Learning
Berkshire House
168-173 High Holborn
London WC1V 7AA
United Kingdom

Asia
Thomson Learning
60 Albert Street, #15-01
Albert Complex
Singapore 189969

Canada
Nelson Thomson Learning
1120 Birchmount Road
Toronto, Ontario M1K 5G4
Canada

Dedication

To Alex

About the Author

HERBERT ZETTL is professor emeritus of Broadcast and Electronic Communication Arts at San Francisco State University, where he teaches in the areas of video production and media aesthetics. Prior to joining the SFSU faculty, he worked at KOVR (Sacramento-Stockton) and as a producer-director at KPIX, the CBS affiliate in San Francisco. While at KPIX he won an Emmy Award (shared with two colleagues from the San Francisco chapter of the National Academy of Television Arts & Sciences) for innovation in entertainment shows. Zettl has participated in a variety of CBS and NBC network television productions and is currently engaged in various experimental television productions. He was recently inducted into the prestigious Silver Circle of the National Academy of Television Arts & Sciences, Northern California chapter, for outstanding contributions to the television profession. Zettl has also been a consultant on television production and media aesthetics for universities and professional broadcasting operations here and abroad.

Zettl's other books include *Sight Sound Motion* and *Television Production Handbook*, both of which, along with this book, have been translated into other languages. His numerous articles on television production and media aesthetics have appeared in major media journals in this country as well as in Europe and Asia. He has presented key papers on television production and media aesthetics at a variety of national and international communication conventions.

His interactive multimedia CD-ROM, *Zettl's VideoLab 2.1*, published by Wadsworth Publishing Company, has won several prestigious awards, among them the Macromedia People's Choice Award, the New Media INVISION Gold Medal for Higher Education, and INVISION Silver Medals in the categories of Continuing Education and Use of Video.

Preface

DESPITE THE RADICAL TECHNICAL CHANGES from analog to digital equipment, the fundamental objective of *Video Basics 3* remains unchanged from the previous two editions: to show ways of generating worthwhile ideas and translating them into effective video messages.

In this edition, I have included all essential information about digital concepts, equipment, and production techniques, while keeping the material easily accessible and manageable within the time limit of a single semester. This book should give the beginning student a solid foundation for practicing the art of video production, regardless of whether the majority of equipment is analog or digital. I hope that my focus on the *basics* of video will not be misconstrued as implying that video production is simple or easy; yet overwhelming the student in the beginning with a great amount of equipment and production details is unnecessary and, ultimately, counterproductive.

VIDEO BASICS 3 FRAMEWORK

All too often enthusiastic newcomers to video production forget that manipulating equipment is less important than having something worthwhile to say. To show that significant ideas and efficient production processes must precede the use of tools for their encoding, *Video Basics 3* moves from idea and production process to the tools and techniques necessary to bring about the production and, finally, to the production environment and the talent who perform within it.

Specifically, the content is divided into four parts: *Part I* takes a look at production processes and people and at how to generate ideas. *Part II* deals with analog and digital image creation and control. It explains the tools and processes necessary to create effective pictures and sound. *Part III* concentrates on video recording, switching, and editing. Finally, *Part IV* discusses talent as well as the studio and field production environments.

VIDEO BASICS 3 KEY FEATURES

Video

Video is used throughout this text as a more inclusive term than *television*. Many of today's productions are done outside the traditional television station environment for nonbroadcast purposes. *Video,* then, is not meant to distinguish commercial from noncommercial, or highly artistic creations from routine programs; it encompasses the full range of today's electronically delivered moving images, from what we normally call television to corporate productions and multimedia content.

Basics

This book covers concepts, tools, and activities essential to getting started in video production without prior knowledge of the field. If some explanations and descriptions seem more complicated than others, it is because those specific production aspects are more intricate. In any case, the "key concepts," highlighted throughout the text, are intended to reinforce the essential ideas.

Analog and Digital

Today digital technology is an integral part of video production equipment and processes. In some cases the production processes will be the same, regardless of whether analog or digital equipment is used. For example, a digital camcorder is not radically different from an analog one, either in looks or handling. In other processes, such as editing, digital technology has changed not only the equipment and its use, but the entire production concept. Nonlinear editing is not simply an improvement over computer-assisted linear editing; rather, it is an entirely new approach, requiring a totally new way of thinking and performing shot selection and sequencing. An even more radical development is that video images are no longer dependent on the video camera, but can be computer-generated as well. Such synthetic image creation is mentioned in the contexts of special effects, interactive video, multimedia, and virtual reality. Synthetic digital audio and video image making has become an essential activity in video production as well as in film.

Aesthetics

Because *Video Basics 3* is designed as a well-rounded learning tool, the aesthetic principles of video production are extensively featured throughout the text. This emphasis on aesthetics should help you understand not only *how* to achieve a specific video or audio effect, but also *why*. The basic aesthetic principles remain valid despite rapid and often radical changes in production tools and are therefore relevant and readily applicable to the many types of video productions.

Support Materials

The *Video Basics 3 Workbook* retains the successful features of the first edition. It can be used to test student retention and retrieval of the basics of video production and also serve as a primer for actual studio or field work. I use the *Workbook* as a diagnostic tool for advanced production students as well. Having students do various problems at the beginning of the semester (without the aid of the text) quickly reveals the strong and weak points of their production knowledge and skills.

Zettl's Video Lab 2.1 (ZVL) is an interactive CD-ROM that provides students with a truly individual, private, and nonthreatening learning experience. Combined with *Video Basics 3*, it becomes a powerful instructional ally: Students can manipulate production equipment in a virtual studio or field environment and apply numerous studio and field production techniques from the text. Each chapter of *Video Basics 3* contains specific references to the ZVL learning and practice modules.

A GUIDE TO LEARNING WITH *VIDEO BASICS 3*

Here are examples of some of the key features of *Video Basics 3:*

Production Model

The effect-to-cause production model, introduced in chapter 1, is designed to make video production maximally effective and efficient. It also serves as a tool for the evaluation of various production steps.

Synthetic Video

The creation by computer of synthetic (noncamera) video and audio and the various aspects of virtual reality have become an important aspect of video production and are, therefore, discussed in addition to more-traditional production methods.

Multimedia and CD-ROM

More and more video production is done not only for on-the-air or cable transmission to a mass audience, but also for the creation of CD-ROM multimedia programs, distributed to highly select audiences. These processes are introduced where appropriate. At key points in *Video Basics,* students are prompted to the corresponding sections of *Zettl's Video Lab 2.1* through a **READY ZVL** cue, giving them the option to switch to the CD-ROM or wait until the end of the chapter to do the CD exercises. There, the various "RUN ZVL" cues guide them to the desired learning module and explain the principal learning objective.

Studio and Field Productions

Modern television requires us to move freely among multicamera studio and single-camera field productions. Both production techniques are integrated throughout the book.

Key Terms

The key terms in each chapter appear at the beginning of the chapter and reappear as part of the glossary. They are intended to prepare the reader for the terminology in each chapter and serve as a quick reference as needed. The key terms appear in *bold italic* in the text in the context in which they are defined.

Key Concepts

The key concepts are intended to reiterate and emphasize the major ideas and issues in each chapter. They also facilitate the connections among communication purpose, people, equipment, and various production processes.

ACKNOWLEDGMENTS

As with the first two editions of *Video Basics,* I had generous help from many knowledgeable people with this third edition. First and foremost, I am greatly indebted to the "A-Team": Karen Austin, radio, television, and film editor; Cathy Linberg, project editor; Deirdre Cavanaugh, executive editor; and Stacey Purviance, executive marketing manager. Karen managed to keep up my spirits throughout the difficult process of writing such a book. Gary Palmatier and Robaire Ream of Ideas to Images performed their magic and turned my manuscript pages and scribbles into this handsome book. My admiration and high praise for such high professional skills extends to Elizabeth von Radics for her meticulous and knowledgeable copy editing. Ed Aiona contributed many excellent photos to this edition and helped to bridge the ideas and images. Many thanks also to Bobbie Broyer, who obtained many hard-to-get product shots.

I am especially grateful to Dr. Paul S. Rose, University of Utah, who went through the manuscript with great care and helped me clarify complex technical information. I am also much indebted to the following video production experts, who carefully reviewed *Video Basics 2* and recommended a number of improvements for this edition: Karl Bardosh, New York University; Robert Clark, Missouri Southern State College; Marco Dominguez, Butler University; Jim Dove, Arizona State University; Gerald Gibson, Elon College; Craig Kauffman, Pennsylvania State University; Susan Kehoe, George Mason University; Sue Lawrence, Marist College; John Mackerron, Towson State University; Lawrence Mullen, University of Nevada, Las Vegas; Ron Osgood, Indiana University; Fred Owens, Youngstown State University; Paul Rose, University of Utah; Doug Underwood, Central Missouri State University; and Susan Brown Zahn, Indiana State University.

Also thanks to the following reviewers of previous editions: Peter Gershon, University of West Florida; August Grant, University of Texas at Austin; James Keener, University of Hartford; Michael Korpi, Baylor University; Gary Larson, North Dakota State University; Danita McAnally, Amarillo College; Michael Ogden, University of Hawaii at Manoa; Collin Pillow, University of Arkansas, Little Rock; and John Walsh, Black Hills State University, South Dakota.

Finally, my sincere thanks to my colleagues in the Broadcast and Electronic Communication Arts Department of San Francisco State University for sharing their expertise with me—John Barsotti, Ron Compesi, Marty Gonzales, Joshua Hecht, Jerry Higgins, Hamid Khani, Phil Kipper, and Winston Tharp—as well as the following people and organizations: Phil Arnone, Ed Cosci, and Ronald Louie of KTVU, Oakland–San Francisco; Hal Morrison and Jay Warner of Panasonic; Ken Kaplan of KRON-TV, San Francisco; and Michael Fellner and Ben Jenkins of nmtv (National Mobile Television).

I am grateful to the following people who appeared in this edition's photographs: Socoro Aguilar-Uriante, Karen Austin, Gabriella Bolton, Ken Baird, Rudi Benzler, William Carpenter, NeeLa Chakravartula, Christine Cornish, Ed Cosci, Poleng Hong, Michael Huston, Olivia Jungius, Akiko Kajiwara, Hamid Khani, Fawn Luu, Orcun Malkoclar, Johnny Moreno, Anita Morgan, Celeste Mulzer, Genevieve Mulzer, Regina Mulzer, Einat Nov, Cathy Palmatier, Richard Piscitello, Ildiko Polony, Kerstin Riediger, Joaquin Ross, Algie Salmon-Fattahian, Alisa Shahonian, Mike Vista, Andrew Wright, and Arthur Yee.

A big hug for my wife, Erika, whose patience and encouragement helped me get through this extensive revision.

Herbert Zettl

Contents

PART I
Production Processes and People   1

CHAPTER **1** **The Production Process**   4

THE EFFECT-TO-CAUSE PRODUCTION MODEL   6
Basic Idea   8
Desired Effect: Defined Process Message   8
Cause: Medium Requirements   10
Script Formats   12
Real Effect: Actual Process Message   16
Evaluation   16

GENERATING IDEAS   19
Clustering   20
Brainstorming   20

CHAPTER **2** **The Production Team: Who Does What When?**   26

TEAM MEMBERS   28
Preproduction Team   28
Production Team   30
Postproduction Team   30

PASSING THE BUCK   32

TAKING AND SHARING RESPONSIBILITY   36

PRODUCTION SCHEDULE   38
INTERVIEW TIME LINE   38
PRODUCTION SCHEDULE: MAY 25—INTERVIEW (STUDIO 1)   39

PART II

Image Creation and Control

43

CHAPTER **3** ## Digital Video   46

BASIC IMAGE FORMATION   47

Scanning Process   48

Digital Television Scanning Systems   51

PRIMARY COLORS OF VIDEO   51

WHAT IS DIGITAL?   52

The Difference Between Analog and Digital   52

WHY DIGITAL?   54

Quality   54

Compression and Signal Transport   54

Effects and Picture Manipulation   55

CHAPTER **4** ## The Video Camera   58

BASIC CAMERA FUNCTION AND ELEMENTS   59

Function   60

The Lens   61

Beam Splitter   65

Imaging Device   66

Viewfinder   67

TYPES OF CAMERAS   68

Studio Cameras   69

HDTV Cameras   71

ENG/EFP Cameras   72

Consumer Camcorder   73

What's the Difference?   75

CHAPTER **5**   **Looking Through the Viewfinder**   78

FRAMING A SHOT   **80**
  Aspect Ratio   80
  Field of View   82
  Vectors   84
  Composition   85
  Psychological Closure   92

MANIPULATING PICTURE DEPTH   **95**
  Defining the Z-axis   96
  Lenses and Z-axis Length   97
  Lenses and Depth of Field   97
  Lenses and Z-axis Speed   99

CONTROLLING CAMERA AND OBJECT MOTION   **100**
  Controlling Camera Movement and Zooms   100
  Controlling Object Motion   102

CHAPTER **6**   **Operating the Camera**   108

BASIC CAMERA MOVEMENTS   **110**

CAMERA MOUNTS AND HOW TO USE THEM   **114**
  The Handheld and Shoulder-Mounted Camera   114
  The Tripod-Supported Camera   117
  The Studio Pedestal   121
  Special Camera Mounts   123

OPERATIONAL FEATURES   **126**
  White-balancing   126
  Focusing   127
  Zooming   130

GENERAL GUIDELINES   **131**
  CHECKLIST: CAMCORDERS AND ENG/EFP CAMERAS   *132*
  CHECKLIST: STUDIO CAMERAS   *133*

CHAPTER **7** **Light, Color, Lighting** 138

LIGHT **140**

Types of Light 140

Light Intensity 140

Contrast 141

SHADOWS **142**

Attached Shadows 142

Cast Shadows 145

Falloff 146

COLOR **147**

Additive and Subtractive Color Mixing 147

The Color Television Receiver and Generated Colors 148

Color Temperature and White-Balancing 148

LIGHTING INSTRUMENTS **150**

Spotlights 151

Floodlights 154

LIGHTING TECHNIQUES **158**

Operation of Lights 158

CHECKLIST: LIGHTING SAFETY 158

Studio Lighting 160

Field Lighting 165

GUIDELINES: FIELD LIGHTING 169

Measuring Illumination 170

CHAPTER **8** **Audio and Sound Control** 176

SOUND PICKUP PRINCIPLE **178**

MICROPHONES **179**

How Well They Can Hear: Sound Pickup 179

How They Are Made 181

How They Are Used 183

SOUND CONTROL **194**

The Audio Mixer 194

The Audio Console 196

Cables and Patch Panel 197

SOUND RECORDING   200

Analog Recording Equipment   200

Digital Recording Equipment   202

SYNTHESIZED SOUND   205

SOUND AESTHETICS   206

Environment   206

Figure-Ground   206

Perspective   207

Continuity   207

Energy   208

CHAPTER **9**   **Video Effects**   212

STANDARD ELECTRONIC VIDEO EFFECTS   214

Superimposition   214

Key   215

Wipe   218

DIGITAL EFFECTS   220

Digital Image Manipulation Equipment   220

Common Digital Video Effects   221

Synthetic Image Creation   223

Animation   226

PART III

Video Recording, Switching, and Editing   228

CHAPTER **10**   **Video Recording**   230

VIDEOTAPE-RECORDING SYSTEMS   232

Tape- and Disk-Based Recording Systems   232

Basic Videotape Tracks   232

Composite, Y/C Component, and RGB Component Systems   235

Types of Videotape Recorders   237

Time Base Corrector   238

Tape Formats   239

VIDEOTAPE-RECORDING PROCESS   240

THE "BEFORE" CHECKLIST   240

THE "DURING" CHECKLIST   243

THE "AFTER" CHECKLIST   246

NONLINEAR STORAGE SYSTEMS   **247**

     Computer Disks   247

     Electronic Still Store System   248

     Read/Write Optical Discs   248

     CD-ROMs and DVDs   248

USE OF VIDEO RECORDING   **249**

     Interactive Video   249

     Multimedia   250

CHAPTER **11**   **Switching and Postproduction Editing**   254

SWITCHING, OR INSTANTANEOUS EDITING   **256**

     Basic Switcher Layout   256

     Multifunction Switchers   258

     Switcher Operation   260

POSTPRODUCTION EDITING   **265**

     Linear Editing Systems   265

     Nonlinear Editing Systems   274

     Editing Preparations   276

     PRODUCTION TIPS TO MAKE POSTPRODUCTION EASIER   *278*

     Off-line and On-line Editing   282

CHAPTER **12**   **Editing Principles**   290

EDITING PURPOSE   **291**

EDITING FUNCTIONS   **292**

     Combine   292

     Condense   292

     Correct   293

     Build   293

AESTHETIC PRINCIPLES OF CONTINUITY EDITING   **294**

     Mental Map   294

     Vectors   298

     On- and Off-screen Positions   303

AESTHETIC PRINCIPLES OF COMPLEXITY EDITING   **309**

     Intensifying the Event   309

     Supplying Meaning   311

PART IV

Talent and the Production Environment 316

CHAPTER **13** **Talent, Clothing, and Makeup** 318

PERFORMING TECHNIQUES   320
Performer and Camera   320
Audio and Lighting   322
Timing and Prompting   323

ACTING TECHNIQUES   330
Environment and Audience   331
Small Screen and Close-ups   332
Repeating Action   332

AUDITIONS   333

CLOTHING   333
Texture and Detail   334
Color   334

MAKEUP   335
Technical Requirements   335
Close-ups   335
Materials   336

CHAPTER **14** **Production Environment: The Studio** 340

THE VIDEO PRODUCTION STUDIO   342
Physical Layout   342
Major Installations   345

THE STUDIO CONTROL ROOM   346
Image Control   347
Sound Control   351

MASTER CONTROL   352

STUDIO SUPPORT AREAS   353
Scenery and Property Storage   353
Makeup   354

SCENERY, PROPERTIES, AND SET DRESSINGS   354

Scenery   354

Properties   358

Set Dressings   359

SET DESIGN   359

Process Message   359

Floor Plan   360

Prop List   362

Using the Floor Plan for Setup   362

Evaluating the Floor Plan   363

CHAPTER **15   Field Production and Synthetic Environments**   368

ELECTRONIC NEWS GATHERING   370

News Gathering   370

Transmission   371

ELECTRONIC FIELD PRODUCTION   373

EFP Preproduction: Remote Survey   373

Production   377

CHECKLIST: FIELD PRODUCTION EQUIPMENT   377

Postproduction: Wrap-up   382

BIG REMOTES   383

SYNTHETIC ENVIRONMENTS   385

Computer-Generated Settings   385

Virtual Reality   386

Interactive Video   386

Epilogue   390

Selected Readings   391

Glossary   395

Index   407

Photo Credits   414

C O N T E N T S

CHAPTER 1

The Production Process

CHAPTER 2

The Production Team: Who Does What When?

Production Processes and People

IMAGINE that you are an intern at Triple-I, a company that specializes in producing a variety of corporate video programs, such as instructional and promotional videotapes and general commercials that range from advertising breakfast cereals to political candidates. Triple-I has also produced several award-winning MTV programs. In your first meeting, somebody tells you that the most important thing to learn during your internship is how to move from idea to the finished production efficiently and effectively.

What follows will give you some suggestions on how to move from the initial idea to the finished production in a systematic way, with a minimum of wasted effort, time, and money.

actual process message The real effect of the program on the viewer.

defined process message The desired effect of the program on the viewer.

documentary script format A script that indicates major video cues in the left column and partial or fully scripted dialogue and major audio cues in the right column. Also called *two-column script.*

drama script format A script that contains complete dialogue or narration and major action cues. Also called *single-column script.*

effect-to-cause model Moving from idea to desired effect on the viewer, and then backing up to the specific medium requirements to produce such an effect.

medium requirements All personnel, equipment, and facilities needed for a production, as well as budgets, schedules, and the various production phases.

news script format A script that indicates in the left column who is on-camera, the kind and length of videotape inserts, and special effects; the right column shows all the words spoken by the newscaster as well as the audio in- and out-cues of the videotape inserts.

postproduction Any production activity that occurs after the production. Usually refers to either videotape editing or audio sweetening.

preproduction Preparation of all production details.

process message The message actually received by the viewer in the process of watching a video program.

production The actual activities in which an event is videotaped and/or televised.

script Written document that tells what the audience will see and hear.

The Production Process

WHEN watching old movies in which a producer appears, you may get the idea that producers always smoke cigars, never take off their hats, and that their main job is to quarrel with writers about ideas and with stars about money. This image of producers and their activities couldn't be farther from the truth. Today's producers seldom smoke cigars or wear hats, and their main concerns are not in arguing with star performers but in coordinating a great many production details.

One minute, as a producer, you may consult with the writer about the script; the next you may be busy trying to find a reasonable sanitary service to deliver portable facilities for the on-location cast and crew. Both activities are equally important in the production process. The head of the Triple-I production company tells you that a good producer is not the one who comes up with some grand idea once in a great while, but rather the one who works diligently and leaves nothing to chance. A good producer is a stickler for detail. Even if you have a superb team of experienced production people, you need to double- and triple-check with everybody about whether the assigned tasks are accomplished at the specified time. The credo of a good producer is to triple-check everything.

 KEY CONCEPT 1   **A good producer triple-checks everything.**

Over the years certain routines—production processes—have developed that can facilitate your complex coordination job as a producer and help you keep on top of things. These processes include a variety of chores you need to do *before* the production, *during* the actual production activities, and *after* the production. In production lingo, we speak of the preproduction, production, and postproduction phases.

In **preproduction** you develop the initial program idea, define the type of audience you would like to have receive your program, and select the people and equipment necessary to translate your initial idea into effective video and audio images. Meticulous preproduction is a key factor in maximizing your video production efficiency and effectiveness.

In **production** you actually translate, or *encode,* the original program idea into a television program. Production involves the operation and coordination of production and technical people and a variety of production equipment.

In **postproduction** you select the best program bits and pieces, enhance their picture and sound quality as necessary, correct some of the minor production mistakes, and then assemble the shots and scenes into a coherent whole—the television program. For complicated programs that require a great deal of editing, the postproduction phase takes the longest.

READY ZVL 1 *Note: ZVL 1* stands for segment 1 of *Zettl's Video Lab 2.1* CD-ROM. You can run each segment after the "ready ZVL" cue or all segments after having read this chapter. See "Zettl's Video Lab 2.1" at the end of this chapter.

You should now be able to answer Triple-I's question of how you would move from initial idea to the finished video production: from preproduction to production and then to postproduction. But what about Triple-I's request for specific production steps and how to make them effective and efficient? To answer these questions, you need to learn more about an approach—a model—that will guide you in achieving these admittedly difficult goals. This is called the *effect-to-cause production model.* Here are some of the specific ideas we will discuss in this chapter:

■ **THE EFFECT-TO-CAUSE PRODUCTION MODEL**
Basic program idea; defined effect on the viewer; medium requirements (cause), including equipment, facilities, and people; script formats; actual effect on the viewer; and evaluating the actual effect

■ **GENERATING IDEAS**
Clustering and brainstor ming

THE EFFECT-TO-CAUSE PRODUCTION MODEL

Like any conceptual model, the ***effect-to-cause model*** is not a foolproof system that works every time you use it, but it can help you decide on the essential steps for a variety of productions and on how to streamline the various production phases. It is based on the realization that the only message that actually counts is not the one you start with but the one that is perceived by the viewer. This process is a little bit like cooking: The final success of your undertaking is not measured by what ingredients you used (the initial idea), but whether your guests like to eat it (the message actually received). Wouldn't it make sense, then, to start with an idea of how the meal should finally look and taste and then figure out what ingredients you need to make such a meal?

1.1

EFFECT-TO-CAUSE MODEL

The effect-to-cause model shows how to move from show idea to the finished program with maximum efficiency.

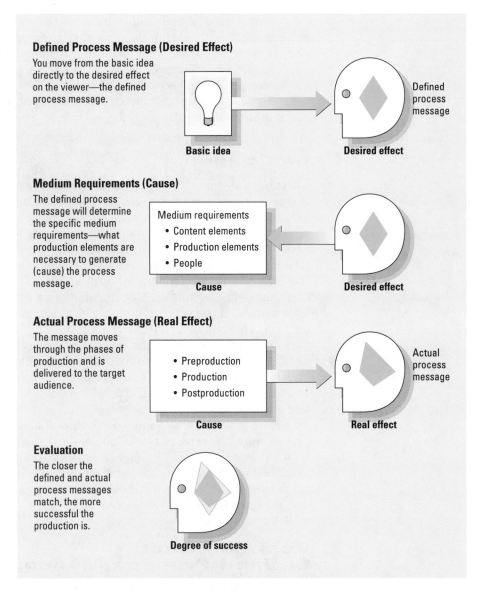

Defined Process Message (Desired Effect)

You move from the basic idea directly to the desired effect on the viewer—the defined process message.

Basic idea — Desired effect — Defined process message

Medium Requirements (Cause)

The defined process message will determine the specific medium requirements—what production elements are necessary to generate (cause) the process message.

Medium requirements
• Content elements
• Production elements
• People

Cause — Desired effect

Actual Process Message (Real Effect)

The message moves through the phases of production and is delivered to the target audience.

• Preproduction
• Production
• Postproduction

Cause — Real effect — Actual process message

Evaluation

The closer the defined and actual process messages match, the more successful the production is.

Degree of success

The effect-to-cause production model works on the same principle: Once you have developed the initial program idea, you move directly to what, ideally, you want the viewers to learn, feel, or do.[1] The model suggests that you jump from the initial idea to a definition of the desired effect. Then, and only then, do you back up and decide on the medium elements necessary to produce the intended communication effect. Because the actual message is generated by the process of viewers watching a video program, this message is called the ***process message***. Like the completed meal, the process message is the only communication effect that actually counts. **SEE 1.1**

---

1. Although the sources cited in this chapter are quite old, they are classics that are unmatched in helping unlock creative ideas and shaping them into effective communication. This concept of the effect-to-cause production model is similar to the writing of instructional objectives. See Robert Mager, *Preparing Instructional Objectives,* 2d rev. ed. (Belmont, Calif.: Lake Publishing Co., 1984).

As you can see, the effect-to-cause model shows four distinct processes: (1) to move from the basic idea to the defined process message (desired effect on the viewer); (2) to determine what medium requirements are necessary to generate the defined effect (the cause); (3) to take the actual process message through the production phases; and (4) to evaluate the actual effect and see to what extent the defined process message and the actual process message overlap. Let's discuss these elements in detail.

Basic Idea

You must have some idea of what meal to prepare before starting to cook. The same is true in video production. Running around and taking pictures with your camcorder before deciding on what it is you want to tell your viewers is a wasteful activity at best. An effective production process depends on a fairly clear idea of what you want to communicate. For example, suppose you have just moved to Big City, and your daily commute prompts you to "do something about these crazy Big City drivers." You are certainly not ready at this point to plunge into production. Changing your idea to "do a documentary on the crazy Big City drivers" is no improvement. If you were proposing such a documentary to the Triple-I people, they would probably ask you what the documentary is all about and why you chose the documentary format in the first place. You need to think more about what exactly you want your viewers to learn through your program about becoming better drivers. The more precise your definition of the intended effect—the *process message*—the easier it is for you to decide on the necessary appropriate production format and procedures.

Note, however, that an initial production idea is usually vague and rarely concise enough to serve as a definition of the desired communication effect. This way of thinking is perfectly normal. As a matter of fact, you should engage in some initial brainstorming about the various program possibilities before defining the desired process message. But you should not move on to specific production details without a precisely defined process message.

Desired Effect: Defined Process Message

To "do something about the crazy Big City drivers" is a noble cause, but it says little about how to go about it. It probably implies that you want to help the drivers become more disciplined, responsible, and courteous and to use television to do so. This is a tall order. You may well decide that you need to devote a whole program series to this goal, rather than a single program, to even partially achieve such a large and difficult task. If so, each program should feature a highly specific learning objective for the viewers. As in most learning tasks, specific objectives are usually more effective than general ones, and small steps are more easily managed by the learner than large ones.

Rather than attack all the bad habits of the "crazy Big City drivers," you can now isolate a single problem that is especially bothersome to you and that you consider important. For instance, you may find that the misuse or nonuse of turn signals has become a serious threat to traffic safety. Rather than attack all the bad habits of Big City drivers all at once, you can now isolate a single objective: to persuade the drivers to make proper use of turn signals. All you need to do now is restate this objective a little so that it can serve as a ***defined process message*** (the desired effect): *The process message should demonstrate to Big City drivers the proper use of turn signals and persuade them to use turn signals accordingly.*

This statement has all the necessary ingredients of a useful process message. It defines the desired audience *(Big City drivers)* and what you want the viewers to learn, feel, or do. In this case, you want them to learn when and how turn signals should be used *(demonstrate…the proper use of turn signals),* and then motivate them to use the turn signals *(persuade them to use turn signals accordingly).* Such precise information will help you greatly in deciding just what the program should contain and how to go about making it. We will return to this example in the context of medium requirements later in this chapter.

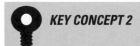

KEY CONCEPT 2   **The defined process message describes the desired communication effect.**

But what do you do when the program objective is much broader or when you want to reach a general rather than a specific audience? Do you still need to come up with a process message? Yes, you do, except that the process message in this case will not be as precise as in the turn signal case. Even a more general process message will give you a clue as to what facilities and people you will need to translate the basic idea into an actual video program.

For example, you may have a sincere desire "to produce a video on the homeless," in order to make the people who have comfortable homes more aware of what it means to be homeless. You will probably think of a documentary that shows people sleeping in the street or on park or subway benches, or pushing shopping carts that hold all of their possessions. You may have some scenes in mind that contrast the homeless against more fortunate members of society, such as elegantly dressed people rushing past the homeless, on their way to some gala performance.

Although you may have many such powerful images in mind, what exactly is it that you want viewers to feel, learn, or do? Is the documentary approach the most appropriate program format to achieve this effect? You can't really answer these questions until you have a more precise idea of the program effect—some kind of process message. Here is one possibility: *The process message should make viewers experience, at least temporarily, what it feels like to be homeless.*

Compared with the turn signal program, this process message is less precise. The audience is much more general (*viewers* instead of *Big City drivers*), and the desired effect is to generate a feeling (to *experience…what it feels like to be homeless*) rather than to accomplish a learning task (to *demonstrate…the proper use of turn signals*). But this process message nevertheless contains significant production clues. The main objective is to make us *feel,* at least for a moment, what it is to be homeless. To learn various statistics about the number of homeless in your city, or how many use public shelters, is much less important than generating empathy, a feeling that reaches into the life of the homeless. This statement opens up new production approaches.

Rather than show a great number of homeless people, you could follow a specific individual for one day and focus on the many problems this person encounters and the frustrations and fears connected with being homeless. The problem with this approach is that people who are not homeless will have a hard time really feeling what this person is going through. To generate real empathy, you may opt to show not a longtime street person, but rather someone who recently became homeless. For example, how would you feel if during a first-time visit to a large city far from home you had your wallet or purse stolen? All of a sudden, you have no money, no identification, no credit cards, no idea of where you are. You have become homeless. Most people you see ignore you or become suspicious and walk away when you ask for help. Fortunately, you remember your long-distance credit code; but the first public phone you find is out of order. The second one works, but connects you with your friend's answering machine. It gets dark and chilly and begins to rain. You can take it from there.

As you can see, even this relatively general process message has opened up new possibilities for approaching the subject and contains some clues to the medium requirements necessary to translate this idea into a television program. You have made a big step toward fulfilling Triple-I's creativity requirement. In addition, your creative efforts are not random, but centered around a specific theme or task. What follows will help you with Triple-I's second major requirement of "exceptional production efficiency and effectiveness."

Cause: Medium Requirements

Once you know what you want to do, you must finally do it. The most ingenious program idea is worthless if it remains in your head. We have now arrived at the production, or "cause," step in the effect-to-cause model (refer to figure 1.1). This translation step is what we normally call *production*. It involves the effective and efficient use of the various *medium requirements*, such as content elements (defined process message, audience analysis, script), equipment and other facilities (cameras, lighting, sound equipment, videotape recorders, editing equipment, studio or field location, and so forth), and people (who work in front of and behind the camera). Just selecting these various medium elements requires a thorough knowledge of what the production people do and what production equipment you need to accomplish the stated communication task. The overall guide to production requirements and specific procedures is, once again, a clearly stated process message.

Without going into too much detail, let's see what the process message of properly using turn signals can tell us about major medium requirements. Here it is again: *The process message should demonstrate to Big City drivers the proper use of turn signals and persuade them to use turn signals accordingly.*

This process message clearly states who the intended audience is (Big City drivers) and what the major content of the show is all about (demonstrate the use of turn signals and persuade drivers to do likewise).

Target audience   Because you are dealing with a learning task (to help drivers use turn signals properly), you need to know as much as possible about the target audience—Big City drivers. The more you know about the target audience, the easier it is for you to decide on what to show and how to show it in order to generate the desired process message.

In this case, you would have to learn all about the driving and living habits of Big City drivers. Do the majority of them actually ignore turn signals? If so, in what situations? This type of information will tell you what examples to use in the video presentation. How can you reach most efficiently the majority of the target audience? Showing the program when most of the target audience is on the road will certainly not help your mission.

Producers of commercial advertising do extensive audience research before moving from the process message to the medium requirements. They would certainly want to know the percentage of male and female drivers in Big City, the various age groups of the drivers, their income levels, education, what kind of work they do, and especially where they live. They would also like to know the driving habits of people who don't commute. These data will give the researchers a *demographic profile* of the typical Big City driver.

If the process message is totally persuasion-oriented, as in commercial advertising, the producers are also interested in what and how much television the target audience watches; what movies they see; what newspapers, magazines, and books they read; what music they listen to; what clothes they wear; what they buy and where they buy it; and so forth. This information on the target audience's general lifestyle provides the producers with *psychographic* data. Such audience analysis is especially important when you are designing a program that is distributed by on-the-air telecast or cable. If you are engaged in corporate or instructional video production, the audience is much more clearly defined. If, for instance, the process message is to help new bank employees cash a check, or third-graders learn the multiplication tables, you do not have to draw up demographic or psychographic profiles. Nevertheless, you need to find out when and under what circumstances the audience will be viewing the program. The more you know about the target audience, the easier it will be to translate the defined process message into medium requirements, and the more efficient the whole production process becomes. The Triple-I people will be happy to hear this.

Now you need to translate your good intentions and process message into an actual video program. Such a translation process requires a clear idea of what you want to show and say—the *content*—and what *equipment, facilities,* and *people* you need to produce the program that will cause the actual process message to occur.

Content To show good or bad driving habits, you need to be out on the streets in traffic. You could, for example, videotape rush hour traffic, point out how many drivers change lanes or turn without bothering to use turn signals, and then explain the potential danger of such omissions. You could then set up driving situations in which you show the benefits of using turn signals properly. By now a detailed *shooting script* is definitely in order. You will read more about the various script formats later in this chapter.

When writing the script, you must consider two more factors: *money* and *time*. Despite your good intentions and desire to rival in your production the style of an elaborate Hollywood movie, you will not succeed unless you have the Hollywood budget and production time to match. Money and time are production factors as real as cameras and microphones. You simply cannot do a six-camera show when you have only two available; likewise, you cannot do a million-dollar production if you have only five hundred to spend. If you have only four weeks to complete a show, don't write, or use, a script that requires on-location shooting in different parts of the world and two months of postproduction.

Equipment and facilities   We already know that most of the production will happen "on location" rather than in a studio. This factor is important in selecting the equipment necessary for a field production of this type. A major portion of this book is devoted to helping you learn exactly what equipment you would need for such a shoot and for the various postproduction tasks.

People   A good script will also help you decide on how many and what kind of production people you need. But, irrespective of the specific process message, you must have a producer who is in charge of the whole production, a director who is responsible for and guides the day-to-day production activities, various assistants, and a skilled production crew. You also need "talent"—people who appear on-camera, do the voice-over narration, or portray various traffic experts if the script calls for that. Finally, you need people who drive the demonstration cars and others who help you facilitate the production.

You can now see why even a simple production can run into quite a bit of money, assuming you have to pay for all the people and equipment involved. It also requires careful planning and coordination of a great variety of people and machines.

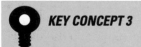

KEY CONCEPT 3   **The medium requirements include content elements (defined process message, audience analysis, script), production elements (equipment, facilities, schedules), and people (talent, nontechnical and technical production people).**

Script Formats

As you can see, the *script* is an important document that interprets the show idea into what the viewers should actually see and hear when watching the program. The script is similar to a recipe that lists the major ingredients of the program and how those elements must be mixed to get the desired result. In the language of the effect-to-cause production model, the script helps you translate the process message into specific medium requirements. Although you may not intend to become a script writer, you must be familiar with the basic script formats used in video production so that you can help make this translation process as efficient and effective as possible.

Despite considerable variations, there are three basic script formats for various video productions: (1) the documentary script format, (2) the news script format, and (3) the drama script format.

Documentary script format   Because this type of script is used for a variety of the nondramatic, *documentary script format* is also known as *two-column script*. The left column contains all video information, and the right column lists all audio information. **SEE 1.2**

1.2

DOCUMENTARY, OR TWO-COLUMN, SCRIPT FORMAT

In the two-column script format, the left column contains all video information, and the right column shows all audio information. The dialogue or narration is fully scripted.

VIDEO	AUDIO
MS Kipper in interview set	KIPPER: Is the problem of not using turn signals really as bad as it is made out to be? I must admit, I don't use mine that often either. So I took a ride with Lieutenant Hewitt during rush hour. What I saw will surprise you . . .
VTR #1 VO	It certainly surprised me . . .
SOT	IN-CUE: "OOPS, HE ALMOST HIT THIS CAR . . ."
	OUT-CUE: ". . . WELL, LIEUTENANT, YOU CERTAINLY TAUGHT ME A LESSON."
CU Kipper in interview set	KIPPER: In this short 10-minute ride, I have seen seven near-misses caused by drivers cutting in and out of traffic without signaling.
	This may not be valid scientific proof, but it was enough to change my mind. The question is still why we don't use our turn signals more often. Lieutenant Hewitt has some ideas about that . . .
VTR #2 SOT	IN-CUE: "PEOPLE ARE JUST IN TOO MUCH OF A HURRY . . ."
	OUT-CUE: ". . . BASIC LACK OF DRIVER COURTESY."
CU Kipper in interview set	KIPPER: What this tells me is that we are barking up the wrong tree. Instead of trying to make drivers use turn signals more often, we should stress good, old-fashioned driver courtesy.

Note that in the audio column, all audio cues, including the names of the talent speaking the lines, are written in uppercase letters. All spoken words are written in the normal upper/lowercase style. The instructions in the video column uses both upper- and lowercase letters. Some script writers maintain the uppercase-only convention because these words are not spoken. Because the upper/lowercase lettering is much easier to read, however, you will find that most scripts use that style for the video column. If there is a considerable amount of ad-libbing to be done by the talent, the audio column indicates only who is speaking and approximately what about; such a script is generally called a *partial two-column script.* **SEE 1.3**

1.3

PARTIAL TWO-COLUMN SCRIPT FORMAT

The partial two-column script shows all video information in the left column, but only partial dialogue or narration in the right column. The questions are usually fully scripted, but the answers are only partially described.

VIDEO	AUDIO
	KATY:
CU of Katy	But the debate about forest fires is still going on. If we let the fire burn itself out, we lose valuable timber and kill countless animals, not to speak of the danger to property and the people who live there. Where do you stand, Dr. Hough?
	DR. HOUGH:
Cut to CU of Dr. Hough	(SAYS THAT THIS IS QUITE TRUE, BUT THAT THE ANIMALS USUALLY GET OUT UNHARMED AND THAT THE BURNED UNDERBRUSH STIMULATES NEW GROWTH.)
	KATY:
Cut to two-shot	Couldn't this be done through controlled burning?
	DR. HOUGH:
	(SAYS YES, BUT THAT IT WOULD COST TOO MUCH AND THAT THERE WOULD STILL BE FOREST FIRES TO CONTEND WITH.)

News script format   The only thing the formats of news scripts from two different newsrooms have in common is that they are, more or less, two-column. In a *news script format,* the right column contains the spoken words of the reporter or anchor, plus the out-cues of the words of previously recorded news segments. The left column contains cues to who is talking; the name, number, and lengths of the various recorded news clips; some shot designations; and whether the recorded insert is to be played with a *voice-over (VO)* of the anchor describing what is happening on the video insert, or with *SOT (sound-on-tape)*—the actual sounds that are recorded on the videotape insert. **SEE 1.4**

1.4

NEWS SCRIPT FORMAT

The news script is also a two-column format. The left column contains such production information as who is on-camera, the kind and length of videotape inserts, and special effects. The right column shows every word spoken by the newscaster as well as the audio in- and out-cues of the videotape inserts.

MARY O/C [on-camera]	NANOTUBES WILL MAKE OUR FASTEST COMPUTERS SEEM LIKE DINOSAURS. PROFESSOR ALEXANDER OF THE UNIVERSITY OF CALIFORNIA HAS UNVEILED THE FIRST SUPERFAST COMPUTER . . . DRIVEN SOLELY BY NANOTUBES INSTEAD OF SILICON CHIPS. IS SILICON VALLEY IN TROUBLE?
VTR # 1 MARY VO	TEN YEARS OF INTENSIVE RESEARCH HAVE FINALLY PAID OFF FOR THE ALEXANDER RESEARCH TEAM AT BERKELEY. THEY BUILT A COMPUTER THAT IS ABOUT THE SIZE OF A MATCHBOX AND A THOUSAND TIMES FASTER THAN THE BEST THAT SILICON VALLEY CAN MUSTER.
SOT	IN-CUE: "The secret is nanotubes . . ." OUT-CUE: ". . . will make silicon chips totally obsolete."
MARY O/C	PROFESSOR ALEXANDER THINKS THAT THIS IS JUST THE BEGINNING . . .

What newswriters don't seem to agree on is just how to format the audio column. Most use capital letters for the spoken words, but some prefer upper/lowercase letters; others use a combination of both. Although it is actually harder to read words written entirely in capital letters, it was long the preferred way of formatting news copy. Typing all words in capital letters with typewriters and teletype machines (which sent copy over telephone wires to electronically activated typewriter terminals) was faster than when using upper/lowercase, and the copy was easier to read on the early teleprompter systems. The word processor and computerized telepromting systems, however, have all but eliminated these handicaps; as a result, more and more news copy today is written in the traditional upper/lowercase documentary script format.

Drama script format   Also known as *single-column script,* the ***drama script format*** contains the complete dialogue, narration over video, and all major action cues in one column. **SEE 1.5**

As you can see, all names of characters (VICKIE, YOLANDA) and audio cues (THEME #2) are written in capital letters. All spoken dialogue (or narration over a scene) is written in upper/lowercase letters. Specific delivery cues (surprised) and directions (getting a chair) are also written in upper/lowercase letters but are clearly isolated from the dialogue by parentheses or brackets. You will, however, find scripts in which these instructions are written in capital letters. The specific shots (close-ups, two-shots) are usually omitted and left for the director to add in the script preparation.

Real Effect: Actual Process Message

Regardless of how much planning and preparation you put into cooking a meal, it is successful only if somebody enjoys eating it. So it is with video production. No matter how much effort you put into a production and how carefully you follow the defined process message, the only thing that really matters is whether the production has the desired effect on the target audience. The closer the ***actual process message***—the message the viewer perceives in the communication process—is to the defined process message, the more successful the production.

Evaluation

If you were to ask a number of television producers how they evaluate their shows, they would probably give you some vague answers: "Well, I just see whether a certain scene works or not," or, "If it feels right, it's usually OK." Others might tell you that they ask their neighbors how they liked the show—or that they don't have time to do formal evaluations. As in any other creative endeavor, the "right feel" for something is an important and often useful criterion. But when asked to be maximally efficient in your production, you need more-precise methods of evaluation. As usual, the effect-to-cause model is of some help.

1.5

DRAMA, OR SINGLE-COLUMN, SCRIPT FORMAT

The single-column drama script contains every word of characters' dialogue and occasional descriptions of their major actions.

SCENE 6

SKY ROOM. TABLE BY THE BANDSTAND.

THEME #2

We hear the last bars of dance music. The band is taking a break. ALAN and YOLANDA are coming back to their table to join STUART, who has been watching them dance. During their dance, VICKY joined STUART and is now sitting in ALAN'S chair.

                    ALAN
                  (surprised)
            You're sitting in my chair.

                    VICKY
    Oh, it's YOUR chair? No wonder it felt so good. But I didn't see any
    name on it. You know—reserved for . . . what's your name again?

                    ALAN
                    Alan

                    VICKY
                  Alan who?

                    ALAN
          Alan Frank . . . like in frank!

                    VICKY
          Reserved for Mr. Alan Frank!

                    STUART
              Dr. Alan Frank

                    VICKY
    Oh, DOCTOR! What are you a doctor of?

                    STUART
          (getting an extra chair for Alan)
          He's a doctor of philosophy.

                    VICKY
                  (laughing)
    A doctor of philosophy? You look like one!

                    ALAN
          What's that supposed to mean?

Formative evaluation   To have some control over the building of your show, you need to check every major phase *during* the production and see whether you can proceed to the next step or whether you must back up to improve the previous one. This procedure is often called *formative evaluation.*

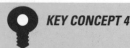

KEY CONCEPT 4   **Formative evaluation is the evaluation of each production phase while the production is in progress.**

Before moving to the medium requirements, for example, you should reexamine the original program idea and especially the definition of the process message. Does it contain all the necessary and useful elements, such as target audience and the desired communication effect? Is it precise enough to guide you toward the production steps? If yes, you can move on to the medium requirements; if not, you need to do more thinking about what it is you want to accomplish with the production.

When moving to the medium-requirement section of the model, you first examine whether you really need all the equipment and people you have listed. If you had to cut your budget severely, what would you eliminate? Could you still function properly in light of the defined process message, or would you have to come up with a new one?

Summative evaluation   This step includes the final evaluation of the finished production and, more important, the true effect of the production on the intended audience—the actual process message.

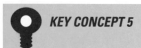

KEY CONCEPT 5   **The summative evaluation is the final evaluation of the finished production and its actual effect on the audience.**

When you are done with a video production, you need to look at it as objectively as possible and evaluate it in the context of the defined process message. Does the production seem to trigger the desired communication effect? With all due respect to your keen judgment and evaluation skills, the ultimate success of the production depends on its real effect on the viewer. The closer the actual and defined process messages match, the more successful the communication.

Be aware that your final evaluation is easily influenced by what you know about the production and the various major and minor production crises you had to overcome. For instance, you may be dismayed over a missed shot, even if the one that is in the show is perfectly appropriate. In any case, don't ever apologize for a missed shot or sound effect; once you have committed yourself to showing your production in public, you must stand solidly behind it. After all, your show is judged by the shots that are on the tape, not by the ones you may have missed.

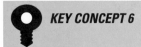

KEY CONCEPT 6　　**The closer the actual and defined process messages match, the more successful the communication.**

The problem with this type of summative evaluation is that it is very hard to assess the actual effect of a program on a large, general audience. This is why rating services are content with projecting the number of viewers rather than measuring the program's impact. The problem with ratings is that we have erroneously come to equate the number of viewers with the quality of the program and a good match between defined and actual process messages.

When you have a small, highly specific audience—such as high-school or college students taking a particular class—a summative evaluation is much easier to do. In this case, you can simply have the students fill out a questionnaire at the end of the program. Although such a response is much harder to get from the audience of an over-the-air telecast, you could still try to solicit responses by telling the audience what you want and where to write, e-mail, or call. By asking the right questions, you can assess the emotional impact of your show, at least to a certain extent. Once your television system is interactive, audience responses to the perceived impact of your program are much more feasible.

Although the effect-to-cause production model cannot guarantee a perfect production, it can guide you to a reasonably effective approach without a lot of trial and error. Properly applied, it should certainly help you meet Triple-I's requirement of making the "production process maximally efficient and effective." *READY ZVL 2*

GENERATING IDEAS

But that's not all. There is one more condition put forward by the Triple-I people. They would like you to eventually combine production efficiency and effectiveness with "exceptional creativity" in generating significant project ideas and in translating those ideas into effective video programs. This condition is a tall order. You could argue that creativity is difficult to define and that the creative process remains largely a mystery. But such an argument is unlikely to be viewed as creative—and you would probably not score too highly as a new intern.

In video production, creativity means coming up with good ideas on a relatively consistent basis and according to a strict time schedule. You need to be able to call up your creativity on demand, as often the clock dictates when to be creative. The production schedule will not allow you to wait for a natural inspiration or creative spark.

You need to develop some practical techniques that will help ignite your imagination and inventiveness on cue. These techniques may not generate creativity, but they will help you unlock creative ideas buried somewhere inside you, help bring them into your consciousness, and make them readily available.

Two well-known and often-used devices for unlocking ideas are *clustering*[2] and *brainstorming*.[3]

Clustering

Take a piece of paper and, in the middle of the page, write a single word that seems somehow central to your basic program idea or process message and circle it. Now write down and circle another word that is somehow associated with your key word and connect the two with an arrow. Write down other word associations and connect them to the last one circled.

In a short time, you will have created a cluster of words or ideas. Don't try to *design* a cluster or be logical about it. Work fast so that you will not be tempted to ponder over your associations. Let your mind flow freely. When you feel that your ideas are exhausted, don't force yourself to find more connections or more-logical ones. According to Gabriele Rico, one of the clustering pioneers, the idea cluster has a natural limit.[4] You will probably know when you have enough branches and when it is time to stop. Once you are at that point, look at the finished diagram and search for possible patterns. These patterns will inevitably reveal some novel connections and relationships that were not obvious before. They will likely provide you with new insights. **SEE 1.6**

These cluster patterns can serve as springboards for the general program idea, the process message, and the medium requirements. If one word or phrase is especially intriguing yet seems out of place, start a new cluster—but leave the old one alone.

Although clustering is basically a solitary activity, you can also do team clustering. In this case, the team members design their individual clusters, but then share and compare them. Such sharing produces new patterns and new clues to various relationships and ideas and, ultimately, to new process messages and their productions.

Brainstorming

A friend tells you that the Triple-I people engage frequently in brainstorming or, as one Triple-I member calls it, "conceptual blockbusting."[5] By freely tossing around all sorts of ideas, regardless of whether they make any immediate sense, they hope to break through the usual conceptual blocks and generate novel ideas and approaches. She describes one of their usual brainstorming procedures as follows.

---

2. "Clustering" as an idea-unlocking technique was developed by Gabriele Lusser Rico in *Writing the Natural Way* (Los Angeles: J. P. Tarcher, Inc., 1983).

3. See James L. Adams, *Conceptual Blockbusting*, 3d ed. (Reading, Mass.: Addison-Wesley, 1990).

4. Rico, *Writing the Natural Way*, pp. 28–37.

5. Adams, *Conceptual Blockbusting*. See also Robert H. McKim, *Experiences in Visual Thinking*, 2d ed. (Boston: PWS Engineering, 1980).

CLUSTERING

Note that clustering starts with a central idea and then branches out in various directions, depending on what you consider connected to it. Once you have listed the connections most apparent to you, stop. The cluster will then suggest new ideas or novel approaches to old ideas. It may also trigger new clusters.

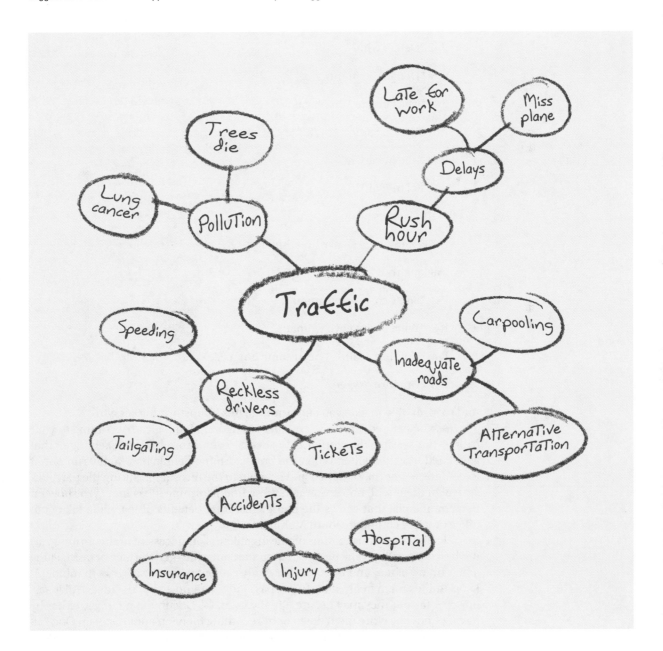

Ten or twelve people sit in a circle. In the middle of the circle is a small audiotape recorder. One of the people (P-1 = person 1) starts with:

P-1: "Knock, knock!"

P-2: "Who's there?"

P-3: "Denali."

P-4: "Denali who?"

P-5: "Denali the mountain."

P-6: "Must be the Himalayas."

P-7: "Alaska. Same as McKinley."

P-8: "The president."

P-9: "All thin air!"

P-10: "Politics again."

P-1 (again): "No. Heavy breathing!"

(All laugh)

P-2: "Snow cave—cave man."

P-3: "What about cave woman?"

P-4: "Not that again—I need some hot tea."

P-5: "Or more oxygen."

And so forth. (If you like, you can continue this brainstorming session.)

As you can see, the idea sequence is anything but logical. According to your friend, the session developed into several even more bizarre exchanges that generated much laughter. When the brainstorming people had finally run out of ideas and energy, they stopped and listened to the recording. During the playback several of them took notes. Some of these brainstorming ideas may well show up in a commercial that shows the energy-restoring benefits of tea while taking an office break or climbing Mount McKinley.

Triple-I's session contains all the ingredients of successful brainstorming: (1) It is best done with several people. (2) You start out with a general idea or task (selling a new brand of tea) and then let everybody call out whatever springs to mind. (3) Let all minds roam freely, and do not pass judgment on any of the ideas. All ideas, however far-out they may be, are equally valid. (4) Document all ideas, either by having someone write them down or by recording them on audiotape. (5) Once all ideas are documented, the team reviews what was said and looks for relevant ideas or associations.

This technique is similar to clustering, except that during a clustering session you create a *visual* pattern that reveals some of the interrelationships of the various ideas. Brainstorming may generate ideas of greater variety and profusion than clustering, but they are trickier to pattern and more difficult to use in defining a process message or in translating it into a video experience. 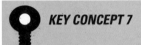 *READY ZVL 3*

 KEY CONCEPT 7　　**Successful clustering and brainstorming depend on a free, intuitive, and noncritical flow of ideas.**

To make sure that you will not miss any of the important production aspects when talking with the Triple-I producer, let's go over the main points in this chapter. Or, to borrow the favorite and frequent advice of the senior director to the production crew: "Once again, remember . . ."

ONCE AGAIN, REMEMBER...

▦ Production Process

This process is divided into three phases: preproduction, production, and post-production. In preproduction the program idea is developed and the medium requirements (people, equipment, and facilities) are determined. Production involves coordination, production, technical people, and a variety of production equipment. In postproduction the best program bits and pieces are selected and put into a coherent whole—the video program.

▦ Effect-to-Cause Production Model

This model shows how to move from the basic program idea to the definition of the intended effect on the viewer and how this defined process message dictates what medium elements (people, equipment, and facilities) to use to generate—cause—the intended effect. The script is an essential element in charting how to move from idea to the finished product. The model also implies evaluating the production process and the actual effect on the viewers. The more closely the actual process message (real effect) matches the defined one, the more successful the production.

▦ Generating Ideas

In video production, creativity means coming up with good ideas on a consistent basis within strict time and budget limits. Two helpful methods are clustering and brainstorming. Clustering means connecting in a graphic fashion words that are somehow related to a central idea. The finished cluster contains important clues to formulating the basic idea and defining the process message. Brainstorming is a free, noncritical expression of ideas that may or may not have anything to do with the basic program idea. It frees the mind from set patterns.

Z E T T L ' S   V I D E O   L A B   2 . 1

Now, let's run the Zettl's Video Lab segments you readied. In many cases, the various segments will be interactive and will let you actually practice with equipment or choose among several possibilities. After loading a tape, click on the title above the list of modules to play the introduction to that tape. The quizzes will give you immediate feedback. At the least, the segments will help you learn and aid you in retrieving the knowledge you already acquired from this book.

RUN ZVL 1

Click on the **process** monitor and load tape 1 **Meet Herb**. Herb, a longtime executive producer, is concerned that you keep in mind that video productions inevitably involve selection and judgment. Mind especially his advice to exercise responsibility whenever you subject the audience to your video messages.

Go back to Master Control and load tape 2 **Phases**. Click on **PHASES** to play the introduction to this tape. This tape reinforces the importance of each of the three production phases. As you can see, preproduction is the key to a successful and efficient production process. Although Herb tells you that one of the functions of postproduction is to correct mistakes, it is much easier to fix mistakes during rather than after the production. Although not specifically mentioned at this point, audio postproduction is often more important and more time-consuming than video postproduction.

RUN ZVL 2

Go back to Master Control, load tape 3 **Effect-to-Cause**, and play the introduction. Here you see how another program idea—Telebytes—is developed into the final production and how the production is evaluated. Note that this segment points, again, to the importance of a precise process message *before* producing this idea for a specific audience. Try to come up with a different, and perhaps more precise, process message. How, if at all, would it influence your production phase? The overall benefit of such a production model is that it helps make your production extremely efficient.

RUN ZVL 3

Tape 4 **Ideas** should stimulate you to do some clustering and brainstorming with a friend to see the benefits of such idea-generating techniques. Both techniques need practice to become effective. Even if you don't have too much initial success, don't give up. You may be surprised by the positive results after a few tries.

KEY CONCEPTS

- A good producer triple-checks everything.

- The defined process message describes the desired communication effect.

- The medium requirements include content elements (defined process message, audience analysis, script), production elements (equipment, facilities, schedules), and people (talent, nontechnical and technical production people).

- Formative evaluation is the evaluation of each production phase while the production is in progress.

- The summative evaluation is the final evaluation of the finished production and its actual effect on the audience.

- The closer the actual and defined process messages match, the more successful the communication.

- Successful clustering and brainstorming depend on a free, intuitive, and noncritical flow of ideas.

above-the-line Category for nontechnical personnel, such as producers, directors, and talent. Also used as a budget category.

below-the-line Category for technical personnel, including camera operators, floor persons, and audio engineers. Also used as a budget category.

floor plan A diagram of scenery, properties, and set dressings drawn on a grid.

postproduction team Normally consists of the director, a video editor, and, for complex productions, a sound designer who remixes the sound track.

preproduction team Consists of people who plan the production. Normally includes the producer, writer, director, art director, and technical supervisor, or TD. Large productions may include a composer and a choreographer. In charge: producer.

production schedule A time line that lists the start times of major production events. Also called *time line*.

production team Consists of a variety of nontechnical and technical people, such as producer and various assistants (associate producer and PA), the director and assistant (AD), and the talent and production crew. In charge: director.

The Production Team:
Who Does What When?

IF you are a painter, you can do everything yourself: come up with the idea, buy the materials, prepare the canvas, struggle with form and color, and finally sign and date the finished work. You could even do the selling without any other people involved. The entire creative process is under your control.

This is not the case in video production, unless you are simply videotaping your vacation adventures. Although you could possibly do a simple production all by yourself, professional productions usually involve a group of people—a production team—each member performing a clearly defined function. This chapter will help you understand the roles involved in video production—what the people do and how they work together.

■ THE PRODUCTION TEAMS
The preproduction team, the production team, and the postproduction team

■ PASSING THE BUCK
What happens when production people do not work as a team

■ TAKING AND SHARING RESPONSIBILITY
What happens when production people know their functions and work as a team

■ PRODUCTION SCHEDULE
How to set up an effective time line for the production

You may best understand who does what by dividing the team into people involved in the *preproduction, production,* and *postproduction* phases. The preproduction team includes people primarily involved with the planning of the production; the production team is made up of people who translate the ideas into actual video pictures and sound; and the postproduction people put all the various videotape segments together and give the whole production the final polish.

Some production people are involved in only one of these phases; others may be involved in all three of them. As you can readily see, no single individual has complete control over the entire creative process. Unlike the painter, you must learn to work as an effective team member, which means that you know exactly what is expected of you when assigned to a specific production position, and also what everybody else is supposed to be doing. Once you know who is supposed to do what, you can establish effective communication among the team members and let them know when specific things need to be done. A *production schedule,* or *time line,* is essential in coordinating the efforts of all the different team members.

TEAM MEMBERS

The size and makeup of the production team depend on the scope of the production. You will find that a specific production away from the studio, called *electronic field production (EFP),* may need only three people: camera operator, audio- and videotape recorder (VTR) operator, and director. But a live sports telecast may keep thirty people very busy.

Let's find out who is normally involved in the three primary production stages: preproduction, production, and postproduction.

Preproduction Team

The primary responsibility of the **preproduction team** is to develop the idea for the video and plan its production so that the translation process of idea to pictures and sound is as efficient as possible. The people normally involved in this initial idea-generating phase are the producer, writer, director, scene designer or art director, and sometimes the technical supervisor or technical director.

The original idea may come from the corporate manager ("Do a 15-minute videotape showing that the customer is our most precious commodity"), or the producer ("Do a pilot of our new medical series"), or it may come from a concerned citizen ("I would like to do a show on the pros and cons of timber clear-cutting"). Often specific show ideas are the product of several people brainstorming together.

Producer   Once the general idea is born, it is nurtured through all preproduction stages by the *producer,* who states the specific purpose of the show—the process message—and prepares a budget for the entire production.

Once you have the necessary funding, you need to hire and/or coordinate all additional personnel, equipment, and production activities. You or your associate producer will then have to come up with a production schedule that indicates specifically who is supposed to do what and the times when the assigned tasks are to be completed.

Writer   The next step is writing the script. The *writer* interprets the defined process message into a video production and writes down what he or she wants the viewers to see and hear. This production step is obviously a crucial one. It often determines the production format—such as instructional show, interactive multimedia show, or documentary—and the style and quality of the production. The script serves as the guide for all production activities.

Scripts are almost always rewritten several times. Sometimes the original content isn't accurate and needs some corrections. At other times the words sound too stilted and academic when actually spoken, or there may be some shots that are unnecessary or too difficult to produce. For all these reasons, good video writers do not come cheaply. Settle on a fee before delivery of the script.

Director　The *director* translates the script into specific video and audio images and selects the necessary production crew and equipment. The sooner the director is brought into the preproduction process, the better. The director may work with the writer early on, for example, to ensure the most effective interpretation of the defined process message. He or she may even help the writer with the basic approach, such as changing the original idea of producing a brief instructional tape into an interactive multimedia experience, or a documentary into a dramatic format, or a company president's address into a town hall–type forum. The director can also help the art director with ideas about the specific environment in which the event is to take place, or even a specific style of graphics to be used.

Art director　The *art director* uses the script and the director's comments for the set design or the specific location for a show. He or she is also in charge of decorating the set and designing the various graphics, such as titles and charts. The art director must create an environment that fits the overall style of the show and that facilitates the anticipated production procedures. Even the most beautifully designed set is useless if there is not enough room for camera movement and microphones or if it cannot be properly lighted.

The art director prepares a ***floor plan***, which is a diagram of scenery, stage properties (tables, chairs), and set dressings (wall hangings, lamps, plants) drawn on a grid. (See figure 14.14 and its context for a more detailed discussion of the floor plan.) The floor plan is an important preproduction guide for the director. With a good floor plan, the director can visualize the major shots and place the cameras accordingly.

Lighting director　The *lighting director (LD)* can use the floor plan to determine the basic lighting setup before ever entering the studio.

Floor manager　Finally, the floor plan enables the *floor manager* to put up and decorate the set. When the production takes place at a remote location, such as in a hospital hallway or in the corporate manager's office, the art director will probably want to do some rearranging of furniture, wall hangings, or equipment to make the location look good to the video camera rather than to the naked eye. Sometimes a *property manager,* who selects all the props used in the show, is involved in the preproduction process.

Technical director　The preproduction team may also include a *technical director,* or *TD,* especially if the production is complex and happens "in the field." The TD can determine ahead of time the technical facilities necessary for the proposed production. For instance, the TD may want to check on the available electric power, or what lights are needed to boost the illumination in a lecture room. A preproduction technical survey is especially important if the production is to be a live telecast.

Small production companies or television stations often combine the various roles. The functions of the producer and director, and even the writer, might be carried out by a single person—the producer-director—and the floor manager might also act as art director and property manager.

Large productions may also include graphic artists, a costume designer, a composer, and a choreographer on the preproduction team.

Production Team

The actual *production team* consists of a variety of people. The nontechnical members include the producer and various assistants—associate producer (AP) and production assistant (PA)—the director, the associate director (AD) if it is a complex show, and the talent. Whereas the major part of the producer's job is in preproduction, the director is totally involved in the actual production phase.

The production crew, which is made up of technical and nontechnical personnel, normally includes the floor manager and floor persons (grips), the TD (technical director), camera operators, the LD (lighting director), video and audio engineers, the videotape operator, the C.G. (character generator) operator, and the VO (video operator), who adjusts the cameras during the production for optimal video output. In single-camera productions, the camera operator is sometimes also taking care of the lighting. This dual job is carried out by the DP (director of photography)—a carryover from film production. In a large production, there is an additional engineering supervisor as well as various costume people, a property manager, makeup artists, and hairdressers.

Postproduction Team

The *postproduction team* is relatively small and normally consists of a video editor and the director. The editor will try to make sense of the various videotape segments and put them into the order indicated by the script. The director will guide the editor in the selection and sequencing of shots. If you (as the director) have a good editor and a detailed script, you will have relatively little to do. You may want to see a *rough-cut*, or an "off-line" editing version, before you give the editor the go-ahead to prepare the final "on-line" videotape. If the postproduction requires more-complex editing, you may have to sit with the editor throughout the process to select most of the shots and determine their sequence.

Complex postproduction may also include extensive manipulation of sound, called *audio sweetening*. It consists of remixing, adding, or replacing small or large portions of the original sound track and can take more time and effort than editing pictures. Major sound postproduction is done by a *sound designer*.

Most producers do not get involved in postproduction, at least not until the first rough-cut is done. Some producers cannot stay away from the editing room, however, and get intimately involved in every decision. Such fervor is, despite all good intentions, not always appreciated by the editor and director.

The accompanying tables summarize the major *nontechnical* and *technical* personnel and their principal functions. **SEE 2.1 AND 2.2**

Sometimes the production people are divided into *above-the-line* and *below-the-line* personnel. These designations are not clear-cut and have more to do with who pays whom than who does what. In general, *above-the-line* personnel are

2.1

NONTECHNICAL PRODUCTION PERSONNEL

PERSONNEL	FUNCTION
A B O V E - T H E - L I N E	
Executive producer	In charge of one or several programs or program series. Coordinates with client, station or corporate management, advertising agencies, investors, and talent and writer's agents. Approves and manages budget.
Producer	In charge of an individual production. Is responsible for all personnel working on the production and for coordinating technical and nontechnical production elements. Often doubles as writer and director.
Associate producer (AP)	Assists producer in all production matters. Often does the actual production coordination jobs, such as telephoning talent and making sure that deadlines are kept.
Studio and field producers	In large operations, studio and field producers are assigned different producing responsibilities: The studio producer takes care of all studio productions, the field producer of all field productions.
Production assistant (PA)	Assists producer and director during the actual production. Takes notes of comments made by the producer or director during rehearsals, which serve as a guide for the crew to fix minor production flaws before the final taping.
Director	In charge of directing talent and technical operations. Is ultimately responsible for transforming a script into effective video and audio messages. In smaller operations also assumes the producer's responsibilities.
Associate director (AD)	Assists director during the actual production. Often does timing for director. In complex multicamera productions, helps to "ready" various operations (such as presetting specific camera shots or calling for a special graphic effect).
Talent	Refers, not always accurately, to all performers and actors who regularly appear on video.
Actor	Someone who portrays someone else on-camera.
Performer	Someone who appears on-camera in nondramatic activities. Always portrays himself or herself.
Announcer	Reads narration but does not appear on-camera. If on-camera, the announcer moves up into the talent category.
Writer	Writes video scripts. In smaller-station operations or in corporate video, the writer's function is often assumed by the director or the producer or by somebody hired on a freelance basis.
Art director	In charge of creative design aspects of show (set design and location, graphics).
Music director/conductor	Responsible for music group in large productions, such as the band that plays in variety shows. Can also be the person who picks all the recorded music for a specific show or show series.
Choreographer	Arranges all movements of dancers.

2.1

NONTECHNICAL PRODUCTION PERSONNEL *(continued)*

PERSONNEL	FUNCTION
BELOW-THE-LINE	
Floor manager	Also called *floor director* or *stage manager*. In charge of all activities on the studio floor, such as setting up scenery, getting talent into place, and relaying all director's cues to talent. In the field the floor manager is basically responsible for preparing the location for the shoot and for cuing all talent.
Floor persons	Also called *grips, stagehands*, or *facilities persons*. Set up and dress sets. Operate cue cards or other prompting devices. Sometimes operate microphone booms. Assist camera operators in moving camera dollies and pulling camera cables. In small operations also act as wardrobe and makeup people. Set up and ready all nontechnical facilities in the field.
Makeup artist	Does the makeup for all talent (in large productions only).
Costume designer	Designs and sometimes constructs various costumes for dramas, dance numbers, and children's shows (in large productions only). Sometimes classified as above-the-line personnel.
Property manager	Maintains and manages use of various set and hand properties, such as tables, chairs, and office furniture (set properties), and telephones, coffee cups, and flashlights (hand properties)—for large productions only. In smaller operations props are managed by the floor manager.

preproduction and supervisory people; ***below-the-line*** personnel are involved in production and postproduction. **SEE 2.3** *READY ZVL 1*

PASSING THE BUCK

In preparation for your Triple-I internship and to learn as much as possible about the basic workings of the production team, you managed to get permission from a medium-sized local television station to watch the videotaping of a visiting rock group.

When you get to the studio well before the scheduled time for videotaping, the production is already in the wrap-up stage. Neither the musicians nor the production people look too happy. The PA (production assistant) tells you that the taping session had been pushed ahead by three hours because of the band's tight schedule. It becomes obvious that the taping session did not go as planned. There are small groups of people on the studio floor engaged in rather lively discussions. Let's listen in on what they are saying.

In one group, the band manager is complaining about poor scheduling and the "static look" of the show, and the lead singer about the "bad sound." The executive producer tries to appease the band members, while the producer is

2.2

TECHNICAL PRODUCTION PERSONNEL

This category includes engineers who are actually engaged in engineering functions, such as installing and maintaining new electronic equipment; it also includes people who operate such equipment. Because operating much of the electronic equipment, such as cameras, switchers, character generators, and videotape editing machines, does not require engineering knowledge, most of the operation of television equipment is performed by nonengineering personnel.

PERSONNEL	FUNCTION
ABOVE-THE-LINE	
Chief engineer	In charge of all technical personnel, budgets, and equipment. Designs electronic systems, including signal transmission facilities, and overseas installations, day-to-day operations, and all maintenance.
Assistant chief engineer or technical supervisor	Assists the chief engineer in all technical matters and operations. Is often involved in preproduction activities of large productions.
BELOW-THE-LINE	
Technical director (TD)	In charge of all technical setups and operations during a production. Does the actual switching in a studio production. Often acts as technical crew chief.
Lighting director (LD)	In charge of studio and field lighting; normally for large productions only.
Director of photography (DP)	Carryover from film production. Takes care of lighting and camera operation in single-camera productions.
Camera operators	Also called *videographers* or *shooters*. Operate studio and field cameras. Sometimes also do the lighting for a show.
Video operator	Also called *video engineer* or *shader*. Adjusts the camera controls for optimal camera pictures (also called *shading*). Sometimes doubles as maintenance engineer.
Videotape operator	Operates videotape recorders during the production. In small field productions, the audio technician doubles as VTR (videotape recorder) operator.
Videotape editor	Operates videotape editing equipment. Often makes creative editing decisions as well.
Sound designer	In charge of "designing" the sound track of a complex production, such as a drama, commercial, or large corporate assignment. Sometimes listed as above-the-line nontechnical personnel.
Audio engineer	Often called *audio technician*. In charge of all audio operations in production and, in the absence of a sound designer, in postproduction. Operates audio console during the show.
Maintenance engineer	A true engineering position. Maintains all technical equipment and troubleshoots during productions.

2.3

ABOVE-THE-LINE AND BELOW-THE-LINE PERSONNEL

ABOVE-THE-LINE

Production people	Executive producer
	Producer and associates
	Director and associates
	Chief engineer and associates
	Technical supervisor
Idea people	Writer
	Art director
	Composer
	Choreographer
Talent	Performers
	Actors

BELOW-THE-LINE

Technical people	Technical director
	Director of photography
	Lighting director
	Maintenance engineers
Production—technical	Camera operator
	Video operator
	Audio engineer
	Videotape operator
	Videotape editor
Production—nontechnical	Floor manager
	Floor persons
	Grips
	Property manager
	C.G. operator
	Makeup and wardrobe

accusing everybody of not communicating with him. The director defends his overall visual concept and personal style and accuses the musicians of not understanding the "true nature of video." The band manager mutters something about the sloppy contract and the lack of coffee during rehearsals.

Some crew and band members vent their frustrations about technical problems. They argue about which microphones should have been used and where they should have been placed, and about light levels that were much too low and uneven for good pictures. The LD counters by saying that she had practically no time for adequate lighting, mainly because she lost three hours of setup time. The musicians complain that the sound levels were too low, while the camera operators say that the music was too loud and they could not hear the director's instructions in their headsets. They felt lost, especially since the director had not briefed them ahead of time on what shots to get.

The floor manager and his crew wonder why they had no floor plan. It would have prevented them from having to move the heavy platform from place to place until the director was finally satisfied with its location.

Everyone seems concerned with passing the buck and blaming everybody else for the various production problems.

But what should have been done to minimize or avoid these problems? Before reading on, write down the major complaints of the band and production members and, by referring to figures 2.1 and 2.2, try to figure out who should have done what. Now compare your notes with the following recommendations.

Situation: Taping session was pushed ahead by three hours because of the band's tight schedule.

Responsibility: Producer. He should have coordinated the band's schedule more carefully with his production schedule. Moving up a shooting schedule by three hours forces the crew to work unreasonably fast, inviting serious production mistakes.

Situation: The band's manager complains about poor scheduling and the "static look" of the show. The lead singer is unhappy with the sound as recorded.

Responsibility: Again, the producer is responsible for scheduling and should have double-checked with the band manager exactly when the band would be available for the studio production. The "static look" complaint is aimed at the show's director, and the "bad sound" at the audio engineer, who chose the type and position of the microphones and who did the sound mixing. Ultimately, the TD is responsible for all technical processes, including the sound pickup and mixing. The producer should have brought the lead singer, the band manager, and the audio engineer together in the preproduction phase to discuss the particular sound requirements. The producer should also have arranged for the band manager to meet with the director to discuss the visual requirements and the overall "look" of the performance. The director could then have discussed his ideas about the "true nature of video" with the band manager. Even if the initiative did not come from the producer, the director and audio engineer should have pressed for such a meeting. Obviously, there was little communication among the members of the production team. The blame for the sloppy contract goes to the band manager and the executive producer, and the PA should have arranged for coffee.

Situation: The choice of microphones and their placement is being challenged. The band members complain that sound levels of the "foldback"—during which the sound as mixed is played back to the band members—were too low. The camera operators could not hear the director's instructions because of the music's high volume and were without direction.

Responsibility: The type of microphones used and their placement is clearly the responsibility of the audio engineer. As pointed out before, a preproduction meeting with the key members of the band could have prevented most of the sound problems, including the low playback levels, despite the drastically reduced setup time. The intercommunication problems between the director and the camera operators should have been anticipated by the director or the TD. Even the best intercom headsets will not function when used close to high-volume sound sources such as a rock band. The director could have minimized this problem by meeting with the camera operators ahead of time to discuss with them the principal shots for each camera.

Situation: The light levels were too low for good pictures.

Responsibility: The LD is responsible for the low light levels. Her excuse is that the setup time was shortened by a full three hours and she had no floor plan to do even the most rudimentary preproduction planning. But she could have contacted the director during the preproduction stage, or at least two days before the production, and asked about the floor plan and the lighting requirements for the show. In addition, when there is a lack of time it is more sensible to illuminate the set with a generous amount of overall light rather than with highly specific light beams in limited areas. (See chapter 6 for more-detailed lighting techniques.)

Situation: The floor manager and his crew lacked a floor plan, which resulted in needlessly moving a heavy platform.

Responsibility: A floor plan would have told the floor crew the exact location of the platform on which the musicians perform. It would also have helped the LD decide on the basic lighting setup, and the director on the basic camera positions. The lack of a floor plan is a direct result of poor communication among the preproduction team and, therefore, the ultimate responsibility of the producer. The director should have consulted the art director about the set and the floor plan during preproduction, and then asked the art director why the floor plan was not done according to schedule. The TD, LD, and floor manager should have asked the director for the floor plan before the actual production date.

As you can see, a production team can operate properly only if every member is aware of and fulfills his or her specific function. All members must be in constant communication with one another during the preproduction and production phases, and everyone must take full responsibility for the task assigned. More-thorough preproduction could have averted many of these problems.

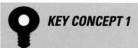

KEY CONCEPT 1   **Know the functions and responsibilities of each member of the nontechnical and technical production staffs.**

TAKING AND SHARING RESPONSIBILITY

Fortunately, a subsequent visit to a Triple-I field production of an MTV segment turns out to be a much happier experience than your studio encounter.

When you get to the location where the MTV shoot is taking place, you find a whole section of the street already blocked off by the local police and you have to show your pass. You find action everywhere. The audio engineer and assistants are adjusting the loudspeakers, and the camera operators are checking out some shots. You are greeted by the floor manager and introduced to the producer and director of the show segment. Despite the bustling activity, the producer seems amazingly calm and takes time out to explain to you what the MTV segment is all about: The lead singer drives an old Cadillac convertible down the street to a stop sign, where the dancers are to mob his car.

Some of the dancers are already practicing their routine, while others are coming out of a large trailer that serves as the talent's makeup and dressing facility. Everybody seems relaxed, and you sense purpose and competence in what each team member is doing. The director checks the schedule, posted by the trailer, and asks the floor manager to call for a run-through. There is instant activity: The dancers take their positions, the car is moved to the starting point, the camera operators get their opening shots, and the audio people start the playback of the specific sound track. So far as you can tell, the run-through goes very smoothly. The crew and talent also seem happy with the outcome. Nevertheless, the director calls for a brief meeting of crew and talent to discuss some production problems.

The PA (production assistant) reads the notes that were dictated to him by the producer and director during the run-through:

☐ "Dancers in the back can't hear music."

☐ "Johnny [the lead singer driving the Cadillac] can't see the mark."

☐ "Shadows too harsh on him when stopped."

☐ "Need a tighter shot of Johnny."

☐ "We should be looking up at Johnny, not down on him."

☐ "Johnny is sweating too much. Light reflects off his nose."

☐ "Lots of dirt in the dancing area."

☐ "We can see audio cables in the background."

☐ "Some dancers are blocking Johnny on a close-up."

Which people would you ask to take care of these minor production problems? Let's look at the notes again.

"Dancers in the back can't hear music."

Correction by audio engineer.

"Johnny can't see the mark."

This means that Johnny can't see the mark on the curb that tells him exactly where to stop the car. The mark has to be moved higher up, to a telephone pole.

Correction by floor manager.

"Shadows too harsh on him when stopped."

Correction by floor persons (grips) under the direction of the LD.

"Need a tighter shot of Johnny."

Correction by director and, ultimately, by camera operator.

"We should be looking up at Johnny, not down on him."

The producer looks at the director. She turns to the specific camera operator.

Correction by director and, ultimately, by camera operator.

"Johnny is sweating too much. Light reflects off his nose."

The director looks at the makeup artist. This problem has nothing to do with lighting.

Correction by makeup artist.

"Lots of dirt in the dancing area."

Correction by floor manager and floor crew.

"We can see audio cables in the background."

The audio engineer says that he will take care of it.

Correction by audio assistant and floor persons.

"Some dancers are blocking Johnny on a close-up."

Correction by director and choreographer.

After this brief meeting, the director calls for a 15-minute "reset" break during which the various production crew members go about correcting the problems mentioned. After the reset period, she checks the production schedule and calls for another run-through. The following three hours are taken up by more rehearsals, two more such brief production meetings (often called "notes"), and several "takes."

The floor manager calls for a "wrap" (the completion of all production activities) a half-hour ahead of schedule.

Contrary to the studio show of the rock band, this MTV field production was obviously well prepared in preproduction. During production the members of the nontechnical and technical staffs knew what they had to do, how to communicate, and how to share responsibilities. The various "notes" meetings were an effective and efficient way to identify major and minor production problems and to make sure that the people responsible took care of them. You may find that in complex productions, some directors schedule as much as one-third of the total rehearsal time for such "notes" meetings and "reset" periods.

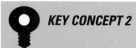

KEY CONCEPT 2   **Establish and maintain effective communication among all production personnel.**

PRODUCTION SCHEDULE

As you recall from the Triple-I MTV field production, the producer, floor manager, and PA periodically checked the schedule to see whether the production was on time. Like the script, a **production schedule**, or *time line*, is essential to proper production coordination. The production schedule can show large blocks of time, such as the various due dates for preproduction, or it can be detailed and show a minute-by-minute breakdown of the actual production activities.

Here is an example of a rather loose production schedule for a 15-minute studio interview with the president of City College.

INTERVIEW TIME LINE

March 1	Confirmation by college president.
March 2	First preproduction meeting. Interview format ready.
March 4	Second preproduction meeting. Script ready. Floor plan ready.
March 5	All facilities requests due, including set and prop requests.
March 9	Production. Studio 1.
March 10	Postproduction, if any.
March 14	Air date.

The time line for this relatively uncomplicated production shows only the major meeting and due dates. Note the four-day lead from the due date for all facilities requests (March 5) to the actual production date (March 9). This lead time is necessary to ensure that the studio and all facilities requested are available.

The schedule for the actual production is much more detailed, and breaks the day into blocks of time for certain activities.

PRODUCTION SCHEDULE:
MAY 25—INTERVIEW (STUDIO 1)

8:00 A.M.	Crew call
8:30–9:00 A.M.	Technical meeting
9:00–11:00 A.M.	Setup and lighting
11:00–12:00 P.M.	Meal
12:00–12:15 P.M.	Notes and reset
12:15–12:30 P.M.	Briefing of guest (Green Room)
12:30–12:45 P.M.	Run-through and camera rehearsal
12:45–12:55 P.M.	Notes
12:55–1:10 P.M.	Reset
1:10–1:15 P.M.	Break
1:15–1:45 P.M.	Taping
1:45–1:55 P.M.	Spill
1:55–2:10 P.M.	Strike

Let's examine more closely each of the scheduled activities.

Crew call   This is the time when all production crew members (floor manager and assistants, TD, LD, camera operators, audio people, and other equipment operators) are expected to show up and start working.

Technical meeting   This meeting includes the major nontechnical and technical people: producer, director, host, PA, floor manager, TD, LD, and audio engineer. The director will briefly explain the process message and how she expects the show to look (bright lighting, fairly tight shots of the college president). This meeting is also to double-check all technical facilities and the scenery and props.

Setup and lighting   According to the floor plan, the setup is relatively easy for the floor manager and his crew. The lighting is routine and does not require any special effects. The two hours allotted should be sufficient for both activities.

Meal   It is important that everybody be back from lunch at exactly 12:00 P.M., which means that everyone has to be able to leave the studio at exactly 11:00 A.M., even if there are still minor setup and lighting details left. Minor adjustments can be made during the reset time.

Notes and reset   If there are no major setup and equipment problems, the period set aside for notes may be considerably shorter. The available time can then be spent on a more leisurely reset, that is, fine-tuning the lighting, moving a plant that may interfere with the person in front of it, cleaning the coffee table, and so forth.

Briefing of guest   While the production crew is getting ready for the first run-through and camera rehearsal, the producer, the interview host, and the PA (and sometimes the director) meet with the college president in the Green Room to go over the aspects of the program. The Green Room is a small, comfortable room specifically set up for such briefing sessions.

Run-through and camera rehearsal   This run-through is to familiarize the guest with the studio environment and procedures, to check on the various camera shots, and to rehearse the opening and closing of the show. It is intentionally brief, to keep the guest as fresh as possible. Because of severe time constraints, news interviews are normally not rehearsed. The producer may brief the guest during camera setup and lighting.

Notes and reset   The run-through and camera rehearsals will inevitably reveal some minor problems with the lighting or audio. The floor manager may want to straighten the president's tie and put a little makeup on his forehead to hide the perspiration.

Break   Even if working within a tight schedule, it is important to give the talent and crew a brief break just before the production. This will help relax everybody and separate the rehearsal from the actual taping.

Taping   The scheduled time allows for a few false starts or closings. The fewer takes there are, however, the fresher the interview will be.

Spill   This is a grace period to fix up things that went wrong unexpectedly. For example, the director might use this time to redo the introduction by the host because the president's name was inadvertently misspelled in the opening titles.

Strike   This activity does not refer to a protest by the crew, but to the clearing of the studio of all scenery, properties, and equipment.

Such a detailed production schedule is especially important for an EFP (electronic field production). The EFP schedule normally includes additional items, such as loading and unloading equipment, and transportation to and from the remote location.

Once you have a production schedule, you must stick to it. The best schedule is useless if you don't observe the deadlines or the blocks of time designated for a specific production activity. Experienced producers and directors move on to the next segment according to the production schedule, regardless of whether they have accomplished everything in the previous one. If you ignore the time limits too many times, your schedule becomes meaningless.   *READY ZVL 2*

KEY CONCEPT 3   **Establish a realistic production schedule and stick to it.**

As you can see, knowing the functions of every member of the production team and coordinating them according to a precise schedule are essential to effective and efficient video productions.

ONCE AGAIN, REMEMBER...

▥ Team Members

The members perform nontechnical and technical functions. Nontechnical people do not normally operate equipment; technical people do. The nontechnical people are also called above-the-line personnel, and the technical people, below-the-line personnel.

▥ Preproduction Team

These people plan the production. This team normally includes the producer, writer, director, art director, and technical director (TD). Small production companies or television stations often combine preproduction functions (such as producer-director); larger productions employ additional preproduction personnel, such as a composer or a choreographer. The floor plan and script are essential guides for the preproduction team.

▥ Production Team

This team consists of a variety of nontechnical and technical people, including the producer and various assistants (associate producer and PA), the director and associate director (AD), and the talent. The production crew usually includes the floor manager and floor persons (grips), TD, camera operators, lighting director (LD), video engineer, audio engineer, videotape operator, and C.G. operator. In preproduction the producer is in charge of coordinating the various people and production details; in the production phase, the director is in charge.

▥ Postproduction Team

This team normally consists of the director, the editor, and, in more-complex productions, a sound designer, who remixes the sound track. The director and occasionally the producer guide the editor in the selection and sequencing of shots.

▥ Floor Plan

The floor plan shows the type and location of a studio set, the necessary stage properties (furniture), and set dressings (wall hangings, lamps, plants).

▥ Production Schedule

A schedule, also called a time line, is essential for proper production coordination and efficiency.

ZETTL'S VIDEO LAB 2.1

*You should now have a pretty good idea about who does what on a production team. Just to make sure, click again on the **process** monitor.*

RUN ZVL 1 Load tape 7 **People**. Play the **Technical** module to see what you remember about the functions of the technical personnel. For starters, move the cursor over the picture of the TD. Do not click on it. The red rectangle around the TD indicates that you selected the right person, and you now see the function of the TD spelled out in the green field to the right of the TD's picture. Now move it over the LD, and you get an explanation of the LD's function. Before moving the rectangle over the other technical personnel, try to recall their specific jobs. Then check whether you were right. Do the same with the **Non-technical** module.

RUN ZVL 2 Tape 2 **Phases** gives you another opportunity to test your understanding of the preproduction, production, and postproduction phases. Check the production schedule again in the **Preproduction** module. Devising a workable production schedule is not easy and requires some production experience. But even if you don't yet know exactly how long each production step should take, write a simplified time line that includes at least some of the most essential deadlines.

KEY CONCEPTS

○ **Know the functions and responsibilities of each member of the nontechnical and technical production staffs.**

○ **Establish and maintain effective communication among all production personnel.**

○ **Establish a realistic production schedule and stick to it.**

P A R T II

C O N T E N T S

CHAPTER 3

Digital Video

CHAPTER 4

The Video Camera

CHAPTER 5

Looking Through the Viewfinder

CHAPTER 6

Operating the Camera

CHAPTER 7

Light, Color, Lighting

CHAPTER 8

Audio and Sound Control

CHAPTER 9

Visual Effects

44

Image Creation and Control

NOW that you have some idea** of who does what in video production, the Triple-I people want you to learn as much as possible about video and audio equipment and its optimal use.

In part II you learn the basics of digital video and how to create effective video images and good sound.

Video images are created by the video camera or by computer. Because the video camera produces electronic images that the camera lens sees, the images are called *lens-generated*. Images created exclusively by computer, such as the letters in titles or animated graphics of weather maps, are *synthetic,* or *computer-generated,* images. Most video productions are a combination of both.

The creation of "audio images," or sound, can be a reproduction of real sounds or the generation of synthetic sounds. *Microphone-generated* sounds are similar to lens-generated images: Both are faithful reproductions of the sights and sounds around us. *Computer-generated* audio images, generally called *synthesized* sound, can either imitate natural sounds or create a whole new idiom. As in video, reproduced and synthesized sounds are often combined for heightened effect.

Image control implies not only the *technical* control of pictures and sound, such as specific lighting techniques or audio mixing techniques, but also *aesthetic* control—how to compose pictures and sound for maximum communication effect.

K E Y   T E R M S

480p The lowest-resolution scanning system of DTV (digital television). The *p* stands for *progressive*, which means that each complete television frame consists of 480 lines that are scanned one after the other.

720p A scanning system of DTV (digital television). The *p* stands for *progressive*, which means that each complete television frame consists of 720 lines that are scanned one after the other.

1080i A scanning system of HDTV (high-definition television). The *i* stands for *interlaced*, which means that a complete frame is formed from two interlaced scanning fields. Each field consists of 539½ lines. As with the traditional NTSC analog television system, the 1080i produces 60 fields, or 30 complete frames, per second.

analog A signal that fluctuates exactly like the original stimulus.

binary digit (bit) The smallest amount of information a computer can hold and process. A charge is either present, represented by a 1, or absent, represented by a 0. One bit can describe two levels, such as on/off or black/white. Two bits can describe four levels (2^2 bits), three bits eight levels (2^3 bits), four bits sixteen (2^4 bits), and so on. A group of eight bits (2^8) is called a *byte*.

compression The temporary rearrangement or elimination of redundant picture information for easier storage and signal transport.

digital Pertaining to data in the form of digits (on/off pulses).

DTV Stands for digital television. Sometimes called ATV (advanced television).

field One-half of a complete scanning cycle, with two fields necessary for one television picture frame. There are 60 fields, or 30 frames, per second.

frame A complete scanning cycle of the electron beam (two fields), which occurs every $\frac{1}{30}$ second. It represents the smallest complete television picture unit.

HDTV Stands for *high-definition television.* The 1080i standard uses 60 fields per second, each field consisting of 539½ lines. A complete frame consists of two interlaced scanning fields of 539½ lines. There are 30 complete 1,080-line frames each second.

interlaced scanning The scanning of all odd-numbered lines (first field) and the subsequent scanning of all even-numbered lines (second field). The two fields make up a complete television frame.

progressive scanning The consecutive scanning of lines from top to bottom.

quantizing A step in the digitizing of an analog signal. It changes the sampling points into discrete values. Also called *quantization.*

refresh rate The number of complete scanning cycles per second.

RGB Stands for *red, green,* and *blue*—the basic colors of television.

sampling Taking a number of samples (voltages) at equally spaced intervals of the analog video or audio signal.

scanning The movement of the electron beam from left to right and from top to bottom on the television screen.

Digital Video

TRIPLE-I has just finished an extensive (and expensive) conversion from analog to digital equipment, and you want to know why they spent so much money. After all, the shows they produced with analog equipment looked fine. This chapter is a partial answer to why such a conversion took place. It will help you understand how video images are created, what the major advantages are of digital over analog video, and what digital processes are all about.

▪ **BASIC IMAGE FORMATION**

Interlaced scanning, progressive scanning, and digital television scanning systems

▪ **PRIMARY COLORS OF VIDEO**

Red, green, and blue—the basic colors of television

▪ **WHAT IS DIGITAL?**

Analog versus digital signals, and sampling

▪ **WHY DIGITAL?**

Artifacts, picture quality, compression and signal transport, and effects and picture manipulation

BASIC IMAGE FORMATION

You may have sometime been annoyed by the large back of your television set or your computer monitor, especially when trying to place it in a tight corner. But that large back is necessary for the creation of the video image. The principle of image formation is the same for black-and-white television, color television, standard analog television (which you have in your home), and digital HDTV (high-definition television). To explain the basic principle, let's use a black-and-white television set.

VIDEO IMAGE FORMATION

The electron gun in the back of the picture tube generates an electron beam. This beam is guided through the long neck of the tube to scan the thousands of dots covering the face of the tube.

The back end of the monochrome (black-and-white) picture tube houses the *electron gun,* which emits a tiny but sharp *electron beam.* This beam is guided through the long neck of the picture tube to scan the face of the tube, which is covered with thousands of tiny phosphorous dots called *pixels.* The stronger the beam, the brighter the dots will light up. **SEE 3.1** When the beam is too weak to illuminate the dots, the screen appears to be black. When the beam hits the pixels at full strength, the screen looks white.

A color set, on the other hand, has three electron guns in the back of the tube that emit three separate electron beams. The face of the color picture tube has neatly arranged groups of RGB—red, green, and blue—dots or tiny rectangles, which are activated by these three beams. One of the beams is always designated to hit the red dots, the second to hit the green dots, and the third to hit the blue dots. **SEE COLOR PLATE 2** Various combinations of these three beams provide all the colors you see on the video screen. We discuss these three primary colors and how they mix into all others in chapter 7.

Scanning Process

The electron beam, emitted by the electron gun, uses *scanning* to "read" the television screen, much like how you read a printed page: from left to right and from top to bottom. There is a difference, however, between how the beam scans a standard television set and how it scans a computer monitor. A television set works with *interlaced* scanning, and a computer screen with *progressive* scanning.

Interlaced scanning Standard television, which you use at home, is sometimes called *STV* (for *standard television*) or, more frequently, *NTSC,* which stands for *National Television System Committee,* which approved this system. (We discuss the NTSC system later in this chapter.) This type of system uses *interlaced scanning,* which means that, unlike a person reading, the electron beam skips every other line during its first scan, scanning only the odd-numbered lines. **SEE 3.2A** Then the beam returns to the top of the screen and scans all the even-numbered lines. **SEE 3.2B** When all odd-numbered lines are scanned, which takes exactly $\frac{1}{60}$ second, we have one *field.* The subsequent scanning of all even-numbered lines, which takes another $\frac{1}{60}$ second, produces another field. The two fields, which take $\frac{1}{30}$ of a second to produce, compose one complete picture, called a *frame.* **SEE 3.2C** Thus, there are 60 fields, or 30 frames, per second.

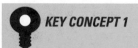 *KEY CONCEPT 1* **A standard television (NTSC) frame is made up of two scanning fields. There are 30 frames (or 60 fields) per second.**

3.2

INTERLACED SCANNING

A In interlaced scanning, the electron beam first scans all odd-numbered lines, from left to right and from top to bottom. This first scanning cycle produces one field.

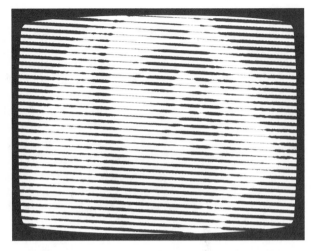

B The electron beam jumps back to the top again and scans all even-numbered lines. This second scanning cycle produces a second field.

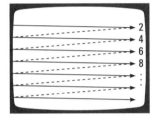

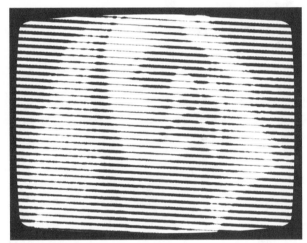

C The two fields make up a complete television picture, called a frame.

A complete television frame in the standard television NTSC system consists of 525 scanning lines.

Progressive scanning In the *progressive scanning* system, the electron beam scans each line in sequence, much like the way we read. As with interlaced scanning, the beam starts at the top left of the screen and scans the first line, then jumps back to the left and scans the second line, then the third, and so forth. After the last line has been scanned, the beam jumps back to its original starting point at the top left and starts the process all over again. The lines are, indeed, scanned in an orderly progression. **SEE 3.3** Contrary to interlaced scanning, which produces half a frame (one field) for each scanning cycle, progressive scanning produces a full frame for each scanning cycle. To avoid flicker in the picture, progressive scanning needs a *refresh rate* (number of complete scanning cycles) of at least 60 frames per second.

3.3

PROGRESSIVE SCANNING

In progressive scanning, the electron beam scans each line from left to right and from top to bottom. This scanning cycle produces a complete frame. The beam then jumps back to the top to start a new scanning cycle to produce another complete frame.

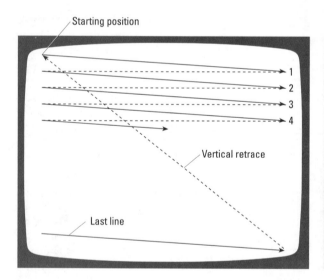

Starting position

1
2
3
4

Vertical retrace

Last line

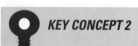

KEY CONCEPT 2   **In progressive scanning, each scanning cycle produces a complete frame. It needs a refresh rate of at least 60 frames per second.**

Digital Television Scanning Systems

High-resolution digital television systems—called *DTV*—use both progressive and interlaced scanning. DTV uses progressive scanning, because it produces sharper pictures and can be more easily compressed. (We discuss compression later in this chapter.) The disadvantage of progressive scanning is that it needs more bandwidth (a wider highway to transport the signal) than does the NTSC system. DTV also uses interlaced scanning, because it allows more lines without taking up too much bandwidth (making the highway too wide).

Three DTV systems have emerged as the most practical for television production and home viewing: the 480p and the 720p systems (for progressive scanning) and the 1080i system (for interlaced scanning). All produce high-quality digital video that is superior to that of standard television. Digital television comprises the *HDTV—high-definition television*—systems. HDTV has much more picture detail than standard (NTSC) television. Both 720p and 1080i are HDTV systems.

The 480p system   The picture of the *480p* system is made up of 480 lines (just a few less than what you actually see of the 525 lines of the NTSC system) that are progressively scanned. It produces 60 complete frames (not fields) per second. Although its pictures look extremely crisp, it is not considered HDTV.

The 720p system   The *720p* system produces 720 lines that are progressively scanned. Its scanning cycle is 60 frames per second. The high number of lines and frames (twice as many as with the NTSC system) results in very sharp pictures that are considered high-definition.

The 1080i system   The *1080i* system uses interlaced scanning, which produces only 30 frames (60 fields) per second. But because of its extremely high number of scanning lines, it produces superior pictures that are officially classified as HDTV.

 KEY CONCEPT 3   **The established DTV scanning standards are 480p, 720p, and 1080i.**

PRIMARY COLORS OF VIDEO

When technical people talk about *RGB*, they are referring to the red, green, and blue primary light colors or their corresponding signals. Red, green, and blue are called "primaries" because they are the basic colors of light from which all others can be mixed. All the colors of the lens-generated image are separated by the beam splitter into these three light primaries (see chapter 4). Do not confuse the light primaries, also called *additive primaries,* with the subtractive primary colors used in painting. In chapter 7 we discuss why they are called additive primaries and how they mix into other colors.

WHAT IS DIGITAL?

All digital video and computers are based on a binary code that uses on/off, either/or values for all their operations. The *on* value is represented by a 1, and the *off* value by a 0. These **binary digits**, or **bits** for short, operate on the light-bulb principle: If you have a 1, the light bulb is on; if you have a 0, the light bulb is off. In the **digital** world—that pertaining to data in the form of digits, or on/off pulses—there is nothing between the 1 and the 0; the light bulb cannot burn at half-intensity.

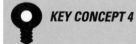 *KEY CONCEPT 4*   **All digital systems are based on the binary on/off, either/or principle. The *on* state is represented by a 1, the *off* state by a 0.**

The Difference Between Analog and Digital

Because the technical difference between analog and digital signals is quite complex, you may want to visualize the **analog** signal—a signal that fluctuates exactly like the original stimulus—as a ramp, which is a continuous way to reach a certain height. It matters little if you take many small steps or a few big ones; you will eventually reach the top of the stairs. **SEE 3.4**

The digital signal is more like a staircase with a certain number of equal steps that lead you to the same elevation. Very much in the either/or spirit of the digital world, you either stand on a certain step or you don't. You can't stand on the space in between the steps. **SEE 3.5**

3.4

ANALOG SIGNAL

The analog signal can be represented by a ramp that leads to a certain height.

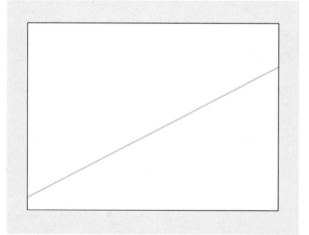

3.5

DIGITAL SIGNAL

The digital signal can be represented by a staircase that leads to a certain height in discrete steps.

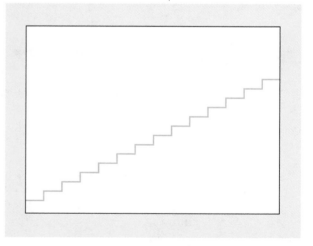

Technically, the elevation has now been divided into a series of steps, each of which can be assigned a number. Although there are several phases involved in digitizing an analog signal, the two most important ones are sampling and quantizing.

Sampling In *sampling,* the number of points along the ramp (analog signal) are determined for building the steps (digital values). With a low sampling rate, you will have only a few points along the ramp, which translates into several large steps. Obviously, those few large steps are not a good representation of the ramp (the original analog signal). **SEE 3.6**

A high sampling rate, on the other hand, will produce many little steps that approximate much more closely the original ramp. **SEE 3.7**

Quantizing At the *quantizing* digitization state, we are actually building steps and checking how high or low each step is relative to a scale—the *quantizing levels.* The height of each step is measured. An 8-bit quantizing has a maximum number of 256 steps (2^8).

Because each step is assigned a binary number, consisting of 0's and 1's, the computer can now identify each signal step.

 KEY CONCEPT 5　**A high sampling rate is desirable in digitizing an analog signal.**

3.6

LOW SAMPLING RATE

Sampling selects a portion of the original analog signal. A low sampling rate transforms this ramp into a few large steps. Much of the original signal is lost.

3.7

HIGH SAMPLING RATE

A high sampling rate selects more parts of the original signal. The ramp is made of more, smaller steps, so they better conform to the original ramp. The higher the sampling rate, the higher the quality of the digital signal.

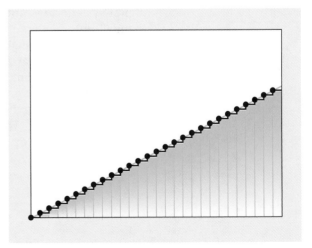

WHY DIGITAL?

Why do we go through all these technical maneuvers when we already have a workable analog signal? The basic answer lies in this seemingly crude either/or, on/off principle: It eliminates, or reduces to a minimum, all unwanted in-between values, called *artifacts*. You either stand on a certain step or you don't. A light is either on or off. Light bulbs that want to burn at only half-intensity are simply ignored or eliminated by the digital (binary) system. In technical language, the digital system is highly robust. In the video field, the major advantages of using digital systems are: (1) quality, (2) compression and signal transport, and (3) effects and picture manipulation.

Quality

Besides higher-resolution (sharper) pictures, DTV also produces better colors and black-and-white contrast than do analog video systems. This advantage is especially apparent in video recording and editing. Digital recordings do no deteriorate in quality even after many tape generations. A *generation* is one of a number of dubs (copies) away from the original. For example, the first-generation dub is struck directly from the original; the second generation is two dubs away from the original.

With analog equipment each subsequent generation amplifies the slight deterioration of the previous one, much like printed text deteriorates when you progressively duplicate photocopies. Even the best analog video equipment will show marked picture deterioration after a few generations. When you use digital videotape recorders, subsequent generations produce pictures that are very close in quality to the original recording, an attribute called *transparency*. Some digital recording systems produce images that show little or no deterioration even after thirty generations. This is of great advantage when building complex effects in postproduction.

Compression and Signal Transport

What can you do when you have only one suitcase and too much stuff to fit into it? This type of dilemma faces digital systems all the time. Even a high-capacity digital system does not normally have enough room to store or a freeway (bandwidth) wide enough to transport all the video and audio information necessary for high-quality moving pictures and sound. The solution to this problem in the digital domain is *compression*. You use compression in your computer when "stuffing" (on a Macintosh platform) or "zipping" (on a Windows platform) large files for storage or transport and then "unstuffing" or "unzipping" them when reopening the file.

Lossless compression   This means that you don't want to leave anything behind when packing your suitcase, so you need to repack it and hope that you get all the stuff into the suitcase. With *lossless compression,* you don't lose any information, but simply rearrange it for easier storage and transport. The problem is that the system still has to manage superlarge files.

Lossy compression   Now you have to make choices about what items to pack into the suitcase and which ones to leave behind. Do you really need three pairs of shoes or will one do? How about one instead of four sweaters, especially if you might not even need one? The *lossy compression* systems have to make similar choices: They throw away, or "lose," any digital information that is not absolutely necessary. For example, the computer estimates that the green grass you are walking through will not turn red from one frame to the next. Subsequently, the system does not bother with green-grass information for each frame, but borrows that information from the one frame that showed the grass as green. The great advantage of lossy compression is that you can travel with a relatively small suitcase—you need less digital storage capacity and can transport the digital information more efficiently. Both popular compression standards, *JPEG* ("jay-peg," which stands for Joint Photographic Experts Group, which established it) and *MPEG-2* ("em-peg two," which stands for the Moving Picture Experts Group) are the lossy kind.

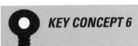 **KEY CONCEPT 6**   **Compression eliminates redundant information to increase storage capacity and speed up signal transportation.**

▪ Effects and Picture Manipulation

Digital video effects (DVE) are much more flexible than analog effects. For example, shrinking a large image to fit a smaller frame without losing any picture content cannot be done with an analog system. But with digital equipment, you can build a great number of complex effects and store them for easy recall. In digital, or nonlinear, editing, you can display a number of individual frames simultaneously on the computer screen and arrange them in any given sequence by simply moving them with the mouse. *READY ZVL 1* With digital equipment, such as a scanner, you can digitize any lens-generated image and manipulate it at will. You can change its size, shape, light, color, and contrast and have it bounce around the frame in various ways. Digital systems also allow the construction of video and audio images synthetically. With a computer you are no longer dependent on the actual sights and sounds around you, but can create your own digital world. We explore the major analog and digital effects in chapter 9. *READY ZVL 2*

ONCE AGAIN, REMEMBER...

■ **Basic Image Formation**

A standard (NTSC) television frame is made up of two scanning fields. There are 30 frames (made up of 60 fields) per second. Interlaced scanning scans every other line, progressive scanning every line. In progressive scanning, each scanning cycle produces a complete frame.

■ **Digital Scanning Systems**

The most prevalent digital television (DTV) scanning systems are the 480p system, the 720p system, and the 1080i system. The 720p and 1080i system are the legitimate high-definition television (HDTV) systems.

■ **Sampling**

The higher the sampling rate, the better the digital signal will be.

■ **Compression**

Compression means reducing digital information to be stored or transmitted by packing the data into less space (lossless compression) or, more common, by throwing away some of the least important data (lossy compression).

ZETTL'S VIDEO LAB 2.1

This entire CD-ROM is a good demonstration of digital processes. It allows you to select the audio monitor's Aesthetics module as readily and quickly as the camera monitor's Focusing tape, which is arranged closer to the beginning of the series. Also, the text, still and moving images, and all sounds are digitally processed and sometimes even digitally generated.

RUN ZVL 1 Click on the **editing** monitor and load tape 2 **Functions**. Play the **Quiz** module and move the available shots in a specific sequence. Without running the selected sequence, change the sequence. Once you have selected a sequence that seems logical to you, run the sequence. You are now engaged in nonlinear editing, a process that is possible only with digital technology.

RUN ZVL 2 The zoom lens that turns toward you at the beginning of this CD-ROM is an example of a synthetically generated image. So are the sounds that accompany the brief opening montage of production images. As you undoubtedly noticed, the Master Control display and the stacks of videotapes that make up the ZVL 2.1 interactive interface design are all digitally generated.

KEY CONCEPTS

- A standard television (NTSC) frame is made up of two scanning fields. There are 30 frames (or 60 fields) per second.

- In progressive scanning , each scanning cycle produces a complete frame. It needs a refresh rate of at least 60 frames per second.

- The established DTV scanning standards are 480p, 720p, and 1080i.

- All digital systems are based on the binary on/off, either/or principle. The *on* state is represented by a 1, the *off* state by a 0.

- A high sampling rate is desirable in digitizing an analog signal.

- Compression eliminates redundant information to increase storage capacity and speed up signal transportation.

K E Y   T E R M S

aperture Iris opening of a lens; usually measured in *f*-stops.

beam splitter Optical device within the camera that splits the white light into the three primary colors: red, green, and blue.

camcorder A portable camera with the VTR built into it.

camera chain The camera and associated electronic equipment, consisting of the power supply, the sync generator, and the CCU (camera control unit).

camera control unit (CCU) Equipment, separate from the actual camera, that allows the VO (video operator) to adjust the color and brightness balance before and during the production.

CCD Stands for *charge-coupled device*. An image-sensing element that translates the optical image into a video signal.

ENG/EFP camera Highly portable, self-contained camera for electronic news gathering (ENG) or electronic field production (EFP).

fast lens A lens that permits a relatively great amount of light to pass through at its largest aperture (lowest *f*-stop number). Can be used in low-light conditions.

focal length With the lens set at infinity, the distance from the iris to the plane where the picture is in focus. Normally measured in millimeters (mm) or inches.

***f*-stop** The scale on the lens indicating the aperture. The larger the *f*-stop number, the smaller the aperture; the smaller the *f*-stop number, the larger the aperture.

iris Adjustable lens-opening mechanism. Also called *lens diaphragm*.

slow lens A lens that permits a relatively small amount of light to pass through (high *f*-stop number). Can be used only in well-lighted areas.

viewfinder A small video monitor on a camera that displays the picture the camera generates.

zoom lens Variable-focal-length lens. All video cameras are equipped with a zoom lens.

zoom range How much the focal length can be changed from a wide shot to a close-up during a zoom. The zoom range is stated as a ratio, such as 20:1. Also called *zoom ratio*.

The Video Camera

BEFORE going to the next Triple-I shoot, you feel that you should get a camcorder and try it out so you have some idea of how to take effective pictures. The camera operator you met at the Triple-I shoot of the MTV segment tells you that knowing how a camera works is an essential prerequisite to producing effective video and understanding the general requirements of visual communication.

This chapter will help you understand how video images are created and how a video camera works.

■ **BASIC CAMERA FUNCTION AND ELEMENTS**
Function, lens, beam splitter, imaging device, and viewfinder

■ **TYPES OF CAMERAS**
Studio cameras, HDTV cameras, ENG/EFP cameras and camcorders, and their various cable connectors

BASIC CAMERA FUNCTION AND ELEMENTS

Regardless of their size, cost, and quality, whether digital or analog, all video cameras operate on the same basic principle: To translate (transduce) the optical image that the lens sees into a corresponding video picture. More specific, *the camera converts an optical image into electrical signals that are reconverted by a television receiver into visible screen images.*

Function

To fulfill this function, each video camera needs three basic elements: (1) the lens, (2) the camera itself, and (3) the viewfinder. **SEE 4.1**

   The *lens* selects a portion of the scene at which you point the camera and produces a sharp optical image of it. The camera contains a *beam splitter* and an *imaging* or *pickup device* that converts the optical image of the lens into weak electric currents or signals, which are amplified and further processed by a variety of electronic components. The *viewfinder* reconverts these electrical signals into video pictures of the lens-generated scene. **SEE 4.2**

4.1

BASIC CAMERA ELEMENTS

The video camera has three main elements: the lens, the camera itself, and the viewfinder.

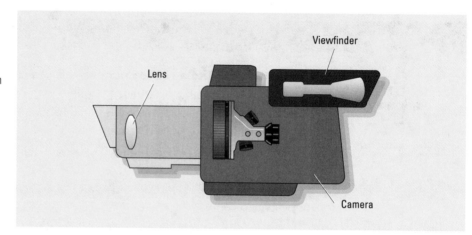

4.2

FUNCTIONS OF THE CAMERA

The video camera translates the optical light image as seen by the lens into a corresponding picture on the screen. The light reflected off an object is gathered and transmitted by the lens to the beam splitter, which splits the white light into red, green, and blue light beams. These light beams are then transformed by CCDs into electric energy, which is amplified and processed and then reconverted into video pictures by the viewfinder.

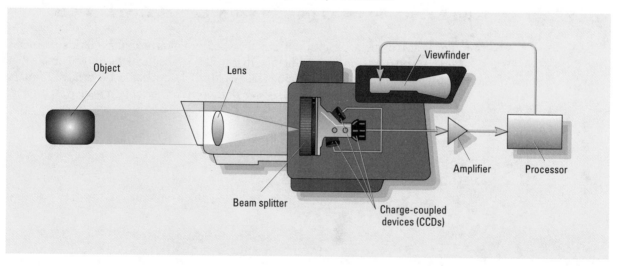

To explain this process, we start with how a lens operates and sees a particular portion of a scene, then we move on to how the beam splitter and the imaging device work, and, finally, to how the video signal is reconverted into a video picture by the television receiver. Knowing this basic process will help you use a camera effectively and understand how other production elements, such as lighting, must be adjusted to meet the various requirements of the camera.

The Lens

Lenses determine what cameras can see. They are classified by *focal length*, which is a technical measure of the distance from the iris inside the lens to the plane where the projected image is in focus. This measurement assumes that the lens distance calibration is set at infinity. This distance is normally given in millimeters (mm); thus, a still camera can have a 24mm or a 200mm lens. Lenses can also be classified by how wide a view you get from a specific camera position. A *wide-angle lens* (short-focal-length lens) gives a relatively wide vista. A *narrow-angle lens* (long-focal-length-lens) gives a relatively narrow vista with the background greatly magnified. *Speed* refers to how much light a lens can let through.

The optical quality of the lens determines to a great extent how good the video picture will look. If you have a low-quality mic, even the best audio recorder will not be able to produce high-quality sounds.

Focal length   The *zoom lens* on a camera can change from a short-focal-length, or wide-angle, position to a long-focal-length, or narrow-angle, position and back in one continuous move. A *short-focal-length* zoom position gives you a *wide-angle* view: You can see more than with a lens in the narrow-angle position. To bring a zoom lens into the *extreme-wide-angle* position, you need to zoom *all the way out.* You will see a relatively large portion of the scene in front of you, but the middle and background objects look quite small and, therefore, far away. **SEE 4.3**

4.3

WIDE-ANGLE VIEW

The wide-angle lens shows a wide vista, with the faraway objects looking quite small.

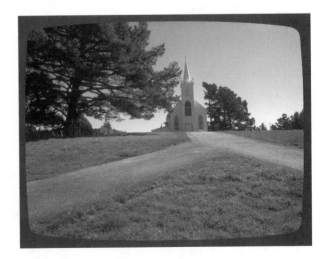

Zooming all the way in puts the zoom lens in a *long-focal-length* or *narrow-angle* lens position. The zoom lens will now give a much narrower, but enlarged, view of the selected scene. Because the narrow-angle lens position functions similar to binoculars, it is also called a *telephoto lens*, or telephoto zoom lens position. **SEE 4.4**

4.4

NARROW-ANGLE VIEW

The narrow-angle, or telephoto, lens shows only a narrow portion of the scene, with the background objects appearing much larger relative to the foreground objects than in a wide-angle view.

When you stop a zoom in the middle of the zoom range (between the extreme-wide-angle and narrow-angle positions), you are more or less in the *normal lens* position. The angle of view of a normal lens approximates what you would see when looking directly at the scene. **SEE 4.5**

Because the zoom lens offers a great variety of focal lengths between its extreme-wide-angle and narrow-angle positions, it is also called a *variable-focal-length* lens.

4.5

NORMAL VIEW

The normal lens shows a vista and a perspective that are similar to what we actually see.

4.6

MAXIMUM WIDE-ANGLE AND NARROW-ANGLE POSITIONS OF A 10:1 ZOOM LENS

A 10:1 zoom lens can narrow the angle of view by ten times. It seems to bring a portion of the scene closer to the camera.

 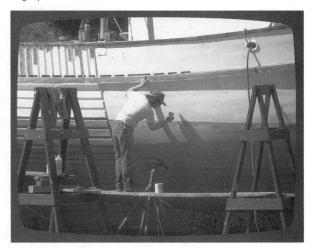

Zoom range   The *zoom range*, also called *zoom ratio*, refers to how close a view you can achieve when zooming in from the farthest wide-angle position to the closest narrow-angle position. The higher the first number of the ratio, the closer you can get to the object from the farthest wide-angle position. A 20:1 zoom lens lets you narrow the *field of view* (your vista) twenty times when zooming in from the farthest wide-angle position to the closest narrow-angle position. In practical terms you can move in to a pretty good close-up from a wide-angle shot. The 20:1 zoom ratio can also be indicated as 20× ("twenty times"). **SEE 4.6**

There is a great difference between optical and digital zooms. In an *optical zoom*, the lens elements inside the lens activate the change of angle of view. In a *digital zoom*, the *pixels* (picture elements) are simply made larger, simulating a changing field of view of zooming in. The problem with digital zooms is that the enlarged pixels make the picture less sharp. A digital zoom-in inevitably produces a slightly fuzzy image. An optical zoom does not influence the sharpness of the picture, which is why optical zooms are preferred.

Some of the large cameras used in covering sports or other outdoor events have lenses with zoom ratios of 40:1 or more. These lenses are as large as, or sometimes even larger than, the camera to which they are attached. With such a lens, you can zoom in from a wide shot of the total football field to a close-up of the quarterback's face. The large zoom range is necessary because these cameras are usually fixed on top of the stadium, far away from the event. Instead of the camera moving closer to the event, as is possible with a camcorder, the zoom lens must bring the event closer to the camera.

The focal length of a lens influences how much you see of a scene and how close it seems to you (the field of view). It also influences how much you can move the camera and how the pictures look to the viewer. You will read more about these aspects in chapters 5 and 6.   *READY ZVL 1*

Lens speed   As pointed out earlier, speed refers to how much light can pass through a lens to the imaging device. A *fast lens* can let a relatively great amount of light pass through; a *slow lens* is more limited in how much light it can transmit. In practice, a fast lens allows you to produce acceptable pictures in a darker environment than does a slow lens. Fast lenses are therefore more useful than slow ones, but they are also larger and more expensive.

You can tell whether a lens is fast or slow by looking at the lowest *f-stop* number on the lens, such as *f*/1.4 or *f*/2.0. The lower the number, the faster the lens.

Lens iris and *f*-stops   Like the pupil of your eye, all lenses have an *iris* that controls the amount of light transmitted. In a bright environment, the iris of your eye contracts to a smaller opening, restricting the amount of light passing through; in a dim environment, it expands to a larger opening, admitting more light.

The iris, or *lens diaphragm,* operates in the same way. The center of the iris has an adjustable hole, called the ***aperture****,* that can be made large or small. By changing the aperture, you control how much light the lens transmits. When there is little light on a scene, you can make the hole bigger and let more light through. This is called "opening the lens" or "opening the iris." When the scene is well illuminated, you can make the hole smaller to restrict the light going through. In so doing, you "close down" the lens. You can thus control the exposure of the picture so that it looks neither too dark (not enough light) nor too washed out (too much light).

Now you can explain a fast or slow lens in more technical terms: A fast lens transmits more light at its maximum aperture (iris opening) than does a slow one.

The standard by which we measure how much light is transmitted through the lens is called the *f-stop.* All lenses have a ring at their base with a series of *f*-stop numbers printed on them (such as 1.7, 2.8, 4, 5.6, 8, 11, 16) that control the iris opening. **SEE 4.7**

When you turn the ring so that *f*/1.7 lines up with the little mark on the lens, you have "opened" the lens to its maximum aperture; it now transmits as much light as it possibly can. When you turn the ring to *f*/16, the lens is "stopped down" to its minimum aperture, letting very little light pass through. A fast lens should have a maximum aperture of *f*/2.8 or better. Good lenses go as low as *f*/1.4, or occasionally even *f*/1.2. With these lenses you need considerably less light to produce good pictures than with slower lenses whose maximum aperture is *f*/4.5.

Notice that the *f*-stop numbers mean just the opposite of what you expect them to be: The lower the *f*-stop number, the larger the aperture and the more light is transmitted. The higher the *f*-stop number, the smaller the aperture and the less light is transmitted. **SEE 4.8** *READY ZVL 2*

4.7

IRIS CONTROL RING

The *f*-stop calibration is printed on a ring that controls the iris opening, or aperture, of the lens. The *C* on the control ring of this lens refers to *cap,* which means the iris is totally closed and acts like a physical cap covering the lens.

Iris control ring with *f*-stops

f-STOP SETTINGS

The higher the *f*-stop number, the smaller the iris opening and the less light is transmitted by the lens.
The lower the *f*-stop number, the larger the iris opening and the more light is transmitted by the lens.

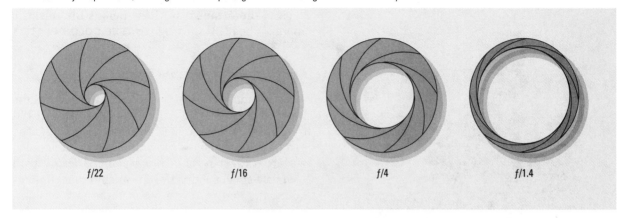

f/22   f/16   f/4   f/1.4

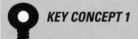

KEY CONCEPT 1   **The lower the *f*-stop number, the larger the aperture and the more light is transmitted. A fast lens has a low minimum *f*-stop number (such as *f*/1.4).**

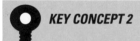

KEY CONCEPT 2   **The higher the *f*-stop number, the smaller the aperture and the less light is transmitted. A slow lens has a relatively high minimum *f*-stop number (such as *f*/4.5).**

Auto iris   Rather than your having to turn the iris control ring to the proper *f*-stop by hand, the auto iris adjusts itself automatically to the optimal aperture. The camera reads the light level of the scene and tells the auto iris to open up or close down until the resulting picture is neither too dark nor too light. Such an automated feature is not without drawbacks, however. We consider the advantages and disadvantages of an auto iris in chapter 6.   *READY ZVL 3*

■ **Beam Splitter**

One of the main components within the camera itself is the ***beam splitter***, which separates ordinary white light into the three primary light colors—red, green, and blue (RGB). When mixed in various proportions, these three primary colors account for all colors you see on the television screen.

PRISM BLOCK

The prism block contains prisms and filters that split the incoming light images as produced by the lens into the three light primaries and direct them into their corresponding CCDs.

Red CCD

Green CCD

Blue CCD

The actual beam splitter consists of a series of prisms and filters locked into a *prism block*. **SEE 4.9** The prism block splits the incoming light into the three colored beams and then directs the RGB light beams into their corresponding imaging devices. The imaging devices then transform these beams into electric energy—the RGB video signals. **SEE COLOR PLATE 1**

Imaging Device

A second main component inside the camera is the *imaging device*. Also called the *pickup device*, it transduces (changes) light into electric energy. The imaging device in most cameras is a CCD, often called a "chip"; *CCD* stands for *charge-coupled device*. It is a relatively small solid-state silicon chip that contains horizontal and vertical rows of thousands of light-sensing picture elements, called *pixels*. Each pixel can translate the light energy it receives into a corresponding electric charge.

Pixels function very much like the individual tiles in a mosaic or the dots in a magazine photo. The more pixels in a given picture area, the sharper the image will be. **SEE 4.10** Similarly, the more pixels a CCD contains, the sharper the resulting screen image. A high-resolution chip has a great many pixels and produces a sharp image. As you can see, the *resolution* (sharpness) of a video image is determined not only by the number of scanning lines, but also by the camera lens and the number of pixels on the imaging device.

PICTURE RESOLUTION

The picture on the right is made up of more pixels than the one on the left. It has a higher resolution and looks sharper.
The more pixels a CCD contains, the higher the resolution of the video image.

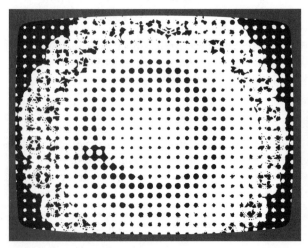

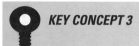

KEY CONCEPT 3   **The CCD imaging device converts the light variations of an image into electric energy—the video signal.**

High-quality consumer and all professional cameras contain three CCDs—one for each of the RGB light beams. But most small consumer camcorders have only a single chip. In this case, the incoming white light is divided by a filter into the three primary colors, which are then processed as individual signals by the single CCD. Even if the single chip is of high quality, with many thousands of pixels, it can devote only one-third of its pixels to each color. The color information and resolution therefore have less fidelity than if three chips were used.

The advantage of single-chip cameras is their small size. You will find that some digital single-chip cameras can produce pictures of astonishing quality that can seriously challenge the three-chip camera in color fidelity and resolution.

Video signal processing   The electric charges that come from the pixels are extremely weak and need to be amplified before they can be further processed into a video signal. The final video signal, which produces the pictures on a television set, is then transported to the camera viewfinder and to the built-in videotape recorder (or one attached to the camera), as shown in figure 4.2. This signal processing consists of combining the RGB color signals with another signal that carries the brightness, or black-and-white, information of the image. The color signals make up the *chrominance channel,* or *C* signal (*chroma* is Greek for *color*). The black-and-white signal is called the *luminance,* or *Y,* signal (*lumen* is Latin for *light*). Both the C and the Y signals are merged into a composite signal, called the *NTSC signal,* or *NTSC* for short. **SEE COLOR PLATE 3** (As you may recall, *NTSC* stands for National Television System Committee.)

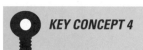

KEY CONCEPT 4   **The composite color signal combines an RGB chrominance (C) channel with a black-and-white luminance (Y) channel.**

▪ **Viewfinder**

The *viewfinder* is a small video monitor attached to the camera that shows an image of what the camera sees. Most viewfinders are *monochrome,* which means that they show in black-and-white the color pictures the camera produces. Several of the high-end consumer camcorders and some professional studio cameras have color viewfinders, which greatly aid the camera operator in picture composition. Because the resolution of small color viewfinders is inferior to monochrome viewfinders, many camera operators prefer the latter. In addition to the regular viewfinder, some small digital cameras have a flat-panel *LCD (liquid crystal display)* viewfinder that can be folded out for more-convenient viewing when you handhold the camera rather than carry it on your shoulder. **SEE 4.11**

4.11

FOLDOUT VIEWFINDER

This relatively large LCD (liquid crystal display) viewfinder gives the operator great flexibility in camera handling.

TYPES OF CAMERAS

When looking at studio cameras, you may wonder why they are so much bigger than ENG/EFP camcorders or cameras. Even the relatively small and portable ENG/EFP cameras are considerably larger and heavier than the typical consumer camcorder. Although it is generally true that large cameras are of higher quality than small consumer camcorders, you cannot always go by size to judge image quality. Several models of digital camcorders are relatively small yet they produce pictures and sound that are far superior to some of the large analog camcorders. In this section we use camera size mainly to explain how they are used. That use is relatively unchanged, whether they are analog or digital, or HDTV (high-definition television) or STV (standard television) cameras.

The large, high-quality cameras you normally find in television studios are, appropriately enough, called *studio* cameras. The smaller cameras used in field production are called *ENG/EFP* (electronic news-gathering/electronic field production) or simply *field* cameras. Although small camcorders that you can find in the electronics section of department stores are often referred to as "consumer" camcorders, various small digital consumer camcorders are also used professionally. These high-quality consumer models are sometimes called *prosumer* (for *pro*fessional and con*sumer*) cameras.

The difference between a camera and a camcorder is that the camcorder (for *cam*era and re*corder*) has a videotape recorder attached to it or solidly built into it to form a single, inseparable unit. Other ENG/EFP cameras must be connected to a separate VTR for recording.

4.12

STUDIO CAMERA

High-quality studio cameras contain three CCDs and many electronic controls. They have a large lens and a viewfinder attached, which makes the whole camera head much heavier than an ENG/EFP camera.

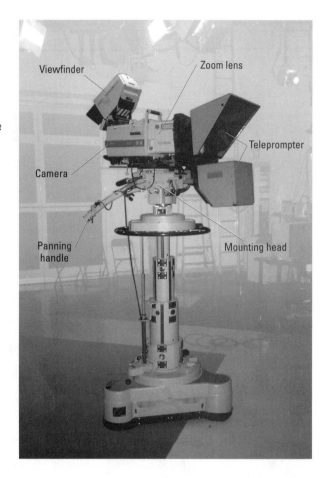

Viewfinder

Zoom lens

Camera

Teleprompter

Panning handle

Mounting head

Studio Cameras

Studio cameras are large and too heavy to be maneuvered without the aid of a pedestal or some other kind of camera mount. What makes the equipment so heavy is not necessarily the camera itself, but the large zoom lens and, most often, the teleprompter attached to it. **SEE 4.12** Studio cameras are typically used in studio productions such as interviews, news, and game shows, and also in big-remote telecasts, such as sporting events, where high-quality video is a must.

Studio cameras are built to produce exceptionally high-quality pictures under a variety of conditions. They all have three CCDs, control equipment, and a large, high-quality zoom lens. To ensure optimal picture quality at any given moment during the production, the studio camera is hooked up via cable to a variety of equipment that supplies power and permits manual control of various electronic and optical functions, such as the lens iris. Unlike the ENG/EFP camera or a small camcorder, the studio camera cannot function by itself but must be connected to external power and control equipment. Because the camera and the associated equipment are necessarily linked together, they are called a *camera chain*.

STANDARD CAMERA CHAIN

The standard camera chain consists of the camera head (the actual camera), the power supply, the sync generator, and the camera control unit (CCU).

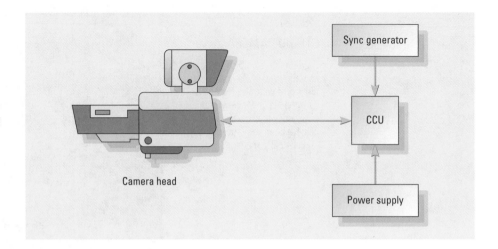

Sync generator

CCU

Camera head

Power supply

Camera chain The standard *camera chain* consists of four parts: (1) the camera itself, which—as the front part of the chain—is called the *camera head;* (2) the power supply; (3) the sync generator; and (4) the camera control unit or, simply, CCU. **SEE 4.13**

CAMERA CONTROL UNIT (CCU)

The CCU has a variety of controls with which the VO (video operator) can continuously monitor and adjust picture quality.

Monitors

CCU operational units

The *power supply* feeds the necessary electricity to the camera head through the camera cable. Unlike ENG/EFP cameras or camcorders, studio cameras cannot be powered by batteries. The power supply is built into the CCU.

The *sync generator* produces the uniform electrical pulse that is necessary to synchronize the scanning of the video pictures in all cameras used in a multicamera telecast with a variety of other equipment (such as video monitors and viewfinders).

The *camera control unit (CCU)* has two major functions: setup and control. *Setup* refers to the adjustments made when the camera is first powered up. The video operator (VO), who is in charge of the camera setup and picture control during the production, makes sure that the colors the camera delivers are true, that the iris is at the proper setting, and that the camera is adjusted for the brightest spot (white-level adjustment) and the darkest spot (black-level or pedestal adjustment) in the scene so that we can see the major steps within this contrast range. Fortunately, the VO is greatly aided in this task by a computerized setup panel.

Assuming the camera is fairly stable, which means that the camera retains the setup values over a period of time, during production the video operator usually needs to adjust only the lens iris, by moving a remote iris control knob or lever on the CCU. **SEE 4.14**

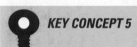 ***KEY CONCEPT 5*** **The camera chain consists of the camera head (actual camera), the power supply, the sync generator, and the camera control unit (CCU).**

Camera cable   The camera cable carries the power to the camera and transports the picture signal, the intercommunication signal, and various technical information between the camera and the CCU. Some cables are designed for analog (nondigital) camera systems and have a great number of wires packed into them. These cables, called *multicore* cables, have a limited reach (up to 2,000 feet or 600 meters). Newer cameras use the thinner, lighter, and more flexible *triax* or *fiber-optic* cables, which have a considerably farther reach than do multicore cables. A triax cable can reach about 5,000 feet (1,500 meters), and a fiber-optic cable can reach almost 2 miles (3,000 meters).

Why do studio cameras need such a great reach? Because they are used not only in the studio, but also at *remotes*—scheduled events that happen outside the studio—that require extremely high-quality video. When covering sporting events such as golf tournaments, downhill ski races, or football games, the cameras are often so far away from the rest of the camera controls that even a 2-mile cable may prove too short to connect the camera to the CCU.

Connectors   Whenever you work with several pieces of equipment that must be hooked together to form a video or audio system, you need the appropriate cables and especially the right connectors. Despite careful preproduction, many productions have been delayed or even canceled because the connectors for camera or audio cables did not fit. You will find that one of the most important tasks when taking equipment out in the field is checking the interconnecting cables and connectors. Although you may hear production people call all connectors "plugs," regardless of whether they represent the male or female part of the connector, it is more precise to call the male part of the connector a *plug*, and the female part a *jack*.

Most studio cameras have specific connectors for their cables that link the camera to the CCU. The coax cables that link various professional video equipment use *BNC* connectors. Consumer equipment normally uses *RCA phono* plugs and jacks for connectors. **SEE 4.15** (Figure 4.15 shows the standard video connectors; the standard audio connectors are shown in figure 8.25.). Because we are constantly seeking to make video equipment smaller and more compact, you may well find that small connectors will be used also for professional-quality equipment.

4.15

STANDARD VIDEO CONNECTORS

The standard video connectors are BNC and RCA phono (also used for audio). There are adapters available that let you join each of these connectors with the others.

BNC   RCA phono plug

HDTV Cameras

As you recall from chapter 3, not all DTV (digital television) cameras produce true HDTV pictures. So far the highest-quality studio cameras operate with the 720p or 1080i scanning standard. In general, HDTV cameras produce much sharper pictures, better colors, and more subtle light/dark contrast steps than do STV cameras. The HDTV camera was developed originally to replace the film camera in the production of electronic cinema. But with the new mandate by the

Federal Communications Commission (FCC) to broadcast in HDTV by 2006, such cameras are also used in studio and large field productions.

To achieve an extremely high-resolution image, HDTV cameras need their own lenses, high-quality CCDs, signal-processing equipment, viewfinders, and monitors that can accommodate the horizontally wider 16 × 9 aspect ratio (see chapter 5), and videotape recorders. As you can see, the HDTV system is not compatible with standard video equipment.

ENG/EFP Cameras

The *ENG/EFP camera* is designed to be carried by the camera operator during electronic news gathering or electronic field production. Although it is considerably smaller than the studio camera, it contains the whole camera chain in the camera itself. The camera is usually battery-powered, but can also be powered through an adapter that uses regular household current, or through power fed by the camera cable. It has built-in automatic controls that greatly aid the camera operator in maintaining high-quality pictures with a minimum of adjustment. ENG/EFP cameras have much smaller zoom lenses and viewfinders than do studio cameras and are lighter in weight. **SEE 4.16**

Why have cables when the cameras are basically self-contained? First, although the ENG/EFP cameras are capable of running on batteries, it is often better for them to receive their power from an external source. External power frees you from having to worry about running out of batteries during a long shoot.

Second, although the built-in CCUs produce good pictures for each individual camera, it is important to control picture quality of all cameras used during the production. With the help of *RCUs* (*remote control units,* for which the actual controls are remote or are portable CCUs), one video operator can ensure that the pictures of all cameras match in color and contrast, even if they shoot against different backgrounds or under different lighting conditions. **SEE 4.17**

Third, without the additional weight of a videotape recorder (VTR), the camera is considerably lighter and easier to operate.

Fourth, because the director can see on a monitor what the camera operators see in their viewfinders, he or she can give the camera operators the necessary instructions over the intercom headsets while the scene is in progress. All these production advantages certainly outweigh by far the slight disadvantage of having the cameras tethered to a remote truck. Apparently, the director and TD of the MTV shoot knew what they were doing.

Camcorders A *camcorder* is an ENG/EFP camera that has a VTR built-in. **SEE 4.18** Some camcorders can be docked with a VTR. *Docking* means that the VTR can be plugged into the back of the camera to form a single camcorder unit. The advantage of a dockable system is that you are not limited to a specific VTR, but you will find that the VTRs of dockable camcorders

4.16

ENG/EFP CAMERA

A high-quality ENG/EFP camera has three CCDs and contains all parts of the camera chain in the camera itself. It can be battery-operated or connected to an external power source and an RCU (remote control unit).

Microphone

Viewfinder

Zoom lens

VTR

4.17

REMOTE CONTROL UNIT (RCU)

The RCU is connected to the ENG/EFP camera by a camera cable. It overrides the controls built into the ENG/EFP camera and enables a VO to continually adjust the pictures for optimal quality. The cable also supplies power to the camera and carries intercommunication between camera operator and the people at the RCU.

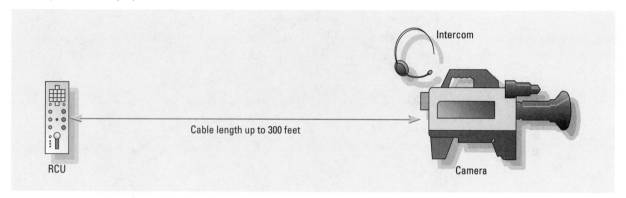

4.18

CAMCORDER

A camcorder is an ENG/EFP camera with a built-in or attached VTR. It has a microphone attached to it and provisions for additional microphones.

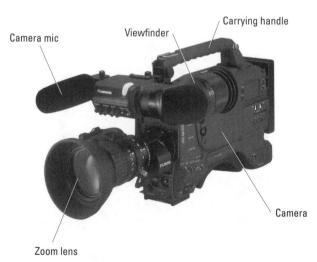

are often not removed but instead used as a single-piece camcorder.

All camcorders—single-unit or dockable—have an external microphone, called the *camera microphone*, attached to the housing or built into the camera. All professional camcorders have an additional jack for an external microphone. Some also have a camera light attached to illuminate a small area during ENG or to provide additional illumination. Note that if you use the built-in light on a camcorder, the battery will drain much faster than without the light.

Studio conversion of ENG/EFP camera

Although the quality of the best ENG/EFP camera is below that of the best studio camera, high-quality ENG/EFP cameras are often used in place of studio cameras. The reasons for this substitution are that ENG/EFP cameras are considerably cheaper and easier to handle than are studio cameras. To adapt an ENG/EFP camera to studio conditions, you need to replace the small viewfinder with a larger one, attach a faster lens (lower maximum *f*-stop number) that has a zoom range more appropriate for studio dimensions, affix cables for focus and zoom controls, and install a frame and mounting devices for a tripod or studio pedestal. **SEE 4.19**

■ Consumer Camcorder

All consumer camcorders have the VTR built into the camera, but the quality among consumer camcorders varies considerably. As pointed out earlier, the three-chip

4.19

STUDIO CONVERSION OF ENG/EFP CAMERA

Converting a high-quality ENG/EFP camera for studio use usually requires a large viewfinder, a lens with a zoom range appropriate for the size of the studio, cables that allow zooming and focusing from the operator's position, and a frame and mounting devices for a tripod or studio pedestal.

camcorders produce pictures that are generally superior to those of the single-chip camcorders. Some digital three-chip consumer camcorders produce such high-quality pictures that they have been elevated to prosumer—low-end professional—camcorders. **SEE 4.20** They can easily outperform more-expensive low-end analog professional camcorders. One big advantage of digital camcorders is that many allow a direct transfer from the camcorder VTR to a desktop computer or a digital editing system for postproduction editing (see chapter 11).

 KEY CONCEPT 6   **A camcorder has its VTR built into the camera.**

4.20

HIGH-END CONSUMER CAMCORDER

This high-end digital consumer camcorder contains three CCDs, automatic control equipment, and a built-in DVCPRO videotape recorder. Its video quality rivals that of the larger and more expensive ENG/EFP camcorders and is, therefore, also referred to as a prosumer camera.

What's the Difference?

When you compare the pictures you took with a consumer camcorder to a similar scene shot with an expensive and much larger, heavier professional camcorder, you may have trouble seeing any difference in picture quality. Even professional camera operators are occasionally surprised by the excellent picture quality of high-end consumer camcorders, especially when there is plenty of light available. What, then, is the difference? Why bother with the heavier and much more expensive equipment?

The most obvious difference is that professional cameras can accept *genlock*—a signal that provides multiple cameras with a general synchronization pulse, called *house sync*, enabling them to scan in exactly the same way. This synchronized scanning is especially important when you want to switch instantly from one camera to another, as during a live pickup of a football game. Also, most professional cameras have much better lenses than do consumer camcorders. ENG/EFP camera lenses have better optics (high-quality lens elements), a higher zoom range, a smoother zoom mechanism, and a wider maximum aperture. Most often, good ENG/EFP lenses allow you to zoom out to a much wider angle than do consumer-camera lenses.

ENG/EFP cameras also have additional electronics that produce high-quality pictures that will not deteriorate substantially when sent over the air or when recorded on videotape. The better the pictures you send to the videotape recorder or transmitter, the better they look when seen on the television receiver. It is often the recording system inside the camcorder, however, that finally determines whether your video and audio will maintain its quality in postproduction. The DVCPRO and DVCAM VTR systems are pretty much the same, regardless of whether they are used in high-end prosumer or the higher-end professional camcorders.

But don't worry: You don't need a high-end ENG/EFP camera to produce interesting videotapes. Good camera operation depends much more on what pictures you shoot and how you frame them than on the technical specifications of the camcorder. The discussion in chapter 5 about looking through the viewfinder will help you obtain maximally effective shots.

ONCE AGAIN, REMEMBER...

Basic Camera Elements

These include the lens, the beam splitter, the imaging device—which is usually a CCD (charge-coupled device)—and the viewfinder.

Lenses

Lenses are classified by the focal length (short and long), angle of view (wide and narrow), and speed (largest aperture expressed in the lowest *f*-stop). The zoom lens has a variable focal length. The zoom range is stated as a ratio, such as 20:1 or 20× (can show the angle of view twenty times narrower than the extreme-wide-angle position with the background greatly magnified). A fast lens lets a relatively large amount of light pass through, a slow lens relatively little. The speed of the lens is determined by the maximum aperture, or iris opening. The specific aperture is indicated by *f*-stops.

Beam Splitter and Imaging Device

These devices change the optical image of the lens to a video signal. The beam splitter divides the light that comes through the lens into red, green, and blue (RGB) light beams. The imaging device—a CCD—transduces (changes) the colored light beams into electric energy.

Studio Camera

This is a large, high-quality camera typically used in the studio. It is normally mounted on a studio pedestal. The camera chain consists of the camera itself, a power supply, a sync generator, and the CCU (camera control unit).

ENG/EFP Camera

This is a portable camera, designed to be carried and operated by a single person. It contains the entire camera chain in the camera itself and is normally battery-powered.

Camcorder

A camcorder is a portable, self-contained camera that has a videotape recorder (VTR) built in or is capable of having a VTR attached (docking). Professional camcorders have genlock capability (the scanning of several cameras and electronic equipment can be synchronized), a high-quality zoom lens, and a high-quality VTR. All consumer camcorders have a built-in VTR.

 Z E T T L ' S   V I D E O   L A B   2 . 1

*Before practicing with an actual camera, you may want to do some zooming and adjusting of the lens aperture for optimal exposure with the virtual zoom lens on the CD-ROM. The first three tapes of the camera monitor also show you the various focal-length positions of the zoom lens and help you understand the relationships among aperture, f-stop, and exposure. Click on the **camera** monitor and listen to what Sonny has to say about camera operation in general on tape 1 **Meet Sonny.***

RUN ZVL 1

Now load tape 2 **Zoom Lens** and play the introduction and the succeeding five modules (**Focal length, Zoom control, Normal, Wide,** and **Narrow**.) Note how a zoom-in results in a progressively narrower focal length, which you perceive as a closer shot. Watch how the zoom ring (showing a focal-length scale in millimeters) moves to a higher number (longer focal length) during a zoom-in, and back to a lower number during the zoom-out. The ratio between the highest and the lowest number on the zoom ring gives you the zoom range of the lens. In this case, its longest focal length is 153mm and its shortest focal length 8.5mm. The zoom range is, therefore, $153 \div 8.5 = 18$. This virtual lens has a hefty zoom range of 18:1—almost twice the $10\times$ (10:1) range of your camcorder.

RUN ZVL 2 Tape 3 **Exposure Control** demonstrates the difference between iris and aperture; aperture and *f*-stop; and *f*-stop setting and exposure. Play module 1 **Aperture**. Note that the iris is the mechanism that makes the aperture larger or smaller, letting more or less light pass through the lens. Module 2 **ƒ-stop** shows the inverse relationship between *f*-stop and aperture, which means that small *f*-stop numbers indicate large apertures, and large *f*-stop numbers indicate small apertures. Notice how when you move the aperture ring to a higher *f*-stop, the picture gets underexposed—and overexposed when you open the lens to a low *f*-stop. Finally, adjust the lens again for optimal exposure and note the *f*-stop.

RUN ZVL 3 Now play module 3 **Auto iris**. Watch how the auto iris can become a hazard rather than a production aid under certain lighting conditions. With some experience, you will probably prefer the manual iris over the automatic iris control.

K E Y   C O N C E P T S

- The lower the **ƒ**-stop number, the larger the aperture and the more light is transmitted. A fast lens has a low minimum **ƒ**-stop number (such as **ƒ/1.4**).

- The higher the **ƒ**-stop number, the smaller the aperture and the less light is transmitted. A slow lens has a relatively high minimum **ƒ**-stop number (such as **ƒ/4.5**).

- The CCD imaging device converts the light variations of an image into electric energy—the video signal.

- The composite color signal combines an RGB chrominance (C) channel with a black-and-white luminance (Y) channel.

- The camera chain consists of the camera head (actual camera), the power supply, the sync generator, and the camera control unit (CCU).

- A camcorder has its VTR built into the camera.

CHAPTER **5**

KEY TERMS

aspect ratio The ratio of the width of the television screen to its height. In STV (standard television), it is 4 × 3 (four units wide by three units high); for HDTV (high-definition television) it is 16 × 9 (sixteen units wide by nine units high).

close-up (CU) Object or any part of it seen at close range and framed tightly. The close-up can be extreme (extreme or big close-up) or rather loose (medium close-up).

cross-shot (X/S) Similar to over-the-shoulder shot, except that the camera-near person is completely out of the shot.

depth of field The area in which all objects, located at different distances from the camera, appear in focus. Depends primarily on the focal length of the lens, its *f*-stop, and the distance from the camera to the object.

field of view The portion of a scene visible through a particular lens; its vista. Expressed in symbols, such as *CU* for close-up.

headroom The space left between the top of the head and the upper screen edge.

leadroom The space left in front of a laterally moving object or person.

long shot (LS) Object seen from far away or framed very loosely. The extreme long shot shows the object from a great distance. Also called *establishing shot*.

medium shot (MS) Object seen from a medium distance. Covers any framing between a long shot and a close-up.

noseroom The space left in front of a person looking or pointing toward the edge of the screen.

over-the-shoulder shot (O/S) Camera looks over the camera-near person's shoulder (shoulder and back of head included in shot) at the other person.

psychological closure Mentally filling in missing visual information that will lead to a complete and stable configuration. Also called *closure*.

vector A directional screen force. There are graphic, index, and motion vectors.

z-axis Indicates screen depth. Extends from camera lens to horizon.

Looking Through the Viewfinder

AS soon as you point your camera at some object or event, you need to make certain decisions about what to shoot and how to shoot it. The relatively small screen of STV (standard television) has made video a close-up medium. Because of this requirement, and often limited presentation time, you cannot usually show an entire event. You must select only the most significant details and then show them in the most effective way possible. When shooting for large-screen HDTV (high-definition television), you have a little more elbow room, but the basic compositional principles of framing a shot still apply.

Which event details you select depends on how much time you have to study the event. If you have to cover a breaking news story, there is little time to research it in depth. Nevertheless, you must try to grasp its substance and select those details that enable the viewer to reconstruct the event as accurately as possible. For example, a close-up of a worried onlooker during a fire may be much more telling about the people trapped inside than flames shooting out of the house. Stay away from sensational or cute shots, especially if they do not tell the real story.

If you are preparing an event, such as the "demo reel" for Triple-I, your selection of event details can, and should, be much more deliberate.

Effective camera operation depends not just on which details you choose to show, but on how you show them on the screen. In addition to a keen and sensitive eye, you need a basic knowledge of picture *aesthetics*—how to frame static or moving objects and events.

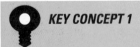

KEY CONCEPT 1   **Select those event details that tell the real story with clarity and impact.**

Familiarity with some basic compositional principles will help you not only produce pictures that have impact and meaning, but also understand how and when to use the camera's operational controls and the zoom lens positions. The technical and operational features of the camera are not designed to make aesthetic decisions for you, but rather to carry out your intentions as faithfully and efficiently as possible.

We have all had, at least once, the rather trying experience of watching someone's vacation videotapes. Unless the person shooting the videotapes was an expert camera operator, you probably saw an incessantly moving view that shifted almost randomly from object to object, annoyingly fast zooms, shots with too much sky or too much ground, and people who seemed to be glued to either the sides or top of the screen, or who had background trees or telephone poles seeming to grow out of their heads.

To help you avoid such aesthetic pitfalls, this chapter takes a closer look at the aesthetics of picture composition.

■ **THE BASICS OF FRAMING A SHOT**
   Aspect ratio, field of view, vectors, composition, and psychological closure

■ **MANIPULATING PICTURE DEPTH**
   Z-axis, lenses and perceived z-axis length, lenses and depth of field, and lenses and perceived z-axis speed

■ **CONTROLLING CAMERA AND OBJECT MOTION**
   Camera movement and zooms, and shooting moving objects

FRAMING A SHOT

The most basic considerations in framing a shot are how much territory you include in the shot, how close an object appears to the viewer, where to place the object relative to the screen edges, and how to make viewers perceive a complete object when only parts of it are visible on the screen. In the terminology of photographic arts, including video, these factors are (1) aspect ratio, (2) field of view, (3) vectors, (4) composition, and (5) psychological closure.

■ **Aspect Ratio**

Your framing of a shot depends to a great extent on the kind of frame you have available, the relationship of the width of the screen to its height, called *aspect ratio*. In video you will most often work with the standard aspect ratio of 4 × 3—the screen is four units wide by three units high. When working in DTV (digital television), many cameras allow you to switch between the standard 4 × 3 ratio to the wide-screen HDTV 16 × 9 ratio. The aspect ratio for HDTV is exclusively 16 × 9. You will

5.1

4 × 3 ASPECT RATIO

The aspect ratio of STV (standard television) is four units wide by three units high.

5.2

16 × 9 ASPECT RATIO

The HDTV (high-definition television) aspect ratio is 16 units wide by nine units high. Most DTV (digital television) cameras permit switching to the standard 4 × 3 ratio or the wide-screen 16 × 9 ratio.

find that on the small screen, your compositions will not differ significantly between the two aspect ratios. **SEE 5.1 AND 5.2**

On a large video screen or when video is projected onto a large movie screen, however, the difference between the two aspect ratios is prominent. A close-up of a face is much more easily and effectively framed in the 4 × 3 aspect ratio than on the HDTV screen. On the other hand, the wide-screen 16 × 9 aspect ratio allows you to frame wide vistas without losing impact. Also, special effects are much more obvious, if not overbearing, on the HDTV screen.

Field of View

Field of view refers to how close the object seems to the viewer, or how much of the "field," or scenery, in front of you is in the shot.

When organized by how close we see the object, there are five field-of-view designations: *extreme long shot* (ELS or XLS), **long shot (LS)**, **medium shot (MS)**, **close-up (CU)**, and *extreme close-up* (ECU or XCU). **SEE 5.3**

5.3

FIELD-OF-VIEW DISTANCE STEPS

The field-of-view distance steps are relative and depend on how a long shot or close-up is visualized.

Extreme long shot (ELS or XLS) or cover shot

Long shot (LS) or full shot

Medium shot (MS) or waist shot

Close-up (CU)

Extreme close-up (ECU or XCU)

When categorized by how much of a person we see, the shots are called: (1) *bust shot*, which frames the upper part of a person, (2) *knee shot*, which shows the person approximately from the knees up, (3) *two-shot*, which shows two people or objects in the frame, (4) *three-shot*, which shows three people or objects in the frame, (5) **over-the-shoulder shot (O/S)**, which shows the camera looking at someone over the shoulder of another person nearer to the camera, and (6) **cross-shot (X/S)**, which looks alternately at one or the other person, with the camera-near person completely out of the shot. **SEE 5.4**

The field of view is relative, which means that what you consider a close-up someone else may think of as a medium shot. Because of the relatively small size of the standard video screen, the close-up is the most frequently used field of view

5.4

AREA FIELD OF VIEW

Other shot designations tell where the subject is cut off by the upper or lower part of the frame, or by how many subjects are in the frame or how they are arranged in it.

Bust shot

Knee shot

Two-shot
(two people in the frame)

Three-shot
(three people in the frame)

Over-the-shoulder shot (O/S)

Cross-shot (X/S)

in video production. These designations hold true regardless of whether you shoot for a 4 × 3 or a 16 × 9 aspect ratio.

You can change the field of view either by moving the camera closer to the event or farther away from it, or by changing the focal length of the lens by zooming in or out. As you learned in chapter 4, zooming in puts the lens in the narrow-angle (telephoto) position and brings the subject closer to the camera for a close-up view. When you zoom out, the lens gradually assumes a wide-angle position and shows more territory farther away. There are important visual differences between moving the camera closer or farther away from the subject and zooming in and out. We discuss these differences in the context of controlling camera and object motion later in this chapter. *READY ZVL 1*

KEY CONCEPT 2   **Video is a close-up medium.**

Vectors

A *vector* is a directional force with various strengths. This concept will help you understand and control the various screen forces generated by someone looking, pointing, or moving in a particular direction or even by the horizontal and vertical lines of a room, desk, or door. A thorough understanding of vectors will aid you in *blocking*—designing—effective movement of talent and cameras. There are three basic vectors: (1) *graphic vectors,* (2) *index vectors,* and (3) *motion vectors.*

5.5

GRAPHIC VECTORS

Graphic vectors are created by lines or an arrangement of stationary objects that lead the eye in a particular direction.

Graphic vectors These vectors are created by lines or an arrangement of stationary objects that lead the eye in a particular direction. Look around you. You are surrounded by graphic vectors, such as the horizontal and vertical lines that are formed by this book you are reading, the window and door frames in the room, or the line where the walls meet the ceiling. Cars neatly lined up in a parking lot create graphic vectors, as do the lines created by a power pole and the wires. **SEE 5.5**

Index vectors These vectors are created by something that points unquestionably in a certain direction, such as an arrow, a one-way-street sign, or somebody looking or pointing in a specific direction. **SEE 5.6** The difference between graphic and index vectors is that index vectors are much more definite as to direction. Going against the index vector of a one-way sign may confuse your mental map as well as physically shake you up.

5.6

INDEX VECTORS

Index vectors are created by someone or something that points unquestionably in a certain direction.

Motion vectors   This type of vector is created by an object that is actually moving, or is perceived to be moving, on the screen. People walking, a car speeding along the highway, a bird in flight—all form motion vectors. For an illustration of motion vectors, look around you where things are moving; they cannot be illustrated by a still picture.

 KEY CONCEPT 3   Vectors are directional forces within the screen that influence composition and the blocking of talent and cameras.

Composition

Our perceptual faculties are always striving to stabilize the chaotic world around us. Good picture composition helps us in this task. Some of the most basic compositional factors involve (1) subject placement, (2) headroom and leadroom, and (3) the horizon line.

Subject placement   The most stable and prominent picture area is screen-center. If you want to draw attention to a single subject, place it there. **SEE 5.7** The same goes for framing a person who is addressing viewers directly, such as a newscaster or a company president. **SEE 5.8**

 KEY CONCEPT 4   The most stable picture area is screen-center.

5.7

SCREEN-CENTER PLACEMENT

The most stable screen position is screen-center. All screen forces are neutralized at this point.

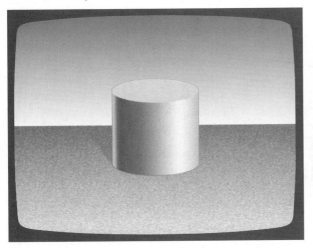

5.8

SCREEN-CENTER PLACEMENT OF NEWSCASTER

A single newscaster should be placed screen-center. This position draws undivided attention to the newscaster and what he is saying.

5.9

PICTURE BALANCE

When the newscaster has to share the screen space with other visual elements, the elements must be placed in opposite screen halves so that they balance each other.

If the newscaster has to share screen space with a visual, such as the secondary frame that contains illustrative material, you obviously need to move the newscaster to one side, not only to make room for the visual, but also to balance the two picture elements within the frame. **SEE 5.9** Sometimes when you frame large vistas that contain a distinct single vertical element, such as a telephone pole, tree, or fence post, you can place the single vertical element off-center, at about the one-third or two-thirds mark of screen width. Such nonsymmetrical framing in which the two unequal parts of the screen contain different visual elements is often called *golden section framing*. It makes the picture look more dynamic and the horizon less divided than if you placed the vertical object exactly at midpoint. **SEE 5.10** 🔘 *READY ZVL 2*

5.10

NONSYMMETRICAL FRAMING

A prominent horizontal line can best be divided by a vertical object located at about two-fifths (for the STV aspect ratio) or one-third (for the HDTV aspect ratio) the distance from either the left or the right screen edge. This way the screen is not divided visually into two equal halves, which makes for a more dynamic and interesting composition.

Headroom and leadroom   Somehow the edges of the video screen seem to act like magnets and attract objects close to them. This pull is especially strong at the top and bottom edges of the screen. For example, if you frame a man so that his head touches the upper screen edge, his head seems to be pulled up, or even attached, to the frame. **SEE 5.11** To counteract this pull, you must leave adequate space, called *headroom*. **SEE 5.12**

5.11

NO HEADROOM

Without headroom, the person seems to be glued to the top edge of the screen.

5.12

CORRECT HEADROOM

Correct headroom neutralizes the magnetic pull of the upper edge and makes the person look comfortable within the frame.

5.13

TOO MUCH HEADROOM

Too much headroom tends to
dwarf the person and push the
image against the lower half
of the screen.

If you leave too much headroom, however, the bottom edge exerts its force
and seems to pull the man downward. **SEE 5.13** Because you inevitably lose some
picture space when showing videotape on a television set, or when actually
transmitting via cable or an on-the-air channel, you should leave just a little more
headroom than what seems appropriate. This way the viewer will see framing with
exactly the right headroom. **SEE 5.14**

  KEY CONCEPT 5   **Headroom neutralizes the pull of the upper screen edge.**

5.14

HEADROOM FOR TRANSMISSION

The framing on the left is correct for the viewfinder display, but the inevitable picture loss during
transmission requires more initial headroom. The framing on the right is, therefore, more appropriate.

Picture loss

5.15

NO NOSEROOM

Without any space between the nose and the screen edge, the person seems to be glued to the screen edge or crashing into it.

5.16

PROPER NOSEROOM

This noseroom is sufficient to counter the pull of the screen and the force of the glance.

The sides of the frame contain similar graphical "magnets" that seem to pull persons or objects toward them, especially when they are oriented toward one or the other side of the screen. **SEE 5.15** Do you feel that this is a good composition? Of course not. The person seems to push his nose into the right screen edge. Correct framing requires some breathing room in front of his nose to reduce the force of his glance and the pull of the screen edge. This is why this type of leadroom is called *noseroom*. **SEE 5.16**

5.17

NO LEADROOM

Without proper leadroom, the laterally moving subject or object seems oddly impeded by the screen edge.

5.18

PROPER LEADROOM

With proper leadroom, the laterally moving subject or object seems to move freely in the given direction.

The same principle operates when you frame someone moving laterally. **SEE 5.17** You must leave some room in the direction of movement to show where the person is going and to absorb some of the directional energy of the vector.

Because the camera must be somewhat ahead of the subject's motion and should lead the action rather than follow it, this is called **leadroom**. It is not always easy to keep proper leadroom for a moving person or object, especially if the subject moves rather quickly. A good rule of thumb is to leave about two-thirds of the screen space ahead of the moving person or object. **SEE 5.18**

With an understanding of vectors, we can explain more accurately the basic compositional principles just discussed. When we frame a telephone pole or fence post somewhat off-center to divide a smooth horizon line, we basically divide a prominent horizontal graphic vector with a strong vertical one. To avoid dividing the screen symmetrically—into two equal halves—we place the vertical vector at approximately the two-fifths mark of the STV screen width. In the HDTV frame, you can place the vertical vector at one-third of the screen width. This way the horizontal vector is divided into balanced yet more dynamic proportions than with a symmetrical division.

If someone is looking or pointing directly screen-left or screen-right, you must give this vector some room to play out by leaving some leadroom in the direction indicated, as shown in figure 5.16. As soon as the person looks straight into the camera, however, the index vector loses its force. Consequently, you must adjust the camera so that the person is placed screen-center. The same principle applies for motion vectors. If someone is running laterally to the camera, you must *pan* the camera (turn it horizontally) ahead of the person to compensate for the strong motion vector, as illustrated in figure 5.18.

As you can see, leadroom must compensate for two screen forces: the magnetic pull of the frame and, especially, the directional force of index or motion vectors. It is this combination of forces that causes a composition to look so bad when inadequate leadroom is given. *READY ZVL 3*

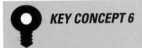 **KEY CONCEPT 6** — **Leadroom neutralizes the index or motion vector force and the pull of the frame.**

Horizon line Normally, we expect to have buildings and people stand upright on level ground. This principle is especially important if you shoot outdoors and where there are distinct vertical and horizontal graphic vectors. For instance, when shooting a reporter standing on a street corner, make sure that the background lines (graphic vectors) are parallel to the upper and lower screen edges. **SEE 5.19** A slight tilt of the handheld camcorder may not readily show up on the foreground person, but is easily detectable by the tilted horizon line.

Sometimes you may want to upset a stable environment and deliberately tilt the camera and, with it, the horizon line. A tilted horizon line can make the picture more dynamic and give it more aesthetic energy. Of course, the subject matter must lend itself to such aesthetic manipulation. **SEE 5.20** Tilting the camera on a dull speaker will not improve his speech; it will simply alert the viewer to sloppy camera work. *READY ZVL 4*

5.19

LEVEL HORIZON LINE

When framing a person standing in front of a prominent background, make sure that the horizon line is level.

TILTING THE HORIZON LINE

A tilted horizon line increases the dynamic tension of the event.

Psychological Closure

Our minds try to make sense out of the multitude of impressions we receive every second and to stabilize the world around us as much as possible. Our perceptual mechanism does this by ignoring most sense impressions that are not immediately relevant and by combining visual cues or filling in missing visual information to arrive at complete and stable configurations. This process is called *psychological closure*, or *closure* for short.

Take a look at the three dots below. Although we see only three separate dots, we perceive a triangle. Through psychological closure we have automatically filled in the missing lines. **SEE 5.21**

Now look at the close-up at the top of the facing page. **SEE 5.22** Again, you mentally fill in the rest of the subject's body although you actually see only her head and shoulders on-screen.

PSYCHOLOGICAL CLOSURE

We perceive these three dots as a triangle by mentally filling in the missing parts.

5.22

FRAMING A CLOSE-UP

A properly framed close-up leads our eyes into off-screen space to complete the figure.

The graphic vectors of the shoulders that led your eye outside the frame helped you to apply closure—to fill in the missing parts. One of the most important principles in framing a close-up in which only part of the subject is shown is to provide sufficient visual clues (graphic vectors) that enable the viewer to complete the figure mentally in off-screen space. Below are two different ECUs (extreme close-ups) of the same person. Which one do you prefer? **SEE 5.23**

5.23

CHOOSING THE PROPER FRAMING

Here are two extreme close-ups. Which one looks better to you?

A   **B**

5.24

PROPER AND IMPROPER FRAMING

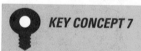 **A** This extreme close-up is improperly framed, because it invites us to apply closure within the frame (a circle) without pointing into off-screen space.

B This framing points properly into off-screen space and makes us apply closure to the whole figure.

Most likely, you chose the framing on the right as the better ECU. You were correct. But why? Because the framing on the right provides ample visual cues that make it easy to extend the lines of the head and neck and to project the missing parts beyond the frame. **SEE 5.24B** The framing in figure 5.23a, however, shows practically no visual cues that would lead us into off-screen space. In fact, our perceptual mechanism is happy with having found a stable configuration within the frame: The head forms a circle. **SEE 5.24A** So far as our automatic perception is concerned, there is no need to go beyond the frame, because we have already found one of the most stable configurations—a circle. The disagreement between our experience—which tells us that there must be a body attached to the head—and our automated perception—which is perfectly happy with the circlelike configuration—is the principal reason why we feel uncomfortable with such a composition. *READY ZVL 5*

KEY CONCEPT 7 **Close-ups that show only part of the object must provide sufficient visual cues for closure in the off-screen space.**

Psychological closure can also produce visual paradoxes and bad composi-tions by having us combine parts of the foreground and background into a single configuration. Examples are the rubber plant on the set that always seems to grow out of the guest's head, or the tree or street sign that extends out of the person standing in front of it. **SEE 5.25** Although we know that such elements are in the

5.25

UNDESIRABLE CLOSURE

Because of our tendency to stabilize the environment, we perceive this background object to be part of the main figure.

background, our perceptual urge for stable figures makes us perceive these visual paradoxes as a single unit.

When looking through the viewfinder, you must learn to see not only the foreground (target) object but also what is *behind* it. By looking behind the target object or scene, you will readily discover potential closure problems, such as the lamp that seems to sit on the performer's head. Looking behind may also reveal other visual hazards, such as billboards, garbage cans, camera cables, or light stands. *READY ZVL 6*

MANIPULATING PICTURE DEPTH

So far we have been concerned mainly with organizing the two-dimensional area of the video screen.[1] This section explores the depth dimension. Whereas the width and height of the video screen have definite limits, the depth dimension extends from the camera lens clear to the horizon. Although illusory, the screen depth, or *z-axis* (a term borrowed from geometry), is the most flexible screen dimension. You can place many more objects along the z-axis than along the width of the screen, and you can have objects move toward and away from the camera at any speed without having to worry about losing the objects in the viewfinder or not leaving enough leadroom.

---

1. For more information on picture composition, see Herbert Zettl, *Sight Sound Motion: Applied Media Aesthetics*, 3d ed. (Belmont, Calif.: Wadsworth Publishing Co., 1999).

Defining the Z-axis

If you point a camera at the cloudless sky, you have just about as long a z-axis as you can get—but it does not show its depth. To show screen depth, you need to define the z-axis by placing objects or people along it. The traditional way of creating the illusion of depth is to have objects placed along the z-axis so that you can identify a distinct foreground, middleground, and background. **SEE 5.26**

Even in a relatively small set, a prominent foreground piece or person will help define the z-axis and suggest screen depth. **SEE 5.27**

5.26

FOREGROUND, MIDDLEGROUND, BACKGROUND

A distinct division of the z-axis into foreground (statue), middleground (bridge), and background (hills) creates the illusion of depth.

5.27

FOREGROUND PERSON IN INDOOR SET

The person standing in the foreground increases the illusion of depth.

Lenses and Z-axis Length

The focal length of a lens has a great influence on our perception of z-axis length and on the distance of objects placed along the z-axis.

Wide-angle position　When zoomed all the way out (wide-angle position), the z-axis appears to be *elongated*, and the objects seem to be *farther apart* than they really are. **SEE 5.28**

Narrow-angle position　When zoomed all the way in (narrow-angle, or telephoto, position), the z-axis seems to be *shorter* than it really is and reduces the distance between the objects placed along it. The z-axis and its objects seem *compressed*. **SEE 5.29**

5.28	5.29
WIDE-ANGLE Z-AXIS	**NARROW-ANGLE Z-AXIS**
The wide-angle lens stretches the z-axis and increases the perceived distance between objects.	The narrow-angle (telephoto) lens shrinks the z-axis and compresses the distance between objects.

Lenses and Depth of Field

You have probably noticed that when you are zoomed all the way in (with the lens in the telephoto position), you have more trouble keeping in focus an object traveling along the z-axis than when zoomed all the way out to a wide-angle position. Also, when zoomed in, the z-axis area that is in focus is considerably more shallow than when zoomed out. We call this area of focus *depth of field*. **SEE 5.30**

In the narrow-angle position, lenses have a shallow depth of field. This means that if you are focused on the foreground object, the middleground and background are out of focus. If you shift your focus to an object in the middleground, the foreground and background objects are out of focus. **SEE 5.31** If you focus on the background, the middleground and foreground objects are out of focus. Also, an object can move only a short distance along the z-axis before it gets out of focus.

5.30

DEPTH OF FIELD

The area of the z-axis in which the objects appear in focus is called depth of field.

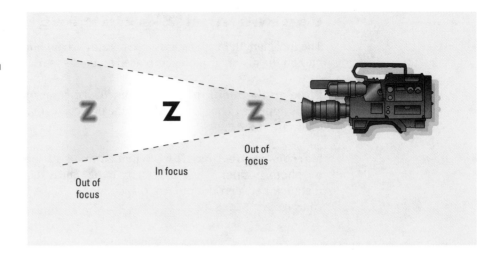

Out of focus

In focus

Out of focus

5.31

SHALLOW DEPTH OF FIELD

Narrow-angle (telephoto) lenses have a shallow depth of field. When zoomed in, the depth of field is shallow.

5.32

GREAT DEPTH OF FIELD

Wide-angle lenses have a great depth of field. When zoomed out, the depth of field is great.

A wide-angle position creates a great depth of field: Objects that are widely scattered along the z-axis are all in focus. For example, when you focus on the foreground object in a large depth of field, the middleground and background objects remain in focus as well, and an object can travel a great distance along the z-axis without getting out of focus. **SEE 5.32**

In addition to the focal length of a lens (zoom lens position), its aperture also influences the depth of field. A large aperture (small *f*-stop number) contributes to a shallow depth of field; a small aperture (large *f*-stop number) to a large depth of field.

You will find that a great depth of field is desirable for most routine productions. Especially when running after a news story, you want to show as much of the event as clearly as possible without having to worry about keeping the picture in focus. This is why you should zoom out and keep the zoom lens in the wide-angle position. When you need a closer shot, you simply move the camera closer to the event. With the lens in the wide-angle position, the depth of field remains great enough to keep in focus, even when you or the object moves.

In a more deliberate production, there are many instances where a shallow depth of field is preferred. For example, you may be asked to show the relationship between two components of a machine. You can do this by having an arrow graphic connect the two parts, but you can also line them up along the z-axis and shift the focus from one component to the other. This *racking focus* will show the relationship in a more subtle, and perhaps more compelling way, than would the arrow. By focusing on the target object while keeping everything else out of focus, you can emphasize the target without eliminating the environment. A shallow depth of field shows the viewer what is important without isolating it from its surroundings. *READY ZVL 7*

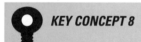

KEY CONCEPT 8   **With the zoom lens in a narrow-angle position (zoomed all the way in), you have a shallow depth of field; keeping focus is difficult. With the zoom lens in a wide-angle position (zoomed all the way out), you have a great depth of field; keeping focus is relatively easy.**

Lenses and Z-axis Speed

Because a narrow-angle lens position compresses the z-axis, the movement of objects along the z-axis is equally compressed. When *zoomed all the way in,* cars seem much more crowded and moving *more slowly* than they actually are. When *zoomed all the way out,* they seem farther apart and moving much *faster* than they actually are. Simply by putting the zoom lens in a narrow-angle or wide-angle position, you can manipulate the viewer's perception of how fast objects move along the z-axis.

If you want to show how crowded a highway is and how slow the traffic moves during rush hour, what zoom lens position would you use? You probably opted correctly for the narrow-angle position. The narrow-angle lens compresses the z-axis and, consequently, shows the cars crowding each other and moving very slowly toward or away from you. But when you want to intensify the speed of a champion bicycler or a dancer's leap, you zoom out. With the lens in a wide-angle position, the z-axis seems elongated and the movement is duly accelerated.

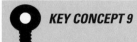

KEY CONCEPT 9   A narrow-angle lens position (zoomed all the way in) compresses the z-axis and slows down z-axis motion. A wide-angle lens position (zoomed all the way out) stretches the z-axis and speeds up z-axis motion.

CONTROLLING CAMERA AND OBJECT MOTION

Here we cover only a few of the main aesthetic principles of camera and object motion. These principles include some of the most obvious do's and don'ts of moving the camera, zooming, and blocking object movement for the camera. Additional information about controlling camera and object motion is presented in subsequent chapters.

Controlling Camera Movement and Zooms

If there is any one sign that points to an inexperienced camera operator, it is excessive camera movement and zooms. Like most of us, you've probably had to sit through a few showings of videotapes in which the camera moved aimlessly from point to point and continually zoomed in and out. The wildly roaming camera reminds us more of a firefighter's hose than photographic artistry, and the fast out-of-focus zooms produce more eyestrain than dramatic impact.

The moving camera   For some reason, inexperienced camera operators think that it is the camera that has to do the moving rather than the object in front of it, especially when there is not much object motion. If nothing moves, so be it. Aesthetic energy does not come from unmotivated camera movement, but from the event itself, whether it is in motion or not.

If there are any hard-and-fast aesthetic rules in camera operation, this is one of them: *Always try to keep the camera as steady as possible and have the people and objects in front of the camera do the moving.* The problem with an incessantly moving camera is that it draws too much attention to itself. It is, after all, the *event* you want to show, not aimless camera movement.

For variety and to provide viewers with different points of view, you can shift camera angles or change the distance of camera to event. Even if there is absolutely no movement in the event, different angles and fields of view will provide enough change to give viewers more information about the event and to keep their interest. To restrict your camera moves, you should mount the camera on a tripod or other camera support whenever possible, even if the camera is small. We discuss handling the camera with or without camera mounts in chapter 6.

KEY CONCEPT 10   Whenever possible, keep the camera still and let the event do the moving.

Fast zooms   Fast, unmotivated zooms are as annoying as the needlessly roving camera. The major problem is that the zoom—even more than camera motion—is a highly visible technique that easily draws attention to itself. The worst thing you can do is follow a fast zoom-in or zoom-out with an equally fast zoom in the opposite direction. Instead, you should rest on the target object for a while after a zoom before switching to another angle and point of view. Constant zooming in and out will make the viewers feel cheated: First you bring the event to them through zooming in, only to take it away again immediately after by zooming out. In the worst case, it may make the viewers slightly nauseated.

Unless you are planning a highly dramatic effect, a zoom should remain largely unnoticed by the viewer. If you have to zoom, do it slowly. Zooming in to a close-up increases tension; zooming out releases it.

Generally, you will find that it is easier to start with a close-up view of the object and then zoom out than to do it the other way around. Zooming out from a close-up also makes it easier to keep in focus than when zooming in, especially if you do not have time to calibrate (preset) the zoom lens. You will learn more about calibrating a zoom lens in chapter 6. Even with auto-focus, fast zooms cause focus problems. The auto-focus "radar" may not have enough time to keep up with constantly changing picture requirements. Consequently, the picture will pop in and out of focus during the zoom.

 KEY CONCEPT 11   **Avoid fast and constant zooming in and out.**

Zoom versus dolly   There is an important aesthetic difference between a zoom and a dolly. *Dollying* means moving the camera along the z-axis toward or away from the object either by carrying the camera or, more often, by means of a camera support (see chapter 6). When you zoom in or out, the event seems to move toward or away from the viewer; in a dolly-in or dolly-out, the viewer seems to move with the camera toward or away from the event. If, for example, you want to show that the ringing telephone bears an important message, you zoom in on the phone, rather than dolly in. The fast zoom virtually catapults the phone toward the screen and the viewer. But when you want to have the viewer identify with a student who is late for class, you dolly the camera toward the only empty chair rather than zoom in on it. The dolly will take the viewer into the classroom and to the empty chair. A zoom would bring the chair to the viewer (and the student), and that rarely happens, even in a rather friendly classroom atmosphere. The reason for this aesthetic difference is that the camera remains stationary during the zoom, whereas during a dolly it is actually moving into the scene.

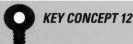 **KEY CONCEPT 12**   **A zoom-in brings the object to the viewer; a dolly-in takes the viewer to the object.**

■ Controlling Object Motion

Despite all the theory on providing leadroom for a laterally moving object, it is hard to keep it properly framed in the traditional 4 × 3 screen, especially if it moves swiftly or if you are composing a tight shot. Sometimes even experienced camera operators have trouble following an object that moves laterally along the x-axis (screen-left or screen-right) in a tight shot. Just try following somebody moving sideways fairly close to the camera; you will be glad just to keep the person in the viewfinder! Framing lateral motion is somewhat easier when shooting with the 16 × 9 HDTV aspect ratio. In any case, when the subject moves in a straight line along the z-axis—toward or away from the camera—you will have little trouble keeping the person in the shot and properly framed—even if he or she walks briskly. Because of the relatively small size of the video screen, blocking people along the z-axis rather than the x-axis not only is easier on the camera operator, but also produces shots that have greater impact.

Blocking means placing people in various precise positions on a set and having them move and do certain things in a predetermined way. *Z-axis blocking* makes it relatively easy to keep several people in a single shot and to capture their movements without excess camera motion. With the lens in a wide-angle position, z-axis movement can look dramatic and spectacular without putting too much strain on the camera operator or the performer. Also, as you have just learned, the wide-angle lens provides a large enough depth of field so that any focus adjustment becomes unnecessary. **SEE 5.33**

Even when you have no control over the event and cannot influence the blocking, as is the case in most ENG (electronic news gathering), you can still place the camera so that the object motion conforms to the aesthetic require-ments of the small screen and the stable camera: Simply position the camera in such a way that most of the object movement occurs along the z-axis. For example, if you cover a parade, don't stand on the sidewalk and try to capture the various bands and floats as they move past you—step onto the street and shoot against the oncoming parade traffic. With a zoom lens in the wide-angle position, you will have little trouble covering the event in long shots and close-ups while staying in focus. 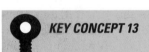 *READY ZVL 8*

KEY CONCEPT 13   **Z-axis movement is well suited to the aesthetic requirements of the small video screen and is relatively simple to shoot.**

Framing effective shots is a basic requirement for competent camera work, regardless of whether you work with a small analog consumer camcorder or an HDTV studio camera.

5.33

Z-AXIS BLOCKING

Blocking along the z-axis suits the small video screen.

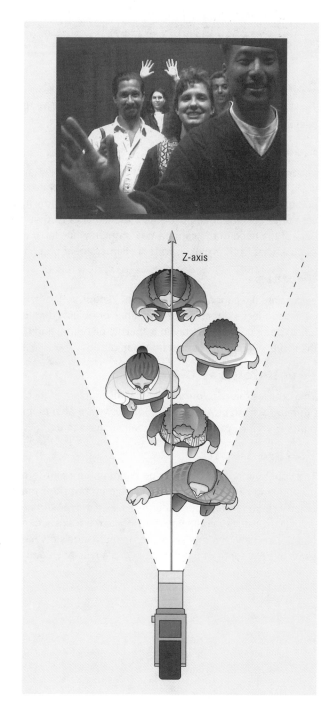

ONCE AGAIN, REMEMBER...

▇ Aspect Ratio

The STV (standard television) aspect ratio is 4×3. The HDTV (high-definition television) aspect ratio is 16×9.

▇ Field of View

The field of view is usually expressed in five shots, ranging from extreme long shot (ELS) to extreme close-up (ECU). Other shot designations refer to how much of a person we see (such as bust shot or knee shot) or how many people we see (two-shot or three-shot). In an over-the-shoulder shot (O/S), we see the shoulder and the back of the head of the camera-near person while looking at the camera-far person. A cross-shot (X/S) is closer, with the camera-near person out of the shot.

▇ Vectors

Vectors are directional screen forces of various strengths. There are graphic vectors, which suggest a direction through lines or objects that form a line; index vectors, which point unquestionably in a specific direction; and motion vectors, which show the actual event or its screen image in motion.

▇ Psychological Closure

This process refers to our perceptual mechanism that completes incomplete figures. Through psychological closure we are able to mentally "see" a complete figure even if it is shown only partially in a close-up.

▇ Picture Depth

The depth dimension depends on defining the z-axis into foreground, middle-ground, and background. Wide-angle zoom positions make the z-axis look longer; objects seem farther apart, and their z-axis movement appears faster than it actually is. Narrow-angle positions make the z-axis look shorter; objects seem more compressed and their z-axis movement appears slower. Wide-angle lens positions show a great depth of field; narrow-angle lens positions show a shallow one.

Z E T T L ' S   V I D E O   L A B   2 . 1

*This time your CD-ROM will work overtime for you and offer you no less than four tapes with many good examples of the compositional basics you have just learned. All these tapes are available by clicking on the **camera** monitor.*

RUN ZVL 1   Load tape 6 **Composition** and play the introduction. Although Sonny tells you that you should have looked at tape 5 **Screen Forces** first, play the **Field of view** module. Compare the field-of-view steps in this module with the figures in this chapter. You can readily see that the shot designations are similar, although the exact field of view—how tight a close-up is framed, for example—depends on the cameraperson's or director's sense of composition and general visual approach.

RUN ZVL 2   Now you can follow Sonny's advice and go back and watch tape 5 **Screen Forces**. Pay particular attention to module 1 **Vectors**. A thorough understanding of the three types of vectors will not only help you compose effective pictures but also achieve smooth continuity in editing. The pull of the frame is explained in module 2 **Frame edge**. You will encounter the magnetic pull of the frame again in tape 6 **Composition** when headroom and leadroom are demonstrated. Save module 3 **Horizon** for the ZVL 4 exercise and move on to module 4 **Balance**. Note that balance can be achieved not only through positioning objects in certain screen areas, but also through prominent vectors. Tape 6 **Composition** gives more-specific information on how vectors influence picture balance.

RUN ZVL 3   Now play the rest of tape 6 **Composition**. Start with module 2 **Headroom** and note how we counteract the magnetism of the top edge of the frame with headroom. Module 3 **Leadroom** shows you how the magnetic pull of the frame edges and the force of index and motion vectors influence composition and how noseroom and leadroom neutralize these screen forces. Run this module again and pay particular attention to how the increased force of the index vector (the woman turning more and more toward the left screen edge) requires that the camera give her progressively more noseroom. The same goes for motion vectors. As you can see, you have to increase the leadroom for the stronger bicycle motion vectors.

RUN ZVL 4   Even if you have run the **Horizon** module on tape 5 **Screen Forces**, go back to it briefly and see how the tilting of the horizon increases the aesthetic energy of the shot and, with it, the speed of the bicyclers.

RUN ZVL 5   Go to Master Control, load tape 6 **Composition**, and play module 6 **Closure**. Now you see vividly how the head of the woman seems bereft of her body and floats in midscreen. The reason is that we do not get any graphic clues (graphic vectors) to extend the figure into off-screen space. You can now see why you should avoid having the natural dividing lines of a person or object coincide with with upper or lower screen edge. Psychological closure is, like vectors, a powerful perceptual factor in composing effective pictures.

RUN ZVL 6

Now play module 4 **Close-ups**. You can use psychological closure as an explanation for why we frame a close-up and an extreme close-up as recommended by Sonny. In module 5 **Background**, psychological closure again plays a role and is the primary reason why you perceive the duck to be growing out of the person's head and why Sonny urges you to be especially aware of the background when framing a shot.

RUN ZVL 7

Sonny's introduction to tape 7 **Picture Depth** and the graphic in module 1 **Z-axis** will give you a good idea of what role the z-axis plays in simulating a three-dimensional effect on the two-dimensional surface of the video screen. See how the feeling of the crowded street changes when the camera switches from a z-axis shot to a later view of the same scene? Play module 2 **Lens choice**. The z-axis, represented by the pier, looks quite a bit longer when shot with a wide-angle lens (wide-angle zoom position) than with a narrow-angle lens (narrow-angle zoom position). As you can see, the narrow-angle (long-focal-length) lens (zoom position) emphasizes dramatically the crowded houses on this city street; they become more comfortably spaced when shot with a wide-angle lens.

Before going on to module 3 **Depth of field**, go back to Master Control and load tape 4 **Focusing**. The introduction to this tape gives you the necessary explanation of depth of field and the various factors influencing it. After Sonny's explanation of focus and depth of field, play module 1 **Focus ring**.

Now move on to module 2 **Depth of field**. You can easily see how a shallow depth of field directs your attention to the man sitting closer to the camera. The wide depth of field, on the other hand, does not isolate the camera-near person and allows you to pay attention to the other man on the bench and the background. In module 3 **Great depth**, watch the setting on the zoom lens to the right of the picture. It shows that the lens is zoomed out to its widest angle (8.5mm), which contributes to the great depth of field. Module 4 **Shallow** shows you again how a shallow depth of field directs attention by focusing on the main subject (flowers) while blurring the rest of the z-axis. Note that racking focus as shown in module 5 **Rack focus** requires a shallow depth of field. What would happen if you attempted the rack-focus effect in a great depth of field? Now view the other demonstrations of depth of field on tape 7 **Picture Depth** in module 3 **Depth of field**.

RUN ZVL 8

On tape 8 **Screen Motion**, Sonny demonstrates one aspect of video images that cannot be done in a book: various types of movement. As you can see, the z-axis again plays a prominent role in module 1 **Z-axis**. Watch the cyclist speeding toward the camera. How much does the camera move? Not at all. The camera needs to move very little, if at all, during z-axis motion. Compare this with the fairly brisk pan of the camera to keep the cyclist properly framed in module 2 **Lateral**. When the camera remains still during lateral motion, which zoom position will accelerate lateral motion, zoomed in (narrow-angle) or zoomed out (wide-angle)? Run module 2 **Lateral** again. Note how the woman moves much faster across the screen on a close-up (zoomed in) than in the long shot (zoomed out). Now go back to module 1 **Z-axis** and compare the perceived speeds of the cyclist traveling along the z-axis. Now the wide-angle zoom position accelerates the perceived motion, and the narrow-angle zoom position slows it down. Obviously, the extreme zoom positions (wide-angle and narrow-angle) produce opposite results when used for lateral and z-axis motions.

K E Y   C O N C E P T S

- Select those event details that tell the real story with clarity and impact.

- Video is a close-up medium.

- Vectors are directional forces within the screen that influence composition and the blocking of talent and cameras.

- The most stable picture area is screen-center.

- Headroom neutralizes the pull of the upper screen edge.

- Leadroom neutralizes the index or motion vector force and the pull of the frame.

- Close-ups that show only part of the object must provide sufficient visual cues for closure in the off-screen space.

- With the zoom lens in a narrow-angle position (zoomed all the way in), you have a shallow depth of field; keeping focus is difficult. With the zoom lens in a wide-angle position (zoomed all the way out), you have a great depth of field; keeping focus is relatively easy.

- A narrow-angle lens position (zoomed all the way in) compresses the z-axis and slows down z-axis motion. A wide-angle lens position (zoomed all the way out) stretches the z-axis and speeds up z-axis motion.

- Whenever possible, keep the camera still and let the event do the moving.

- Avoid fast and constant zooming in and out.

- A zoom-in brings the object to the viewer; a dolly-in takes the viewer to the object.

- Z-axis movement is well suited to the aesthetic requirements of the small video screen and is relatively simple to shoot.

KEY TERMS

arc To move the camera in a slightly curved dolly or truck.

calibrate the zoom lens To preset a zoom lens to keep in focus throughout the zoom.

cam head A camera mounting head that permits extremely smooth tilts and pans.

cant Tilting the camera sideways.

crane or boom To move the boom of the camera crane up or down.

dolly To move the camera toward (dolly in) or away from (dolly out) the object.

jib arm A small camera crane that can be operated by the camera-person.

mounting head A device that connects the camera to its support. Also called *pan-and-tilt head*.

pan Horizontal turning of the camera.

pedestal To move the camera up or down via a studio pedestal.

Steadicam A camera mount that allows the operator to walk and run with the camera remaining steady.

studio pedestal Heavy camera dolly that permits raising and lowering of the camera while on the air.

tilt To point the camera up or down.

tongue To move the boom with the camera from left to right or right to left.

tripod A three-legged camera mount.

truck or track To move the camera laterally by means of mobile camera mount.

white balance The adjustments of the color circuits in the camera to produce a white color in lighting of various color temperatures (relative bluishness or reddishness of white light).

Operating the Camera

L **ET'S watch a tourist** who is itching for something interesting to shoot with his brand-new camcorder. He quickly takes aim at the picturesque clock tower of city hall, tilts his camera up to the flag on top, zooms in on the flag, zooms out again, tilts down to the clock, zooms in on the clock, zooms out again, continues to tilt down to the old oak doors, zooms in on the doors and out again, pans over to the park bench where a bird is finishing its lunch, pans over again to city hall, zooms in on the sign that tells about the city hall's colorful history, zooms out again to catch a small child feeding pigeons, and then zooms in on one of the more aggressive pigeons, who refuses to stay in the frame.

Although such camera handling may be good exercise for the arm and the zoom mechanism, it rarely produces satisfactory footage. Such unmotivated camera motion produces images that seem restless and unsettling for anyone except, perhaps, the person who shot them. The tourist would have done much better had his camera been mounted on a small tripod.

When handling a small camcorder with a fold-out viewfinder, you are virtually unrestrained in moving the camera. But when the camera is mounted on a tripod, its movements become much more restricted. Initially, you will probably feel that a tripod constrains your artistry and that it is much better to handhold the camera, so long as it is not too heavy. After some experience in camera operation, however, you will discover that it is actually easier to operate the camera and control picture composition when the camera is mounted on some kind of support. In fact, the art of operating a camera is not as dependent on its electronic design or basic operational controls as it is on its size and especially on how it is mounted.

This chapter explores the basic camera movements and operations, and how they can be accomplished.

■ **BASIC CAMERA MOVEMENTS**
Pan, tilt, cant, pedestal, dolly, truck or track, arc, crane or boom, tongue, and zoom

■ **CAMERA MOUNTS AND HOW TO USE THEM**
The handheld and shoulder-mounted camera, tripods, the studio pedestal, and special camera mounts

■ **OPERATIONAL FEATURES**
White-balancing, focusing, zooming, and some general operational guidelines

BASIC CAMERA MOVEMENTS

The various camera mounts are designed to steady the camera and help you move it as easily and smoothly as possible. To understand the features and functions of camera mounting equipment, you should first learn about the major camera movements. The terms are the same regardless of whether the camera is carried on your shoulder or mounted on a tripod, studio pedestal, or some other camera support.

There are nine basic camera movements: (1) *pan*; (2) *tilt*; (3) *cant*; (4) *pedestal*; (5) *dolly*; (6) *truck* or *track*; (7) *arc*; (8) *crane* or *boom*; and (9) *tongue*. Sometimes the zoom is also included in the major camera movements, although the camera itself does not normally move during a zoom. **SEE 6.1**

Pan Turning the camera horizontally, from left to right or right to left. To *pan right* means to swivel or move the camera clockwise so that the lens points more to the right; to *pan left* means to swivel or move the camera counterclockwise so that the lens points more to the left. For example, if you need more leadroom for an object that moves screen-left, you pan left. If you need more noseroom for someone standing too close to the right screen edge, you pan right.

Tilt Making the camera point up or down. A *tilt up* means to point the camera gradually up. A *tilt down* means to point the camera gradually down. If you need more headroom to counter the pull of the upper frame, you tilt up somewhat. If you have too much headroom and want to see more of the neck and shoulders of a person in a close-up, you tilt down.

Cant Tilting the camera sideways. You can cant the camera either left or right. When you *cant left*, the horizon line will be slanted uphill; its low point will be screen-left, and its high point screen-right. The *cant right* move will produce the opposite effect. Recall that a slanted horizon line makes a picture appear less stable, thereby increasing the energy of the event. Canting a camera is easy with

CP-1

IMAGE FORMATION FOR COLOR VIDEO

The color receiver has three electron guns, each responsible for either the red, green, or blue signal. Each of the beams is assigned to its color dots.

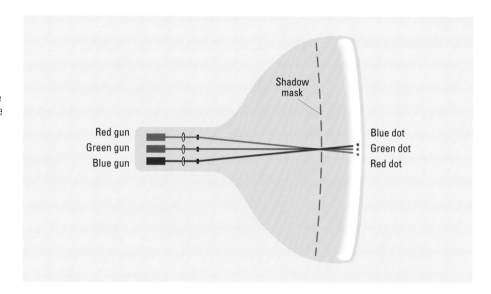

CP-2

RGB BEAM SPLITTER

The prism block consists of prisms and filters that split the incoming white light into the three additive primary colors—red, green, and blue—and direct these colored light beams into their corresponding CCDs.

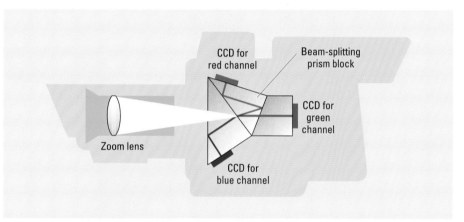

CP-3

NTSC SIGNAL

The NTSC video signal combines the chrominance (C) or RGB color channel with the luminance (Y) or black-and-white channel.

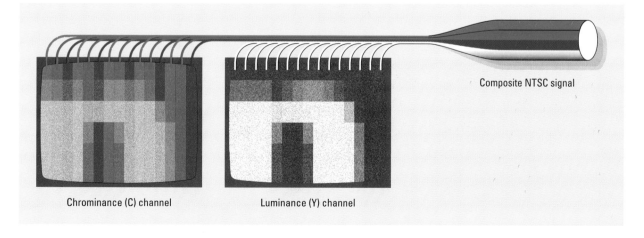

Chrominance (C) channel   Luminance (Y) channel

CP-4

WHITE BALANCE

To counteract tinting caused by variations in color temperature, it is necessary to white-balance the camera.
This adjusts the RGB channels to compensate for the unwanted color cast and make white look white.

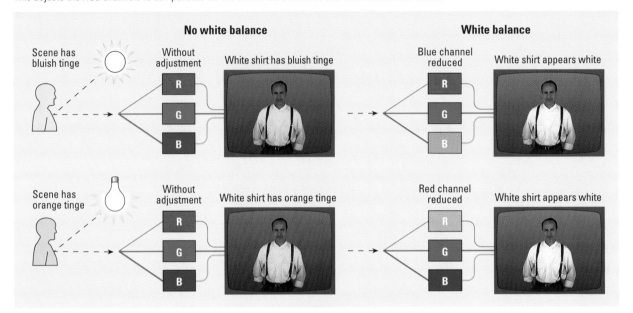

CP-5

ADDITIVE COLOR MIXING

When mixing colored light, the additive primaries are red, green, and blue. All other colors can be achieved by mixing certain quantities of red, green, and blue light. For example, the additive mixture of red and green light produces yellow.

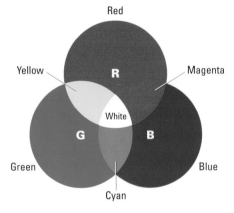

CP-6

CHROMA-KEY EFFECT: WEATHERCAST

A In this chroma key, the weathercaster stands in front of a blue background.

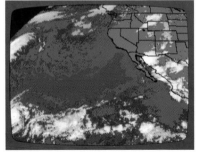

B During the key the blue background is replaced by this computer-enhanced satellite photo.

C The weathercaster seems to stand in front of the satellite photo.

CP-7

GRAPHICS PROGRAM

Graphics programs offer a variety of lines and brush strokes, surface textures, and a wide choice of colors.

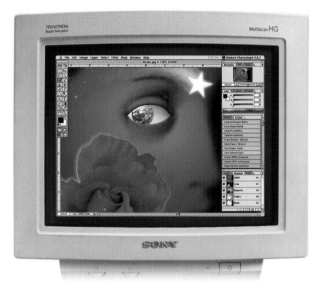

CP-8

FRACTAL LANDSCAPE

Some computer programs allow you to "paint" irregular images using mathematical formulas.

CP-9

MORPHING

Here the image of a person changes gradually into that of a cat.

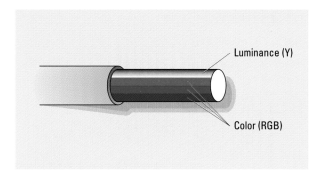

COMPOSITE SYSTEM

The composite system uses a video signal that combines the luminance Y (brightness) and color C information. It needs a single wire to be transported and recorded on videotape as a single signal. It is the standard NTSC system.

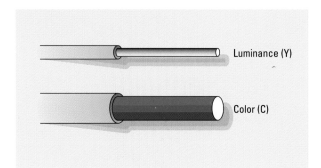

Y/C COMPONENT SYSTEM

The Y/C component system separates the Y (luminance) and C (color) information, but combines the two signals on the videotape. It needs two wires to transport the two separate signals.

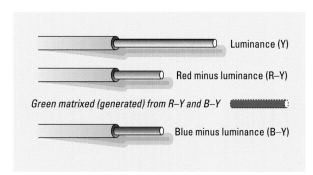

Y/COLOR DIFFERENCE COMPONENT SYSTEM

Like the RGB component system, the Y/color difference component system needs three wires to transport the three component signals: the Y (luminance) signal, the R–Y (red minus luminance) signal and the B–Y (blue minus luminance) signal. The green signal is then matrixed (generated) from these signals.

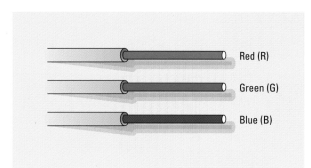

RGB COMPONENT SYSTEM

The RGB component system (also called the RGB system) separates the three RGB signals throughout the recording process. It needs three wires to transport the signal. All accessory equipment must be able to process the three separate channels.

6.1

MAJOR CAMERA MOVEMENTS

The major camera movements are pan, tilt, cant, pedestal, dolly, truck or track, arc, crane or boom, and tongue.

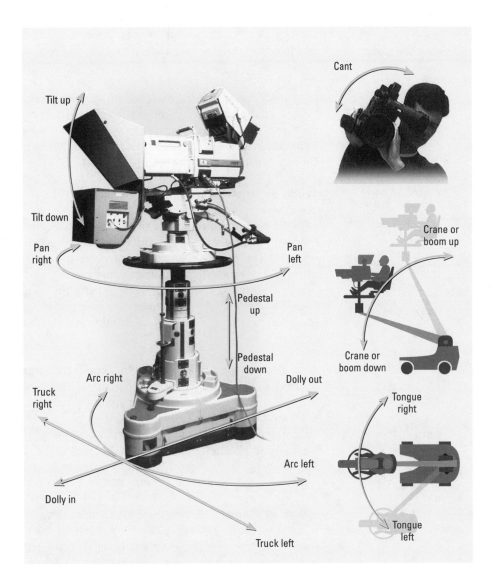

Tilt up

Cant

Tilt down

Pan right

Pan left

Crane or boom up

Pedestal up

Pedestal down

Crane or boom down

Arc right

Dolly out

Truck right

Tongue right

Arc left

Dolly in

Truck left

Tongue left

the handheld or shoulder-mounted camera, but you cannot cant a camera supported by a camera mount.

Pedestal   Elevating or lowering the camera on a center column of a tripod or a studio pedestal. To *pedestal up* you crank or pull up the center column, thereby raising the camera. To *pedestal down* you crank or pull down the center column, thereby lowering the camera. This camera motion puts the camera into different vertical positions, which means that the camera sees the scene as though you were looking at it from the top of a ladder or while kneeling on the floor. You can "pedestal" a handheld camera by simply raising it slowly above your head or lowering it to the ground.

Dolly Moving the camera toward or away from an object in more or less a straight line (along the z-axis) by means of a mobile camera mount. When you *dolly in,* you move the camera closer to the object; when you *dolly out* or *dolly back,* you move the camera farther away from the object. As you recall from chapter 5, in a dolly the viewer seems to be moving with the camera in or out of the scene.

With the handheld or shoulder-mounted camera, you simply walk the camera toward or away from the scene along the z-axis. Some directors call this "dollying" in or out, even if the camera is not mounted on a camera dolly; others simply call for you to get closer or to back up.

Truck or Track Moving the camera laterally by means of a mobile camera mount. When you *truck right* or *truck left,* you move the camera mount to the right or left with the camera pointing at a right angle to the direction of travel. If you want to follow somebody walking on a sidewalk, you would truck with the camera alongside on the street, with the lens pointing at the person. When trucking, you must be especially careful to leave sufficient leadroom for the lateral motion.

Tracking often means the same as trucking. Sometimes tracking refers simply to a moving camera keeping up with a moving object. With a handheld or shoulder-mounted camera, you walk parallel to the moving object while keeping the camera pointed at it.

Arc Moving the camera in a slightly curved dolly or truck movement. To *arc left* means that you dolly in or out in a camera-left curve, or truck left in a curve around the object; to *arc right* means that you dolly in or out in a camera-right curve, or truck to the right in a curve around the object. With the handheld or shoulder-mounted camera, you simply walk in a slight arc while pointing the camera at the scene. Arcing is often required to reveal more of the camera-far person in an over-the-shoulder shot where the camera-near person is blocking or nearly blocking our view of the camera-far person. **SEE 6.2 AND 6.3**

Crane or Boom Moving the camera up or down on a camera crane or jib arm. A crane is a large and bulky device that can lift the camera and its operator, and sometimes a second person (usually the director), up to 30 feet above ground in one impressive sweep. The crane itself is moved by a driver and an assistant. A jib arm is a simpler crane that can be handled by a single camera operator, as shown in figure 6.21. The effect of a crane or boom movement is somewhat similar to pedestaling up or down, except that the camera swoops in a vertical arc over a much greater distance. You could, for instance, use a boom to move the camera from an extreme overhead long shot of dancers to a below-eye-level close-up of one of them, with the camera now shooting from close to the floor. To *crane up* or *boom up* means to raise the boom with the attached camera; to *crane down* or *boom down* means to lower the boom and the attached camera. Simply holding a small camcorder high above your head and then swooping it down close to floor level will not duplicate the feeling of a crane motion. Unless you are 10 feet tall, there is simply not enough height difference between the extreme high and low camera positions to simulate a crane motion.

6.2

CAMERA-FAR PERSON PARTIALLY BLOCKED

In this over-the-shoulder shot, the camera-near person partially blocks the camera-far person.

6.3

ARC CORRECTS BLOCKED SHOT

By arcing right, the camera-far person is properly seen.

Tongue Moving the whole camera from left to right or right to left with the boom of a camera crane or jib arm. When you *tongue* left or right, the camera usually points in the same general direction, with only the boom swinging left or right. Tonguing creates an effect similar to a truck, except that the horizontal arc of the boom with the camera is usually much wider and can be much faster. Tonguing is often combined with a boom-up or boom-down movement. For example, you could use the tonguing effect to follow and intensify the fluid lateral movement of dancers.

The crane and tongue movements are somewhat of a special effect. Even if you have access to a crane, use such extreme camera movements sparingly and only if they contribute to the shot intensity. If the scene is not spread out too much, you may be able to simulate a tonguing motion with a handheld camera by swinging the camera from left to right or right to left while keeping the lens pointed in the same general direction. But without a large crane or jib, you will not be able to duplicate the sweeping lateral motion of tonguing.

Zoom Changing the focal length of a lens through the use of a zoom control while the camera remains stationary. To *zoom in* means to change the lens gradually to a narrow-angle position, thereby making the scene appear to move closer to the viewer; to *zoom out* means to change the lens gradually to a wide-angle position, thereby making the scene appear to move farther away from the viewer. Although the effect of a zoom is one of the object moving toward or away from the screen rather than the camera moving into or out of the scene, the zoom is usually classified as one of the camera "movements." *READY ZVL 1*

CAMERA MOUNTS AND HOW TO USE THEM

You can support a camera (1) by carrying it with your hands or on your shoulder, (2) with a tripod, (3) with a studio pedestal, and (4) with several other special camera mounting devices. They all influence greatly, if not dictate, how you operate the camera.

The Handheld and Shoulder-Mounted Camera

We have already mentioned that the small, handheld camcorder invites excessive camera motion. You can point it easily in any direction and move it effortlessly, especially if you have a foldout viewfinder. Although such high mobility can be an asset, it is also a liability. Too much camera movement draws attention to itself and away from the things you want to show. Unless there is an image stabilizer built into the camera that absorbs minor camera wiggles, you will find it difficult to keep the handheld camera steady. When zoomed all the way in (with the lens in the narrow-angle, or telephoto, position), it is almost impossible to avoid some shaking and unsteadiness in the handheld shot.

6.4

HOLDING THE SMALL CAMCORDER

The small camcorder is steadied by both hands, with the elbows pressed against the body.

To keep the handheld camera as steady as possible, support the camera in the palm of one hand and use the other hand to support the "camera" arm or the camera itself. **SEE 6.4** With a foldout viewfinder, keep your elbows to the body and use your arms as shock absorbers. Try to avoid operating the camera with arms outstretched, which invites annoyingly quick pans and tilts. Inhale and hold your breath during the shot. The lack of oxygen will obviously limit the length of your shot, and that is probably a good thing. Shorter takes that show a variety of viewpoints are much more interesting than a long take with constant panning and zooming. There are small handheld camera mounts (see figure 6.20) that reduce the wobbles of small camcorders. When using your arms as a camera mount, bend your knees slightly when shooting or, better, lean against some sturdy support, such as a building, wall, parked car, or lamppost to increase the stability of the camera. **SEE 6.5**

Always keep the lens in the wide-angle position (zoomed out) to minimize camera wiggles. If you need to get closer to the scene, stop the videotape, walk closer to get the tighter shot, and start the tape again. If you need to zoom, work the zoom controls *gently* during the shot. For a relatively long take without a tripod, try to find something stable on which to place the camera, such as a table, park bench, or the roof or hood of a car.

6.5

STEADYING THE CAMERA OPERATOR

Leaning against some object will steady the camera operator and the camera.

6.6

PANNING THE CAMCORDER

Before panning, point your knees in the direction of the pan, then uncoil your upper body during the pan.

When moving the camera, do it *smoothly*. To pan the camera, move it with your whole body rather than just your arms. Point your knees as much as possible to where you want to end the pan, while keeping your shoulders in the starting position. During the pan, your upper body will uncoil naturally in the direction of your knees and will carry the camera smoothly with it. **SEE 6.6** If you do not "preset" your knees, you will have to coil your body rather than uncoil when panning, which is much harder to do and usually results in jerky camera motion.

When tilting the camera (pointing it up or down), try to bend forward or backward at your waist as much as possible while keeping your arms pressed against your body. As in the pan, your body motion makes the tilt look smoother than if you simply moved your wrists to point the camera up or down.

6.7

WALKING BACKWARD

Walking backward rather than forward makes it easier to keep the camera steady.

When walking with the camera, walk backward rather than forward whenever possible. **SEE 6.7** When walking backward you will automatically lift your heels and walk on the balls of your feet. Your feet rather than your legs will act as shock absorbers. Your body, and with it the camera, will tend to glide along rather than bounce up and down.

For unconventional shots you can tilt the camera sideways, raise it above your head, and shoot over the people or other obstacles in front of you, or you can lower it close to the ground to get some low-angle views. Most regular viewfinders can be adjusted (at least tilted up and down) so that you can see what you are shooting during these maneuvers. The foldout viewfinder offers a great advantage in such situations, especially if you find that the only way to get a good shot is to hold the camera high above your head and aim it more or less in the direction of the event. The foldout display still enables you to see the shot the camera is getting. But even without a viewfinder display, you will probably get some usable shots.

ENG/EFP cameras or camcorders are too large and heavy to be handheld for any length of time and are best supported by your shoulder. Although the shoulder-mounted camera is slightly more restrictive than the small handheld camcorder, the basic moves are much the same.

Assuming that you are right-handed, carry the camera on your right shoulder and slip your right hand through the support strap on the zoom lens to hold the camera and operate the lens. Your left hand is free to steady the camera and work the focus ring at the front of the zoom lens. **SEE 6.8** You need to adjust the viewfinder to fit your prominent (usually right) eye. Some camera operators keep the left eye open to see where they are going; others prefer to close it and concentrate on the viewfinder image. If you are left-handed, reverse the procedures. Some viewfinders can be flipped over for the left eye, and there are lenses with straps and zoom operating controls for the left hand.

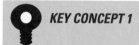

KEY CONCEPT 1   **Keep the handheld or shoulder-mounted camera as steady as possible and zoomed-out when moving.**

6.8

THE SHOULDER-MOUNTED ENG/EFP CAMCORDER

The larger camcorder is carried on the shoulder. One hand slips through a strap attached to the lens, leaving the fingers free to operate the zoom control. The other hand steadies the camera and operates the focus ring.

6.9

TRIPOD WITH SPREADER

The tripod has three adjustable pods that are sometimes secured by a spreader.

Spreader

The Tripod-Supported Camera

Unless you are running after a breaking news story, the best way to keep the camcorder or ENG/EFP camera steady and the movements as smooth as possible is to support it on a *tripod* or some other kind of camera mount. The collapsible tripod has always been the primary camera support for the still photographer and has proved just as effective for the videographer who uses portable cameras.

A good tripod should be lightweight but sturdy enough to support the camera during pans and tilts. Its collapsible legs (pods) must lock securely into place at any extension point and should have rubber cups and spikes at the tips of the legs. The rubber cups prevent the tripod from slipping on smooth surfaces, as do the spikes on rough surfaces.

Most professional tripods come with a *spreader*, a triangular base mount that locks the tips in place and prevents the legs from spreading no matter how much weight is put on them. **SEE 6.9** More-elaborate tripods have a center column that enables you to elevate and lower the camera. All good tripods have an air bubble at the top ring so you can make sure that the tripod is level.

Camera mounting head One of the most important parts of a tripod is its camera *mounting head*. This device, also called the *pan-and-tilt head*, lets you quickly and safely attach and remove the camera unassisted. It also permits smooth pans and tilts. Most tripod mounting heads have a load limit of 30 to 45 pounds—ample to hold even the most elaborate ENG/EFP camcorder. These days the

6.10

MOUNTING HEAD FOR LIGHT CAMERA

The mounting head permits smooth pans and tilts. Its pan and tilt mechanism can be adjusted to various degrees of drag, and it can be locked.

Quick-release plate

Panning handle

problem is not whether the mounting head can support relatively heavy cameras, but whether it can operate smoothly with the lightweight digital camcorders. When using a tripod, check that it is appropriate for the weight of your camera.

You move the mounting head (and with it the camera) with the panning handle that is attached to it. **SEE 6.10** Lifting the handle makes the camera tilt down; pushing it down makes the camera tilt up. Moving the panning handle to the left makes the camera pan right; moving it to the right makes the camera pan left.

A mounting head must provide a certain degree of *drag* (resistance) to panning and tilting to prevent a jerky, uneven movement. The pan and tilt drag can be adjusted to fit the weight of the camera and your personal preference. A small camcorder needs a lighter drag adjustment than does a heavy ENG/EFP camcorder; some people favor rather loose or slightly tighter pan and tilt drag, regardless of camera weight.

6.11

QUICK-RELEASE PLATE

The quick-release plate allows you to attach the camera to the tripod or other mount and balance the camera securely. Sometimes a wedge-shaped plate and receptacle are used for heavier cameras.

Quick release plate attached to camera base

The mounting head also has *pan and tilt lock* mechanisms that prevent the camera from moving horizontally or flopping forward or backward when unattended. Lock the mounting head every time you leave the camera unattended, no matter how briefly.

Quick-release plate This mechanism, also called the *wedge mount,* consists of a rectangular or wedge-shaped plate that attaches to the bottom of the camera. The *quick-release plate* makes it easy to mount the camera and position it so that it is perfectly balanced each time you put it on the tripod or any other camera mount. When mounting the camera, the release plate slides into the receptacle attached to the mounting head. The release plate is especially important for supporting heavy studio cameras (see figure 6.17). Once the camera is slipped all the way into the wedge receptacle, it is mounted in the right position. **SEE 6.11**

When switching from a handheld to a tripod-supported camera, you will find that the tripod severely restricts your use of the camera. When using a tripod, you can no longer run with the camera, lift it above your head, shoot from close to ground level, cant it, or swing it wildly through the air. You are limited to panning and tilting and, if you have a center column, to a rather modest camera elevation. Why use a tripod?

▷ The tripod steadies the camera, whether you are zoomed in or out.

▷ Your pans and tilts are much smoother than with a handheld camera.

▷ The tripod keeps you from moving the camera excessively, which is a positive rather than a negative factor in good camera work.

▷ You get less tired with the camera on the tripod than on your shoulder or in your hand.

KEY CONCEPT 2   **Whenever possible, put the camcorder or ENG/EFP camera on a tripod.**

The tripod dolly To dolly or truck with a tripod-mounted camera, you must put the tripod on a three-caster dolly base, which is simply a spreader with wheels. **SEE 6.12** When the casters are in a freewheeling position, you can dolly, truck, and arc. Most professional dollies let you lock the casters in position for straight-line dollying. Make sure to check that the floor is smooth enough for an

6.12

TRIPOD DOLLY

The tripod can be mounted on a three-wheel dolly, which permits quick repositioning of the camera.

6.13

CABLE GUARDS

The cable guards prevent the dolly wheels from running over the camera cable. They must be close enough to the studio floor to push the cable aside.

Cable guard

"on-air" move while the camera is hot (operating). When moving the tripod dolly, you usually push, pull, and steer the dolly with your left hand while guiding the panning handle and camera with your right hand.

When a camera or camcorder is connected to a camera cable, you must adjust the cable guards so that the cable does not get wedged under the dolly casters. It is also a good idea to tie the cable to one of the tripod legs so that the cable is not pulled by its connector. **SEE 6.13**

The field dolly   When dollying on a rough surface, such as gravel or grass, you need to mount the tripod on a field dolly. A *field dolly* consists of a plywood platform supported by four wheels with pneumatic tires. The steering mechanism works like the one you may remember from your red Radio Flyer wagon: A large handle turns the front wheels in the desired direction and lets you pull or push the entire platform. **SEE 6.14** When operating the camera, you can stand on the dolly or walk alongside while the dolly operator pulls or pushes it along the dolly path. When the surface is especially rough, you can underinflate the tires to make the trip smoother. Many dollies are homemade and constructed from parts readily available in most hardware stores.

6.14

FIELD DOLLY

The field dolly has a platform with four pneumatic tires that support the tripod-mounted camera and the camera operator.

◼ The Studio Pedestal

Studio cameras, or EFP cameras that are converted for studio use, are usually mounted on studio pedestals. A ***studio pedestal*** is a relatively expensive camera mount that supports even the heaviest of cameras and additional equipment, such as a teleprompter. The studio pedestal lets you pan, tilt, truck, arc, and pedestal while the camera is on the air. By turning a large steering wheel, you can move the camera in any direction; by pulling it up or pushing it down, you can change the camera height. The telescoping center column must be balanced so that the camera stays put at any pedestal height, even if you let go of the steering wheel. If the camera begins to creep up or down by itself, the center column must be rebalanced. **SEE 6.15**

6.15

STUDIO PEDESTAL

The studio pedestal permits you to pan, tilt, truck, arc, and pedestal while the camera is on the air. If equipped with a telescoping column, you can move the camera from about 2 feet to about 5 feet above the studio floor.

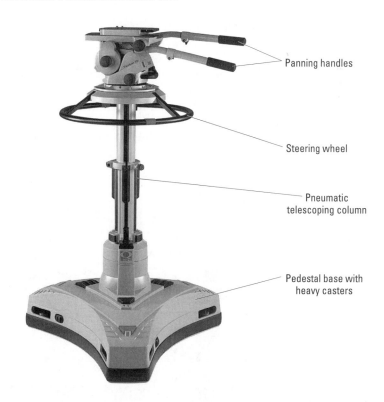

Panning handles

Steering wheel

Pneumatic telescoping column

Pedestal base with heavy casters

6.16

PARALLEL AND TRICYCLE STEERING

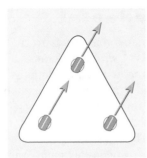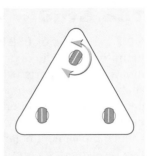

A In the parallel steering position, three casters steer in the same direction.

B In the tricycle steering position, only one wheel is steerable.

Parallel and tricycle steering   You can put the studio pedestal into a parallel or tricycle steering position. In the *parallel* steering position, the steering wheel points all casters in the same direction. **SEE 6.16A** Parallel steering is used for all normal camera moves. In the *tricycle* position, only one wheel is steerable. **SEE 6.16B** You use this steering position if you need to rotate the pedestal itself to move it closer to a piece of scenery or the studio wall.

Cam head   Like the tripod, the center column of the studio pedestal has a camera mounting head attached to it. To accommodate the combined weight of studio camera and teleprompter, the customary tripod head has been replaced by a much heavier camera mount, called a ***cam head***. Its operational controls are similar to those of the mounting heads for lightweight cameras: pan and tilt drags, locking devices, the wedge mount receptacle, and panning handles. **SEE 6.17** The two panning handles allow you to pan and tilt smoothly while simultaneously operating the attached zoom and focus controls. Instead of the three cable guards of the tripod

6.17

MOUNTING HEAD FOR HEAVY CAMERA

The studio camera mounting head is designed for heavy cameras and accessory equipment and permits smooth pans and tilts despite the camera weight. Note that this mounting head has a wedge mount receptacle.

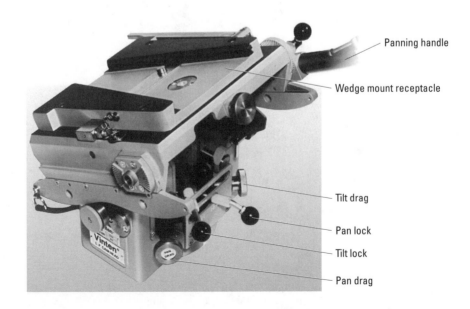

Panning handle

Wedge mount receptacle

Tilt drag

Pan lock

Tilt lock

Pan drag

dolly, you need to adjust the whole skirt (housing) of the pedestal base to prevent the cable from getting caught in the casters.

Before operating the studio camera, always unlock the mounting head and adjust the pan and tilt drags. When leaving the camera unattended, even for a short time, lock the mounting head and cap the lens (put the metal or plastic cap over the front of the lens). At no time should you use the drag controls for locking the mounting head when leaving the camera unattended.

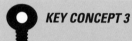

KEY CONCEPT 3   **Always lock the mounting head when leaving the camera unattended.**

◼ Special Camera Mounts

Special camera mounts range from robotic pedestals whose movements are computer-controlled, to large cranes that can swoop the camera with its operator as high as 30 feet above ground, to common beanbags and shopping carts. Here is an area where you can put your imagination and creativity to work. On smooth ground a simple shopping cart or wheelchair can give you almost as smooth a dolly as a studio pedestal costing several thousand dollars more. Mounting a small camcorder on a skateboard and pulling it along a smooth surface can give you an interesting low-angle trucking shot. **SEE 6.18**

6.18

ROBOTIC PEDESTAL

The robotic pedestal is a computer-steered studio pedestal that can pan, tilt, dolly, truck, pedestal, and zoom according to computer instructions instead of those of a camera operator. It is used mainly for news presentations.

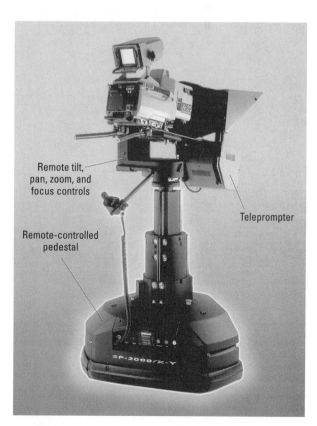

Remote tilt, pan, zoom, and focus controls

Teleprompter

Remote-controlled pedestal

The **Steadicam** is a camera mount that enables you to walk, run, and even jump, with the camera remaining perfectly steady. There are large Steadicam supports for heavy cameras and camcorders, which are worn by the camera operator, and some lightweight ones for small camcorders that you can carry with one hand. The *jib arm* is a counterbalanced camera mount designed for shooting on location. You can clamp it to a door frame, a chair, or a car window and then tongue the camera sideways and boom it up and down. The following five figures show some of the more common special camera mounts. **SEE 6.19–6.23**

6.19

STEADICAM FOR HEAVY CAMERAS

This heavy camera mount allows the camera operator to walk, run, or jump with the camera remaining steady.

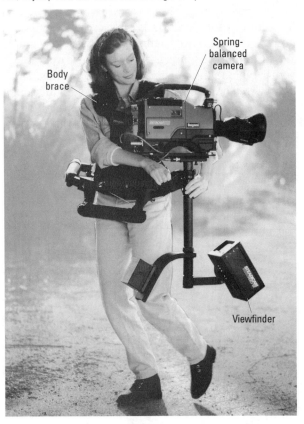

Body brace

Spring-balanced camera

Viewfinder

6.20

STEADICAM FOR LIGHTWEIGHT CAMCORDERS

This Steadicam device is designed for lightweight camcorders and can be carried in one hand.

6.21

COLLAPSIBLE JIB ARM

The lightweight jib arm can do pretty much everything a heavy camera crane can do, except carry the camera operator and the director aloft. It can be easily disassembled and transported in a car to a remote location.

6.22

SHORT-ARM JIB

This counterbalanced camera support can be clamped to just about anything; it can be moved up and down and tongued just like a big crane.

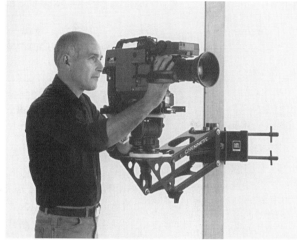

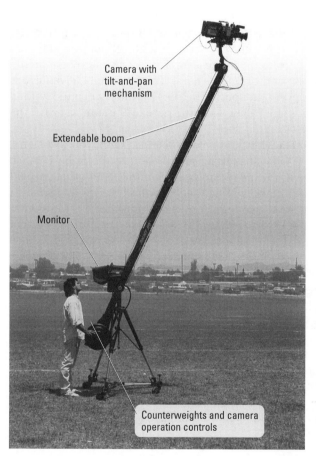

Camera with tilt-and-pan mechanism

Extendable boom

Monitor

Counterweights and camera operation controls

6.23

BEAN BAG

This small canvas bag is filled not with beans but with a highly flexible synthetic material that adjusts to any camera configuration. Like a pillow, it cradles the camera and protects it from minor shocks. You can tie it to practically any moving object.

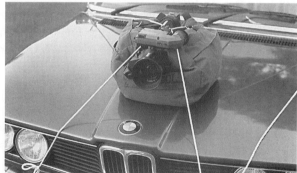

OPERATIONAL FEATURES

Now that you know how to move the camera about and frame a shot, you need to pay attention to (1) white-balancing, (2) focusing, and (3) zooming.

White-balancing

White-balancing means adjusting the red, green, and blue (RGB) chroma channels in the camera so that a sheet of white paper looks white on the television screen, regardless of whether the light that illuminates the sheet is reddish, as a candle, or bluish, as outdoor light. Most small camcorders do this automatically, assuming that you have set the white-balance switch to the proper setting, such as *outdoors* or *indoors*. **SEE COLOR PLATE 4**

Professional ENG/EFP cameras have a semiautomatic white-balance control that is more accurate than the fully automatic ones. The disadvantage is that you need to white-balance every time you move into a new lighting environment, such as from indoors to outdoors or from the fluorescent lights of a supermarket to the manager's office that is illuminated by a table lamp. The overriding advantage is that you white-balance a camera in the specific lighting in which you are shooting. When using a fully automatic white balance, you are never quite sure just what the camera considers to be white.

To white-balance a camera with the semiautomatic system, you focus on a white sheet, a white shirt, or even a clean tissue and then press the white-balance button. Some camera bags have a white rectangle sewn into them so that you will always have something for white-balancing. The viewfinder display (usually a flashing light) will tell you when the camera is seeing true white. Make sure that the white object fills the entire screen area and that it is located in the light that *actually illuminates* the scene you are shooting. For example, don't white-balance the camera in the hallway or outside the stage doors and then run up to the stage runway where models parade the latest designs. If you do, you may find that the video colors are quite different from the actual colors the models wore. (The reason for such color shifts is explained in chapter 7.) You need to white-balance every time you move into a new lighting environment; even if the light seems the same to the naked eye, the camera will detect the difference.

When operating a studio camera or an ENG/EFP camera that is connected to a camera cable, the video operator takes care of the white-balancing from the CCU (camera control unit) or the RCU (remote control unit). Nevertheless, as a camera operator you need to focus the camera on a white card under the actual lighting conditions—very much as you would do in the studio. *READY ZVL 2*

KEY CONCEPT 4   **Unless the camera has a fully automatic white-balance system, you need to white-balance every time you enter a new lighting environment.**

Focusing

Normally, we want all pictures on the screen to appear in focus (sharp and clear). You can achieve focus by *manual* or *automatic* controls.

Manual focus   Most ENG/EFP and all studio cameras must be focused manually. The ENG/EFP focus control is a ring at the front of the lens that you can turn clockwise or counterclockwise. **SEE 6.24** When operating a studio camera, you keep in focus by turning a twist grip mounted on the left panning handle and connected to the zoom lens by cable. **SEE 6.25**

Some small camcorders have a focusing system that is driven by a motor. Instead of turning the twist grip or the focus ring of the lens, you simply press one of two buttons to get the lens into focus. The problem with this system is that it is considerably slower than turning the focus ring, and it is difficult to get the motor to stop at precisely the sharpest focus point without some tweaking.

Presetting the zoom lens   *Calibrating the zoom lens,* or presetting it, means that you adjust the zoom lens so that it will maintain focus during the entire zoom. Let's practice presetting a zoom lens for a simple EFP assignment and for a studio production.

Assume that you are to videotape a sales manager's pep talk to her company. During the videotaping you are asked to zoom in to a fairly tight close-up of the sales chart on an easel slightly behind the sales manager. When you try to zoom in from the medium shot of the sales manager to the tight close-up of the chart, it

6.24

MANUAL FOCUS ON ENG/EFP CAMERAS

The focus control on ENG/EFP cameras is a ring at the front of the lens, which can be turned by hand.

Focus ring   Zoom lever

6.25

MANUAL FOCUS CONTROL ON STUDIO CAMERAS

The focus control on studio cameras is a twist grip attached to the left panning handle. To focus you turn it either clockwise or counterclockwise.

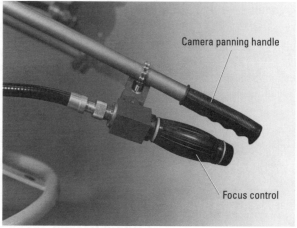

Camera panning handle

Focus control

gets woefully out of focus and becomes unreadable. What happened? You neglected to preset, or calibrate, the lens before zooming in for the close-up.

To preset the lens, you must first zoom in to the desired close-up of the farthest target object—the chart—and bring it into focus by turning the focus ring at the front of the ENG/EFP lens or the focus grip on the panning handle of the studio camera. When you then zoom back to the medium shot of the sales manager, she will be pretty much in focus. You may have to adjust the focus a little, but zooming in to the chart will no longer present a focus problem, provided that she, the chart, and the camera do not move. As soon as you reposition the camera, however, or if the sales manager moves the easel, you will need to recalibrate the lens. This means zooming in on the chart once again, focusing, zooming back a little to include the sales manager, and seeing whether you have to tweak the focus a little to keep her sharp and clear in subsequent zooms.

Now let's move into the studio, where your camera is assigned to cover a classical pianist from the side so that you can zoom in from a medium shot to a tight close-up of the keyboard and the pianist's hands. How do you preset the zoom lens for this? You zoom in for a tight close-up of the keyboard and bring the lens into focus (by turning the twist grip on the left panning handle). But exactly where on the keyboard? Probably the far end, because then you can zoom in and out and stay in reasonably sharp focus regardless of whether the pianist displays his virtuosity at the near or far end. 🔘 *READY ZVL 3*

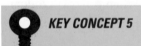

KEY CONCEPT 5   **To preset (calibrate) a zoom lens, zoom in as closely as possible on the target object and bring it into focus. All subsequent zooms will be relatively in focus. Every time the camera or the subject moves, you need to recalibrate.**

Automatic focus   Most consumer camcorders and some ENG/EFP cameras are equipped with an automatic focusing system, called the *auto-focus*. Through some electronic wizardry (reading the angle of a little radar beam or measuring the contrast), the camera focuses on the various objects in a scene all by itself. Most of the time, these systems work well. But there are times when the camera is fooled or gets confused by very bright or low-contrast scenes and leaves you with a blurred image. Or it may not know exactly which object in the picture you want to bring into focus. You may not want to focus on the obvious foreground object but instead on the middleground. The auto-focus will not be able to read your artistic intent and will proudly focus on the most prominent object closest to the camera. To achieve such a *selective focus* (see "Depth of field," which follows), you need to switch from auto-focus to manual. As you recall from our discussion in chapter 5, the auto-focus also has trouble keeping up with the rapidly changing scene in a fast zoom. 🔘 *READY ZVL 4*

Depth of field   As mentioned in chapter 5, the shallower the depth of field, the more critical the focus becomes. The greater the depth of field, the less you have to worry about staying in focus. You also recall that the more you zoom in (with the

6.26

SHALLOW DEPTH OF FIELD IN CLOSE-UPS

Regardless of the focal length of the lens, close-ups have a shallower
depth of field than do long shots.

lens getting progressively more narrow-angle), the shallower the depth of field
becomes; the more you zoom out (to a wide-angle view), the greater the depth of
field becomes. In addition, depth of field is also influenced by the distance from
the camera to the subject.

Which assignment would probably give you more focus problems: the
coverage of evening rush-hour, when you must zoom in to a fairly tight shot to
compress the heavy bridge traffic; or the coverage of a midday parade from street
level with the zoom lens in the extreme-wide-angle position? Definitely the first
one. But why? The low light level, the resulting large lens aperture, and the long-
focal-length (telephoto) position of the zoom lens (see chapter 5) combine into a
relatively shallow depth of field. In contrast, the high midday light levels for the
parade (resulting in a small lens aperture) and the wide-angle position of the zoom
lens give you such a great depth of field that you probably won't have to turn the
focus ring even once.

You will find that if you move the camera extremely close to the object, the
depth of field will shrink even if the lens is zoomed out to the wide-angle position.
Because the distance of camera to object influences the depth of field as does the
focal length of the lens, we can say that, in general, tight close-ups have a shallow
depth of field. **SEE 6.26** *READY ZVL 5*

When working with a a high-definition television (HDTV) camera, you
initially will have quite a bit of trouble focusing. Because everything looks so
much sharper than with standard television (STV), you may not see in the
relatively small viewfinder when your shots are slightly out of focus. The increased
sharpness of the HDTV image also lures you into seeing a much greater depth of
field than you actually have—foreground and background seem to be in focus.
When watching your shots on a high-quality monitor, however, you may discover

that not only is your background out of focus, but your foreground is as well. Racking in and out of focus and looking very carefully will help you determine where the optimal focus lies.

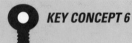 **KEY CONCEPT 6**   **Depth of field is dependent on the focal length of the lens, the aperture, and the distance from camera to object.**

Zooming

All small and ENG/EFP camcorders have a rocker switch on the lens that activates the zoom mechanism. By pressing the front of the switch, usually labeled *T* for telephoto or tight, you trigger a motor that rearranges various elements in the zoom lens for the zoom-in effect; by pressing the back of the switch, labeled *W* for wide, you zoom out. This *servo-zoom* mechanism, which is activated by the zoom rocker switch, keeps your zooming steady and smooth. **SEE 6.27** Some cameras offer a

6.27

CAMCORDER ZOOM CONTROL

Camcorders have a rocker switch near the lens that controls the zooming-in and zooming-out motion.

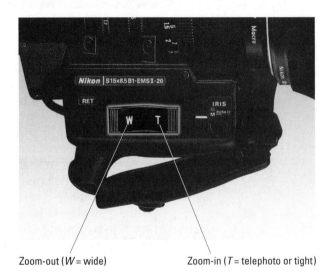

Zoom-out (*W* = wide)   Zoom-in (*T* = telephoto or tight)

choice between a slow and a fast zoom speed. ENG/EFP lenses have an additional manual zoom control that allows you to override the servo-zoom mechanism by turning the zoom lever on the lens barrel for fast zooms (see figure 6.24).

Studio cameras have a similar rocker switch mounted on the right panning handle. This thumb-operated switch is connected by cable to the servo-zoom mechanism of the studio lens. By pressing the *T* (for tight) side of the switch, you zoom in; by pressing the *W* (for wide) side, you zoom out. **SEE 6.28**

6.28

STUDIO ZOOM CONTROL

The zoom control of the studio camera is a rocker switch on the right panning handle that is activated by the thumb of your right hand.

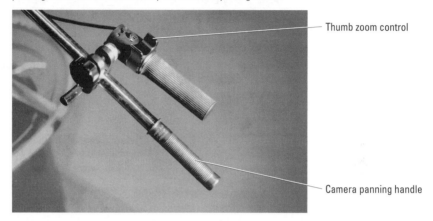

Thumb zoom control

Camera panning handle

Because the servo-zoom mechanism makes zooming relatively easy, you may be tempted to zoom in and out rather than move the camera closer or farther away. Again, remember to keep zooming to a minimum; frequent and unmotivated zooming reveals the inexperience of the camera operator as readily as excessive camera movement. *READY ZVL 6*

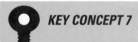 *KEY CONCEPT 7*   **Keep zooming to a minimum.**

GENERAL GUIDELINES

Whether you are operating a small camcorder or a large studio camera, treat it with extreme care—as with all electronic equipment. Always be mindful of your and others' safety. Do not risk your neck and the equipment to get an especially spectacular shot that merely embellishes, rather than tells, the story. Do not abandon standard operational procedures for the sake of expediency. Whatever you do, use common sense.

Like bicycling, you can learn to operate a camera only by doing it. The following guidelines, however, can make learning easier and also serve as useful checklists.

CHECKLIST: CAMCORDERS AND ENG/EFP CAMERAS

☑ **Don't expose the camera to the elements** Never leave the camera unprotected in the sun or in a hot car. Also watch that the viewfinder is not pointed into the sun; the magnifying glass in the viewfinder can collect the sun's rays and melt the viewfinder housing and electronics. Use plastic covers, called "raincoats," when shooting in the rain or extreme cold. In case of emergency, a plastic grocery bag will do.

☑ **Leave the camera with care** Lock the mounting head on the tripod whenever you leave the camera unattended. When putting the camera down, place it upright. Laying it on its side may damage the viewfinder or attached microphone.

☑ **Use the lens cap** Even if a camera can be "capped" internally to prevent light from reaching the imaging device, always put the metal or plastic cap over the front of the lens. This lens cap keeps the light off the imaging device and protects the front surface of the expensive zoom lens.

☑ **Use fully charged batteries** Make sure that the nickel-cadmium (nicad) battery is fully charged. Many batteries develop a "memory," which means that they signal a full charge even when only partially charged. To avoid this problem, always discharge the batteries fully before recharging them. Battery dischargers/chargers are commercially available (sometimes called *battery reconditioners*) that discharge the battery before automatically switching over to the charging cycle.

Do not drop batteries or expose them to extreme heat. Always carry a fully charged spare battery and an AC power pack, which converts the standard 110-volt AC (alternating current) to the appropriate DC (direct current) and serves as a power supply as well as a battery charger.

Unless the main battery recharges the small auxiliary battery in the camera that drives the clock and maintains other electronic values, you need to replace it from time to time, very much like a watch battery. Always carry at least one spare battery and a spare fuse.

☑ **Verify the videotape format** Make sure that the videotape cassettes fit the camera model. Even if the cassettes look similar from the outside, they may not fit the particular camera model. Always take a few additional videocassettes along. Running out of tape in the middle of an important event is as frustrating as running out of battery power.

☑ **Examine all connections** Check *all connectors*, regardless of what they connect, to see whether they fit their designated plugs (see figure 4.15). Use adapters only in an emergency; an adapter is by design a stopgap and, as such, the source of potential trouble. If an ENG/EFP camera is connected to a cable, check its reach.

Plug in the external microphone to verify that the microphone connectors fit the plug on the camera. Small camcorders normally use smaller (RCA phono) connectors; all larger ENG/EFP camcorders have three-pin (XLR) connectors. (See chapter 8 for further information on audio connectors.)

☑ ***Test the camera*** Even when in a hurry, do a brief test recording to verify that the camcorder operates properly. Bring headphones along to check the audio. Use the same power supply and connectors you intend to use during the actual videotaping. Check the full range of the zoom lens and the focus. In extremely cold or damp weather conditions, zoom lenses sometimes stick or give up altogether.

☑ ***Set the switches*** Have all the switches, such as auto- or manual focus, auto-iris, zoom speed, and shutter speed, in the desired positions. The faster the action in front of the camera, the higher the shutter speed must be to prevent the moving object from blurring. Remember, however, that higher shutter speeds require higher light levels.

☑ ***Perform a white balance*** White-balance the camera before beginning the videotaping, unless the system is fully automatic. Be sure to white-balance under the light that actually illuminates the event.

☑ ***Always capture audio*** Always turn on the camera microphone and record sound with the pictures. This sound will help you identify the location of the event and will provide *ambient* (background) sound and continuity for postproduction editing.

☑ ***Heed the warning signs*** Take note of caution signals and try to take care of the problem immediately. You may be able to dismiss the "low light level" warning on the camera if you are not concerned with picture quality; but you simply cannot ignore a "low battery" warning.

CHECKLIST: STUDIO CAMERAS

☑ ***Get in touch and in control*** Put on your headset to establish contact with the control room and the video operator. Unlock the mounting head and adjust the pan and tilt drags. Pedestal up and down to get a feel for the pedestal range and motion. A properly balanced pedestal should keep the camera stable at any given vertical position.

☑ ***Tame the cables*** Make sure that the cable guards are close enough to the floor to prevent the camera from rolling over the camera cable. Uncoil the cable and check its reach. To avoid the inevitable tug of the cable during a dolly, tie it to the pedestal, but leave enough slack so that you can freely pan, tilt, and pedestal.

☑ **Test zoom and focus**   Ask the video engineer to uncap the camera so that you can rack through the zoom and focus ranges and, if necessary, adjust the viewfinder. Practice presetting the zoom lens so that the scene remains in focus during subsequent zooms.

☑ **Practice your moves**   Mark the critical camera positions on the studio floor with masking tape. Write down all on-air camera moves so that you can set the zoom lens in the wide-angle position before the required move.

☑ **Move gracefully**   Ask the floor person to help you steer the camera during an especially tricky move. If the cable gets tangled up during a dolly, don't drag the whole mess along. Signal the floor person to untangle it for you. When dollying or trucking, start slowly to overcome the inertia of the heavy dolly, and slow down just before the end of the dolly. When raising or lowering the camera, brake the pedestal column before it reaches its maximum or minimum height; otherwise, the camera and the picture might receive a hefty jolt.

☑ **Don't jump the red light**   Watch for the *tally light* (the red light inside the viewfinder and on top of the camera) to go out before moving the camera into a new position or presetting the zoom. The tally light tells the camera operator, the talent, and the studio production crew which camera is hot (on the air). During special effects, your tally light may remain on even if you think that your shot is finished. Normally, the ENG/EFP camera or camcorder has only a viewfinder tally light, with no additional one on top of the camera. This viewfinder tally light tells only you—the camera operator—when the camera is operating.

☑ **Avoid nervous camera movements**   Keep your eyes on the viewfinder and correct *slowly* for minor compositional defects. If a subject bounces back and forth on a close-up, do not try to keep it in the frame at all costs. It is better to let it move out of the frame from time to time than to play catchup by rapid panning.

☑ **Let the director direct**   Always follow the director's instructions, even if you think that he or she is wrong. Do not try to outdirect the director from your position. But do alert the director if you are asked to do such impossible things as dollying or trucking on the air with your lens in the narrow-angle (zoomed-in) position.

☑ **Be observant and attentive**   Be aware of all other activities around you. Pay special attention to where the other cameras are and where they are asked to move. By listening to the director's instructions, you will be able to stay out of the way of the other cameras. When moving a camera, especially backward, watch for obstacles that may be in your path. Ask a floor person to guide you. Avoid unnecessary chatter on the intercom.

☑ ***Anticipate***   Try to line up the next shot before the director calls for it, even if you work without a shot sheet that lists the nature and sequence of your shots. For example, if you hear on the intercom that the other camera is on air with a close-up, pull out to a medium shot or get a different angle to provide the director with another field of view. Do not duplicate the shot of the other camera.

☑ ***Put all tools away properly***   At the end of the show, wait for the "all clear" signal before preparing your camera for shutdown. Ask the video operator to cap the camera. As soon as the viewfinder goes dark, release the tilt and pan drags, lock the mounting head, and, for good measure, put the metal or plastic cap on the front of the lens. Park the camera in its usual place and coil the cable in the customary figure-eight loops.

ONCE AGAIN, REMEMBER...

▣ Camera Movements

The movements include the pan, tilt, cant, pedestal, dolly, truck or track, arc, crane or boom, and tongue. The zoom is also included, although the camera does not move.

▣ Camera Mounts

These include a variety of tripods, studio pedestals, or special mounts, such as the jib arm or camera crane.

▣ Camera Mounting Head

This device is a mechanism that connects the camera to the tripod or studio pedestal. It facilitates pans and tilts.

▣ White-balancing

This procedure is necessary to adjust the camera to various lighting conditions. It needs to be done every time the camera operates under new lighting conditions, unless it has a fully automatic white-balance mechanism.

▣ Presetting the Zoom Lens

This step is also called calibrating the zoom lens. It needs to be done every time the camera or the subject in front of the camera moves. To preset a zoom, the lens must be zoomed in on the farthest target object and brought into focus. All subsequent wider-angle zoom positions will be in focus.

Z E T T L ' S   V I D E O   L A B   2 . 1

Let's go into the studio to look at various camera moves. There you will also be able to watch some demonstrations of white-balancing, calibrating the zoom lens, focusing, and fast zooming. For starters, click once on the **camera** *monitor.*

RUN ZVL 1 Load tape 9 **Camera Moves** and play the introduction. Sonny is right when he warns you not to move the camera too much. Even when you move the camera, your movements should remain largely unnoticed by the viewer. Start with module 2 **Pan**, then play the **Tilt**, **Pedestal**, **Dolly**, and **Truck** modules. When looking at these camera moves, watch the background. On the screen you can often tell a specific camera move not so much by the moving foreground object but by how the background changes.

RUN ZVL 2 Now go back to Master Control and click on the **lights** monitor. Load tape 5 **Color Temperature** and play module 1 **White balance**. The idea of shooting the white card is to tell the camera what it should reproduce as white, regardless of whether the light falling on the card is bluish or reddish. Pay particular attention to how the bluish tint and the reddish tint (caused by the bluish outdoor light or the reddish indoor light) of the shirt change to white after white-balancing. Without white-balancing, the "white" shirt would remain light blue or light orange.

RUN ZVL 3 Go back to Master Control and click on the **camera** monitor again. Load tape 9 **Camera Moves** and play module 1 **Zoom**. Watch carefully how calibrating a zoom lens is done and how it helps you keep in focus during subsequent zooms. Without calibrating the zoom lens, you would inevitably lose focus on a zoom-in.

RUN ZVL 4 Load tape 4 **Focusing** and play module 6 **Auto focus**. If you detected similar problems with auto-focus as with auto-iris, you are right. As you can see, the auto-focus is even more problematic than the auto-iris—and all but reliable. If you use your camcorder for anything more than casual vacation pictures, switch to manual focus and turn the focus ring.

RUN ZVL 5 Just to reinforce what you already know about depth of field, play module 2 **Depth of field**. This time note all the variables that influence depth of field. Note that tight close-ups that show the foreground object in focus have a shallow depth of field, regardless of the focal length of the lens.

RUN ZVL 6 You've been adequately warned about unmotivated and especially fast zooms. Just to see how distracting fast zoom-ins followed by fast zoom-outs really are, load tape 9 **Camera Moves** again and watch the zoom demonstration in module 1 **Zoom**. Are you now convinced how bad such zooms are?

KEY CONCEPTS

○ Keep the handheld or shoulder-mounted camera as steady as possible and zoomed-out when moving.

○ Whenever possible, put the camcorder or ENG/EFP camera on a tripod.

○ Always lock the mounting head when leaving the camera unattended.

○ Unless the camera has a fully automatic white-balance system, you need to white-balance every time you enter a new lighting environment.

○ To preset (calibrate) a zoom lens, zoom in as close as possible on the target object and bring it into focus. All subsequent zooms will be relatively in focus. Every time the camera or the subject moves, you need to recalibrate.

○ Depth of field is dependent on the focal length of the lens, the aperture, and the distance from camera to object.

○ Keep zooming to a minimum.

CHAPTER

7

KEY TERMS

additive primary colors Red, green, and blue. Ordinary white light (sunlight) can be separated into the three primary light colors. When these three colored lights are combined in various proportions, all other colors can be reproduced.

attached shadow Shadow that is on the object itself. It cannot be seen independent of (detached from) the object.

background light Illumination of the set pieces and backdrop. Also called *set light*.

back light Illumination from behind the subject and opposite the camera. Usually a spotlight.

baselight Even, nondirectional (diffused) light necessary for the camera to operate optimally. Refers to the overall light intensity.

cast shadow Shadow that is produced by an object and thrown (cast) onto another surface. It can be seen independent of the object.

color temperature Relative reddishness or bluishness of light, as measured in Kelvin degrees. The norm for indoor video lighting is 3,200°K, for outdoors, 5,600°K.

contrast The difference between the brightest and the darkest spots in a video picture.

diffused light Light that illuminates a relatively large area with an indistinct light beam. Diffused light, created by floodlights, produces soft shadows.

dimmer A device that controls the intensity of light by throttling the electric current flowing to the lamp.

directional light Light that illuminates a relatively small area with a distinct light beam. Directional light, produced by spotlights, creates harsh, clearly defined shadows.

falloff The speed (degree) with which a light picture portion turns into shadow areas. Fast falloff means that the light areas turn abruptly into shadow areas and there is a great difference in brightness between light and shadow areas. Slow falloff indicates a very gradual change from light to dark, and a minimal brightness difference between light and shadow areas.

fill light Additional light on the opposite side of the camera from the key light to illuminate shadow areas and thereby reduce falloff. Usually done with floodlights.

floodlight A lighting instrument that produces diffused light.

foot-candle (ft-c) The unit of measurement of illumination, or the amount of light that falls on an object. One foot-candle is the amount of light from a single candle that falls on a 1-square-foot area located 1 foot away from the light source. See *lux*.

incident light Light that strikes the object directly from its source. To measure incident light, the light meter is pointed at the camera lens or into the lighting instruments.

Kelvin degrees (°K) The standard scale for measuring color temperature, or the relative reddishness or bluishness of white light.

key light Principal source of illumination. Usually a spotlight.

light intensity The amount of light falling on an object that is seen by the lens. Measured in lux or foot-candles. Also called *light level*.

light plot A plan, similar to a floor plan, that shows the type, size (wattage), and location of the lighting instruments relative to the scene to be illuminated and the general direction of the light beams.

lux European standard unit for measuring light intensity. One lux is the amount of 1 lumen (one candle-power of light) that falls on a surface of 1 square meter located 1 meter away from the light source. 10.75 lux = 1 foot-candle. Most lighting people figure roughly 10 lux = 1 foot-candle.

photographic principle The triangular arrangement of key, back, and fill lights, with the back light opposite the camera and directly behind the object, and the key and fill lights on opposite sides of the camera and to the front and side of the object. Also called *triangle lighting*.

reflected light Light that is bounced off the illuminated object. To measure reflected light, the light meter is pointed close to the object from the direction of the camera.

spotlight A lighting instrument that produces directional, relatively undiffused light.

triangle lighting The triangular arrangement of key, back, and fill lights. Also called *photographic principle*.

Light, Color, Lighting

THE lighting director of Triple-I, with a reputation for being one of the best LDs around, does strange things: She insists on using large reflectors and additional lights when shooting a beach scene, even with the midday sun blazing down. But later on when the fog has rolled in and the day begins to look rather dreary, she seems unconcerned about additional lights or reflectors. Back in the studio, she complains about the lack of adequate lighting instruments when trying to re-create the light of a single candle in a studio scene.

She tells you that good lighting calls for not only deliberate illumination—where and from what angle the light falls, whether the light used is soft or harsh, and what color the light has—but also for meticulous shadow control—where the shadows fall, and whether or not they should be prominent. It is, after all, the interplay of light and shadows that makes us see objects and their environments and feel about them in a specific way.

 KEY CONCEPT 1   **Lighting means deliberate illumination and shadow control.**

In this chapter, you will learn about the various aspects of light and the art of lighting:

■ **LIGHT**
Directional and diffused light, light intensity and how to measure it, and contrast

■ **SHADOWS**
Attached and cast shadows, and falloff control

■ **COLOR**
Additive and subtractive mixing, the color television receiver and generated colors, and color temperature and white-balancing

■ **LIGHTING INSTRUMENTS**
Spotlights, floodlights, and studio and portable instruments

■ **LIGHTING TECHNIQUES**
Operation of lights, the photographic or triangle lighting principle, field lighting, and measuring illumination

LIGHT

Seeing the many various lighting instruments suspended from the studio can be quite intimidating. But the LD (lighting director) of Triple-I assures you that the art of lighting can be learned. All it takes, she says, is the ability to recognize different types of light and their functions, manipulate their intensities, and control the contrast between light and shadows.

Types of Light

No matter how the light is technically generated, you will work with two basic types: *directional* and *diffused.*

Directional light means that the beam is precise, which causes harsh shadows. The sun, a flashlight, and the headlights of a car all produce directional light. You can aim directional light at a specific area without much spill into other areas.

Diffused light causes a more general illumination. Its diffused beam spreads out quickly and illuminates a large area. Because diffused light seems to come from all directions (is omnidirectional), it has no clearly defined shadows—they seem soft and transparent. A good example of diffused light occurs on a foggy day, when the fog operates like a huge diffusion filter for the sun. Watch the shadows during bright sunlight and on an overcast or foggy day; they are quite distinct and dense in sunlight, but hardly visible in fog. The fluorescent lighting in department stores or elevators uses diffused light exclusively. You cannot use diffused light to illuminate a precisely defined area; rather, diffused light is often used to illuminate large areas. *READY ZVL 1*

Light Intensity

An important aspect of lighting is controlling *light intensity*, or how much light falls onto an object. Intensity is measured in European *lux*, or American *foot-candles* (ft-c). If you have foot-candles and want to find lux, multiply the foot-candle figure by 10. Twenty foot-candles are approximately 200 lux ($20 \times 10 = 200$). If you have lux and want to find foot-candles, divide the lux number by 10. Two thousand lux are approximately 200 ft-c ($2,000 \div 10 = 200$).[1]

You may hear the LD or VO (video operator) complain that there is not enough baselight. *Baselight* refers to the overall light intensity. You determine baselight levels by pointing a light meter (which reads foot-candles or lux) from the

---

1. One lux is the light that falls on the surface of 1 square meter (roughly 3×3 feet), generated by a single candle that burns at a distance of 1 meter.

illuminated object or scene *toward the camera*. As you recall, you need a certain amount of light to activate the imaging device and other electronics in the camera to produce an optimal video signal at a given f-stop. If there is insufficient light even at the maximum aperture (lowest f-stop number), you need to activate the *gain* circuits of the camera. Most consumer camcorders do this automatically. Studio and ENG/EFP cameras need to have the gain activated either via the CCU (camera control unit) or through a switch on the ENG/EFP camera. The gain will boost the weak video signal electronically. Unfortunately, the higher the gain, the "noisier" the picture becomes: The dark portions of the picture will begin to show small colored specks that resemble miniature snowstorms. An adequate baselight level will prevent such problems.

Although the newer cameras (analog and digital) are much more sensitive and need less light than do older ones, for good crisp pictures you still need a generous amount of light. A consumer camcorder may be able to produce recognizable pictures at light levels as low as 1 or 2 lux; but for high-quality pictures, you need simply more light. Top-of-the-line cameras need about 1,000 lux (100 ft-c) at an f-stop of about 5.6 for optimal picture quality.[2] High baselight levels will also slow down the falloff throughout the scene and thus render shadows less dense without eliminating them. If the baselight level is too low, you can open the iris, increase the gain, or—better yet—add one or two floodlights that produce highly diffused light and shine them onto the scene.

You can also control light intensity by adjusting the distance of the lighting instrument to the object. The closer the instrument is to the subject, the more intense the illumination; the farther away the lighting instrument is from the subject, the less intense the light becomes. By putting diffusion material in front of the lighting instrument or, more common, by using an electronic dimmer, you can further reduce light intensity. Like the gas pedal in a car, which controls the amount of gasoline reaching the engine, the electronic *dimmer* controls the amount of electricity (voltage) reaching the light bulb. Most modern dimmers are computer-controlled and highly precise.

Contrast

Contrast refers to difference between the brightest and the darkest spots in a video picture. You measure contrast by taking a light meter reading of *reflected light*. Contrast is usually given as a ratio. If, for example, the light meter reads 4,000 lux or 400 ft-c in an especially bright area, such as against the white tablecloth on the dinner table, and only 100 lux or 10 ft-c in the dark background, the contrast ratio is 40:1 (400 ÷ 10 = 40). The 40:1 ratio is just about the upper limit for most cameras. Anything above such a ratio, such as 60:1, will either make the white areas look overexposed or the subtle shadow differences in the dark areas uniformly black. Even if high-quality cameras can handle such high-contrast scenes, the average television set cannot. *READY ZVL 2*

---

2. An f-stop between $f/5.6$ and $f/8.0$ produces an optimal depth of field. This is why camera specifications use $f/5.6$ as the norm for optimal light levels. Of course, with larger apertures, you can shoot with much less light.

SHADOWS

Although we are quite conscious of light and light changes, we are usually unaware of shadows, unless we seek comfort in them on a particularly hot day or if they interfere with what we want to see. Because shadow control is such an important aspect of lighting, we'll take a closer look at shadows and how they influence our perception.

Once you are aware of shadows, you will be surprised by the great variety of shadows that surround you. Some seem part of the object, such as the shadows on your coffee cup; others seem to fall onto other surfaces, such as the shadow of a telephone pole that is cast onto the street. Some shadows are dark and dense as though they were brushed on with thick, black paint; others are so light and subtle that they are hard to see. Some change gradually from light to dark; others do so abruptly.

Despite the great variety of shadows, there are only two basic types: *attached* and *cast*. The relative lightness and darkness of the shadows and how they vary are aspects of *falloff*.

Attached Shadows

Attached shadows seem affixed on the object and cannot be seen independent of it. Take your coffee cup and hold it next to a window or a table lamp. The shadow opposite the light source (window or table lamp) on the cup is the attached shadow. Even if you wiggle the cup or move it up and down, the attached shadow remains part of the cup. **SEE 7.1**

7.1

ATTACHED SHADOW

The attached shadow is always bound to the illuminated object.
It cannot be seen separate from the object.

7.2

ATTACHED SHADOWS DEFINE SHAPE

The attached shadows help define the basic shape of the object. Without attached shadows we perceive a triangle on the left; with attached shadows we perceive a cone on the right.

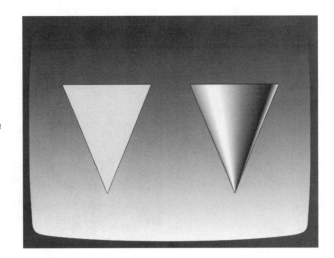

Attached shadows help us perceive the basic form of an object. Without attached shadows the actual shape of an object may remain ambiguous when seen as a picture. In the figure at the top of the facing page, the object on the left looks like a triangle; but when you see it with the attached shadows, the triangle becomes a cone. **SEE 7.2**

Attached shadows also contribute to perception of texture. A great amount of prominent attached shadows emphasizes texture; without them, things look smoother. Attached shadows on a Styrofoam ball make it look like a moonscape; but when the attached shadows are removed through flat lighting, the ball looks smooth and flat. **SEE 7.3 AND 7.4**

7.3

ROUGH TEXTURE

Prominent attached shadows emphasize texture. The surface of this Styrofoam ball looks rough.

7.4

SMOOTH TEXTURE

Here, the attached shadows are almost eliminated, so the surface of the ball looks relatively smooth.

7.5

ATTACHED SHADOWS MINIMIZED

To emphasize the smoothness of this model's face, attached shadows are kept to a minimum.

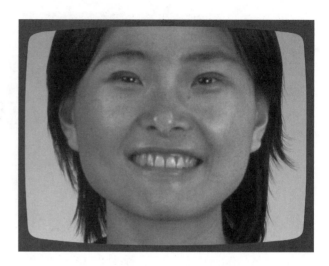

If you had to shoot a commercial for skin lotion, you would want to light the model's face in such a way that the attached shadows are so soft that they are hardly noticeable. **SEE 7.5 AND 7.6** But if you were asked to emphasize the rich, deep texture of the famous stone carving of the Aztec calendar, you would need to light for prominent attached shadows. **SEE 7.7** How to control attached shadows is discussed in the context of lighting techniques later in this chapter.

 KEY CONCEPT 2   **Attached shadows reveal form and texture.**

7.6

ATTACHED SHADOWS MINIMIZED

With the light shining directly on this Aztec calendar stone, the lack of attached shadows make the intricate carvings look relatively flat.

7.7

ATTACHED SHADOWS EMPHASIZED

With the light coming from the side, the attached shadows are more prominent and the rich, deep texture is properly emphasized.

7.8

REVERSAL OF ATTACHED SHADOWS

The below-eye-level light source causes the attached shadows to fall opposite their expected positions. We interpret such unusual shadow placement as ghostly or mysterious.

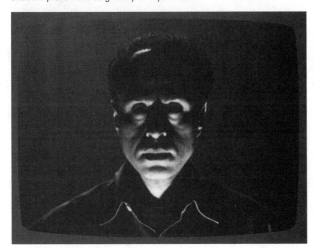

7.9

CAST SHADOWS

Cast shadows are usually cast by the object onto some other surface. In this case, the cast shadows of the trees fall on the snow-covered ground.

Because we normally see the main light source coming from above (the sun, for example), we are used to seeing the attached shadows fall below protrusions and indentations. When you lower the principal light source so that it illuminates an object, such as a face, from below eye level, we experience this departure from the norm as mysterious or spooky. **SEE 7.8** There is probably not a single science fiction or horror movie that does not use such a shadow-reversal effect at least once. *READY ZVL 3*

Cast Shadows

Unlike attached shadows, *cast shadows* can be seen independent of the object that is causing them. If you make some shadow pictures on a wall, for instance, you can focus on the shadows without showing your hand. The shadows of telephone poles, traffic signs, or trees cast on the street or on the wall of a nearby building are all examples of cast shadows. Even if the cast shadows touch the base of the objects causing them, they remain cast shadows and will not become attached ones. **SEE 7.9**

Cast shadows help us to see where the object is located relative to its surroundings and to orient us in time, at least to some extent. Take another look at figure 7.9. The cast shadows of the trees stretch quite far across the snow toward the camera. The relatively long shadows indicate early morning or late afternoon. *READY ZVL 4*

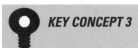 **KEY CONCEPT 3** **Cast shadows help tell us where things are and when events take place.**

FAST FALLOFF

The change of light to shadow areas on these buildings is very sudden. The falloff is extremely fast, indicating an edge or corner.

SLOW FALLOFF

The attached shadow on this balcony gets gradually darker. The falloff is relatively slow, indicating a curved surface.

■ Falloff

Falloff indicates the degree of change from light to shadow. Specifically, it refers to the relative abruptness—the "speed"—with which light areas turn into shadow areas, or the brightness contrast between the light and shadow sides of an object. When the change from light to dense shadow is extremely abrupt, we speak of *fast falloff*; it indicates a sharp edge or corner. **SEE 7.10** *Slow falloff* shows a more gradual change from light to shadow side; the gradual shading indicates a curved object. **SEE 7.11**

Fast falloff can also mean that there is a high contrast between the light and shadow sides of a face. When the shadow side is only slightly darker than the light side and the shadows are highly transparent, the falloff is slow. If both sides of the face are equally bright, there is no falloff. The perception of texture also depends on falloff. Fast-falloff lighting shows wrinkles in a face; slow-falloff or no-falloff lighting hides them.

 **KEY CONCEPT 4** **Falloff defines the contrast between light and dark areas and how quickly light turns into shadow.**

When generating lighting effects with a computer, the relationship between attached and cast shadows and the rate of falloff have to be carefully calculated. For example, if you simulate a light source striking the object from screen-right, the attached shadows must obviously be placed on its screen-left side (opposite the light source). Also, the cast shadows must point in the screen-left direction. If you now move the light source in a counterclockwise direction (closer to the camera), the attached as well as the cast shadows must move with it—to stay opposite the light source. If you move the light source higher, the cast shadows become shorter. If you move the light source lower, they become longer. To make sure the shadows are logically placed, it helps to have actual photos from which to work. Such careful attention to shadow consistency is also important if you cut a live scene electronically into a photographic or painted background.

COLOR

Chapter 4 promised you more-detailed information on color and its use in video. In this section we focus on (1) the basic process of color mixing, (2) the color television receiver and generated colors, and (3) color temperature and white balance. 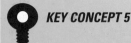 *READY ZVL 5*

Additive and Subtractive Color Mixing

You will undoubtedly recollect the discussion about the beam splitter that divides the white light transmitted by the lens into the three primary light colors—red, green, and blue (RGB)—and how we can produce all video colors by adding the red, green, and blue light in certain proportions. These are called *additive primary colors* because we mix them by *adding* one colored light beam on top of others.

If you had three identical slide projectors, you could put a red slide into one, a green slide in the second, and a blue slide in the third and aim them at the screen so that their beams overlap slightly. **SEE COLOR PLATE 5** What you would perceive is similar to the three overlapping circles shown in the illustration.

As you can see, red light and green light add up to *yellow;* red and blue to a bluish red called *magenta;* and green and blue to a greenish blue called *cyan.* Where all three primary light colors overlap, you get white. By dimming all three projectors equally, you get a variety of grays. By turning them all off, you get black (obviously). By dimming any one or all projectors independently, you can achieve a wide variety of colors.[3] For example, if the red projector burns at full intensity and the green one at two-thirds intensity with the blue projector turned off, you get some kind of orange. The more you dim the green projector, the more reddish the orange becomes.

KEY CONCEPT 5   **The additive primary light colors are red, green, and blue.**

You may remember from your finger-painting days that the primary colors were red, blue, and yellow and that mixing red and green paint together does not

---

3. On some projectors such dimming will also reduce power to the projector's blower motor. If so, do not throttle the power too much or for too long a period or you run the risk of overheating the entire lamp assembly.

produce a clean yellow, but rather a muddy dark brown. But paint mixes differently from light. When paint is mixed, its built-in filters subtract certain colors (light frequencies) rather than add them. We call this mixing process *subtractive color mixing*. Because the video system processes colored light rather than paint, we concentrate here on additive mixing. When mixing colored light (shining colored lights on top of each other), you *add* colors rather than filter them out, hence the term *additive color mixing*.

The Color Television Receiver and Generated Colors

The color television set also works on the additive color-mixing principle. Instead of the three slide projectors, a color television receiver has three electron guns in the neck of the picture tube that shoot their beams at many tiny red, green, and blue dots or tiny rectangles clustered on the inside of the television screen. One of the three guns is designated to hit the red dots, the other the green dots, and the third the blue dots. **SEE COLOR PLATE 1** The harder they hit the dots, the more the dots light up. If the red gun and green gun hit their dots with full intensity with the blue gun turned off, you get yellow. When all three guns fire at full intensity, you get white; at half intensity, you get gray. When they hit their respective dots with little but equal intensity, you get a very dark gray. As you can see, all three guns work overtime when you are watching a black-and-white show on a color television set.

Because the video signal consists of electric energy rather than actual colors, couldn't we produce certain colors without a camera simply by stimulating the three electron guns with certain voltages? Yes, definitely! In a slightly more complex form, this process is used by the computer to generate thousands of colors. The various colors in titles or other graphic displays, and the controversial colorizing of black-and-white movies, are all based on the principle of additive color mixing and generating colors by computer.

Color Temperature and White-Balancing

In chapter 6 you learned how to white-balance; now you will learn *why*. You need to white-balance the camera because not all light sources produce light of the same "whiteness." For instance, a candle produces a more reddish light than does a supermarket's fluorescent lights, which are more blue. Even the same light source does not always produce the same light. The beam of a flashlight with a weak battery looks quite reddish; when fully charged, the flashlight throws a more intense, and also whiter, light beam. The same color temperature change happens when you dim lights. The more you dim the lights, the more reddish they get. The camera needs to adjust to these differences to keep color the same in different lighting environments.

Color temperature The standard by which we measure the relative reddishness or bluishness of white light is called *color temperature*. The color differences of white light are measured in **Kelvin degrees** (°K). The more bluish the white light looks, the higher the color temperature; the more reddish it is, the lower its color temperature.

Keep in mind that color temperature has nothing to do with how hot the actual light source gets. You can touch a fluorescent tube, even though it burns at a high color temperature; but you wouldn't do the same with the incandescent light bulb in a reading lamp, which burns at a much lower color temperature.

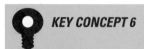

KEY CONCEPT 6   **Color temperature measures the relative reddishness or bluishness of white light. Reddish white light has a low color temperature; bluish white light has a high color temperature.**

Because outdoor light is much more bluish than normal indoor illumination, two color temperature standards have been developed: 5,600°K for outdoor illumination and 3,200°K for indoor illumination. All the lighting instruments you use to simulate outdoor lighting burn at the relatively high 5,600°K color temperature. This means that their white light approximates the bluishness of outdoor light. The standard lighting instruments for indoor use (studio lights or portable lights for EFP used primarily indoors) burn at the lower 3,200°K, and their "white" light is more reddish.

Color temperature is measured by the relative bluishness or reddishness of white light, so couldn't you raise the color temperature of an indoor light by putting a slightly blue filter in front of it, or lower the color temperature of an outdoor lamp by using a slightly orange filter? Yes, you can certainly do this. Such color filters, called *gels* or *color media*, are a convenient way of converting outdoor instruments for indoor lighting and vice versa. Similar filters are used in some cameras for rough white-balancing.

White-balancing   As you recall, *white-balancing* means adjusting the camera so that it reproduces a white object as white on the screen regardless of whether it is illuminated by a high-color-temperature source (the sun at high noon, fluorescent lamps, 5,600°K instruments), or a low-color-temperature source (candlelight, incandescent lights, 3,200°K instruments). When put on automatic white balance, the camera adjusts the RGB signals electronically so that they mix into white. You can also use the manual control, which means that you have to white-balance on a white object. The camera locks in on this balance and remembers it until you rebalance it in a different lighting environment.

Some larger cameras do the first rough white-balancing with a bluish or orange filter to change the color temperature of outdoor and indoor lights. In the high-color-temperature (bluish) outdoor light, the camera uses an orange filter to reduce the bluishness and then fine-tunes the white balance by electronically adjusting the RGB mix. These cameras have a white-balance lever that can be positioned at various Kelvin degrees, or are controlled from the CCU or RCU (remote control unit).

Proper white-balancing is very important for color continuity. For example, if you videotape a performer in a white dress first outdoors and then indoors, her dress should not look bluish in the outdoor scene and reddish in the indoor scene; it should look equally white in both. Even when shooting outdoors in the same location, you may have to white-balance several times to preserve color continuity. Because the outdoor light of an overcast sky has a much higher color temperature than does bright sunlight, you will have to rebalance the cameras when the fog lifts or the clouds dissipate. You will definitely have to rebalance when you move from outdoors to indoors. **SEE COLOR PLATE 4** *READY ZVL 6*

LIGHTING INSTRUMENTS

Despite the many lighting instruments available, there are basically only two types: *spotlights* and *floodlights*. Spotlights are designed to throw a directional, defined beam that illuminates a specific area. They cause harsh, dense shadows. Floodlights produce a great amount of nondirectional, diffused light that yields transparent shadows. Some floodlights generate such slow falloff that they seem to be a shadowless light source. The heavier and more powerful lights are designed for studio use. They are usually suspended from a fixed lighting grid made of heavy steel pipes, or from movable, counterweighted battens. **SEE 7.12** Portable lights for ENG and EFP are more flexible and lightweight but are generally less powerful.

7.12

STUDIO LIGHTING BATTENS

Lighting battens consist of a large grid of steel pipes that support the various lighting instruments. In this case, the battens can be lowered or raised through a counterweight system.

Trough to catch power cable when raising batten

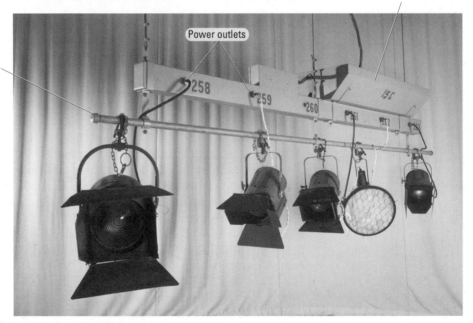

Power outlets

Batten

Spotlights

Spotlights produce a sharp, directional beam that illuminates a fairly distinct area. Most studio spotlights have glass lenses that help collect the light rays and focus them into a precise beam. The most common studio spotlights are the Fresnel and the ellipsoidal. There are also a variety of portable spotlights, which differ greatly in size and beam spread.

Fresnel spotlight   The workhorse of studio spotlights is the *Fresnel* (pronounced "fra-'nel") *spotlight.* Its thin, steplike lens (developed by Augustin Jean Fresnel of France) collects the light into a distinct beam. **SEE 7.13** The spread of the beam can be adjusted from a "spot" or "focus" position to a "flood" position by moving the lamp-reflector unit toward or away from the lens. Some instruments move the mirror relative to the lamp.

To flood, or spread, the beam you move the lamp-reflector unit *toward* the lens. The light beam becomes slightly more diffused (less intense), and the shadows are softer than when focused. To focus the beam, you move the lamp-reflector unit *away from* the lens. This increases the sharpness and intensity of the beam and makes its shadows fairly distinct and dense. Some Fresnel spots have a crank for moving the lamp-reflector unit, others have a ring or knob that can be turned from the studio floor with a lighting pole (a 10-foot wood pole with a metal hook on its tip).

You can further control the light beam by *barn doors,* shown in figure 7.13. They consist of movable metal flaps that swing open and close like actual barn doors, blocking the beam on the sides or, when rotated, on the top and bottom. Barn doors slide into a holder in front of the lens. To prevent them from sliding out and dropping, guillotinelike, on somebody, secure all of them to their instruments with a small chain or steel cable.

The size of Fresnel spotlights is normally given in the wattage of their quartz-halogen lamps. In the studio the most common Fresnels are the 650-watt and 1K (1 kilowatt = 1,000 watts) instruments. For older, less sensitive cameras, the 2Ks (2,000-watt) Fresnels are still the workhorse. All studio Fresnel spots burn at the indoor color temperature of 3,200°K.

7.13

FRESNEL SPOTLIGHT

The Fresnel spotlight is the workhorse of studio lighting. Its lens creates a sharp light beam that can be partially blocked by barn doors.

Barn doors   Fresnel lens

7.14

ELLIPSOIDAL SPOTLIGHT

The ellipsoidal spotlight produces an extremely bright and sharp beam. It is used to illuminate precise areas.

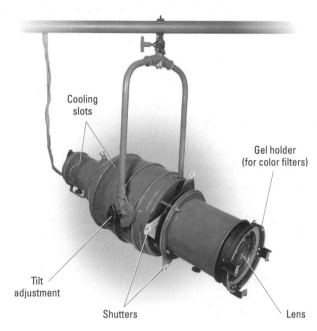

Cooling slots

Gel holder (for color filters)

Tilt adjustment

Shutters

Lens

During an elaborate EFP or a large remote telecast, you may come across another type of Fresnel spotlight, called an *HMI*. These expensive spotlights have highly efficient arc lamps that deliver three to five times the illumination of a normal Fresnel spot of the same size—and use less electricity to do so. HMI spotlights burn at the outdoor standard of 5,600°K. The disadvantage of HMI lights is that they need a ballast (a type of transformer like that used for your fluorescent lights at home) to operate properly.

Ellipsoidal spotlight This spotlight is used for special effects. It produces an extremely sharp, high-intensity beam that can be given rectangular or triangular shapes by movable metal shutters. **SEE 7.14** Instead of sliding the lamp reflector unit toward or away from the lens, you can focus the ellipsoidal spotlight by moving the lens away or closer to the fixed bulb-reflector assembly. Because it delivers such a precise beam, it does not need barn doors. Some ellipsoidals have a slot right next to the beam-shaping shutters that can hold a variety of thin metal sheets with variously patterned holes. Such a metal sheet is called a *cucalorus,* or *cookie*. Cookies are projected by the ellipsoidal spot onto a flat surface to break it up with freeform or geometric patterns. **SEE 7.15** The normal size of studio ellipsoidals is 750 watts.

Portable spotlights Although you can, of course, take small Fresnel spotlights on location, there are portable spotlights that are hybrids between spots and floods. To keep their weight to a minimum, these portable spots are relatively small and "open-faced," which means that they do not have a lens. Without a lens, they cannot deliver as precise a beam as the Fresnel or ellipsoidal spots, even

7.15

COOKIE PATTERN

Some ellipsoidal spotlights double as pattern projectors. You can insert a variety of metal cutouts, called cookies, whose patterns are projected by the spotlight onto a wall or other surface.

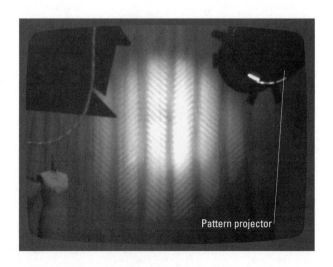

Pattern projector

7.16

LOWEL OMNI LIGHT

This popular lightweight instrument doubles as a spot and floodlight and is used mainly in ENG/EFP. You can plug it into any normal household outlet and hold it or fasten it to a light stand or any other convenient mounting device.

7.17

LOWEL PRO LIGHT

The Pro is a small, powerful (200-watt) ENG/EFP spotlight that can be handheld, clipped on the camera, or mounted on a light stand.

when in the spot or focus position. They are all designed to be mounted on a light stand or on a clip-on device. Some of the more popular models are the Lowel Omni and Pro lights. **SEE 7.16 AND 7.17** An old standby is the clip light, with its reflector built into its bulb. The PAR 38 lamp is especially popular for illuminating outdoor walkways and driveways. Clip lights are useful for supplemental illumination of small areas; you can easily clip them onto furniture, scenery, doors, or whatever the clip will fit. Metal housings with barn doors that fit over the clip light are also available. As with large ones, these barn doors control the spread of the beam. **SEE 7.18**

7.18

CLIP LIGHT WITH BARN DOORS

Small spotlights, which use ordinary internal reflector lamps, are useful for illuminating small areas during field productions.

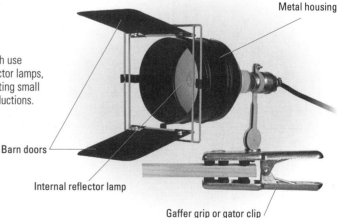

Metal housing

Barn doors

Internal reflector lamp

Gaffer grip or gator clip

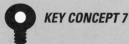

KEY CONCEPT 7   **Spotlights produce a sharp, directional light beam. They cause fast falloff.**

Floodlights

Floodlights have no lens, because their purpose is to create a highly diffused nondirectional light rather than a sharp beam. Because the light is so diffused, the shadows are soft and transparent. When you illuminate an object with floodlights, the falloff is much slower than with a spotlight. The more common studio floods are the *scoop*, the *softlight*, and the *broad*. Special-purpose floodlights include the fluorescent bank, the internal reflector bank, the strip or cyc light, and a great variety of small portable floodlights. All are relatively small, highly portable, and produce a great amount of diffused light.

The scoop　Named after its scooplike reflector, the *scoop* is a relatively small and flexible floodlight that burns at the 3,200°K indoor color temperature. Some LDs prefer it to the broads because its beam, however soft, is somewhat more directional and can therefore illuminate more-precise areas. Scoops are often used as fill light for dense shadow areas to slow down falloff and make the shadows more transparent. To diffuse the light beam even more, you can attach a scrim to the front of the scoop. A *scrim* is a heat-resistant spun-glass material that comes in rolls and can be cut with scissors like cloth. **SEE 7.19**

7.19

SCOOP WITH SCRIM

The scooplike reflector of this floodlight allows you to give its diffused beam some direction, which makes it a good fill light. With a scrim attached to its otherwise open face, it acts more like a broad.

Safety chain

Scrim holder with scrim

7.20

SOFTLIGHT

This floodlight is covered with diffusing material and delivers extremely diffused light. It causes very slow falloff and renders shadows virtually invisible.

7.21

LARGE BROAD

This open-face floodlight illuminates a large area with soft, highly diffused light. It causes slow falloff.

Softlight reflector/diffuser

The softlight   *Softlights* are similar to broads, except that the large opening is covered with a diffusing material that scatters the light so much that it renders the shadows virtually invisible. Because it produces such slow-falloff lighting, it is often used where flat lighting is important, such as for product displays in commercials or instructional shows, or on models, when the softness and smoothness of the skin is especially important. Softlights come in various sizes and burn at an indoor 3,200°K color temperature. Most softlights are quite large and do not fit a cramped production space, but smaller softlights are the mainstay of news sets and interview areas. **SEE 7.20**

The broad   The *broad* is an open-face instrument that houses one or more large tubelike lamps in a square or rectangular reflector. It produces a great amount of highly diffused light. You use the broad to illuminate large areas with even, slow-falloff, 3,200°K light. **SEE 7.21** Some small broads, which are used primarily for filling in the harsh spotlight shadows, have barn doors. The barn doors keep the light from spilling into certain set areas without reducing the softness of their "beam."

Special-Purpose floodlights The *fluorescent bank,* which consists of a row of fluorescent tubes, used to be one of the main lighting devices in the early days of television. After a hiatus the bank has made a comeback. It is highly efficient, produces extremely diffused light and slow falloff, and does not generate the heat of the other floodlights. You can get fluorescent banks that burn at the outdoor norm of 5,600°K or with 3,200°K indoor light. The manufacturers of fluorescent lights try hard to make the light look similar to incandescent floodlights without the telltale greenish look of the fluorescents. The disadvantage of all such lights is that the banks are relatively large and unwieldy. **SEE 7.22**

The *floodlight bank* consists of strips of internal reflector bulbs. The smaller ones have two or three rows of three lamps each; the larger ones can have several rows of twelve or more. They are used to light large areas from some distance, similar to the lights you see in a sports stadium. **SEE 7.23**

The *strip,* or *cyc, light* is used to illuminate *cycloramas* (the seamless background curtain that stretches along studio or stage walls), drapes, or large areas of scenery. They are similar to theater border lights and consist of rows of three to

---

7.22

FLUORESCENT BANK

The fluorescent bank consists of a series of fluorescent tubes. It produces very soft light with slow falloff.

7.23

FLOODLIGHT BANK

The floodlight bank consists of rows of internal reflector lamps. It is used to illuminate large areas from some distance. Large banks are used in lighting scenes at remote locations, such as sporting events.

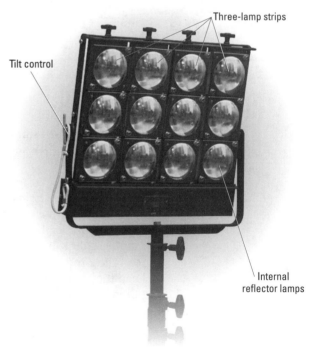

7.24

STRIP, OR CYC, LIGHT

These instruments are used primarily to illuminate cycloramas, drapes, or large scenic areas.

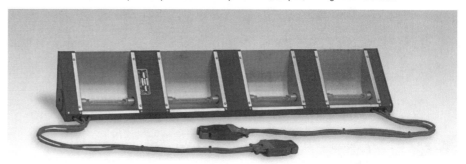

twelve quartz lamps mounted in long, boxlike reflectors. Some of them have color filters at the opening, which allow you to change the colors on the background without adding new instruments. They are usually positioned side-by-side on the studio floor and shine upward onto the background. **SEE 7.24**

Portable floodlights   When choosing a portable floodlight, you should look for one that is small, produces a great amount of diffused light, has a reflector that keeps the diffused light from spilling all over the area, can be plugged into an ordinary 120-volt household outlet, and is lightweight enough to be supported by a small light stand. **SEE 7.25** When mounted inside an umbrella reflector, a portable floodlight serves as a softlight. Many portable lights come with "light

7.25

SMALL EFP FLOODLIGHT

This small EFP floodlight (Lowel Tota light) runs off ordinary household current and can be used to illuminate small areas. When mounted inside an umbrella reflector, it serves as a softlight.

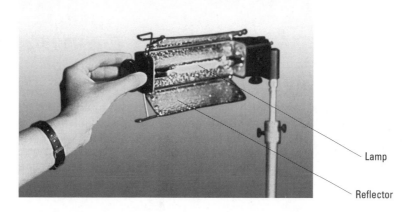

Lamp

Reflector

boxes," or "light tents," which are tentlike diffusers that you can put over the portable light source to change it into an efficient softlight. In an emergency you can always use an ordinary quartz garage light and either diffuse its beam with a scrim or, better, bounce it off a white card or some kind of reflector. 🔵 *READY ZVL 7*

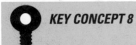 **KEY CONCEPT 8**   **Floodlights produce general, nondirectional illumination. They cause slow falloff.**

LIGHTING TECHNIQUES

Start your lighting task with an idea of how you would like it to look on the video screen, and then choose the simplest way of achieving this look. Although there is no universal recipe that guarantees good lighting for every situation, there are some established techniques available that you can easily adapt to the specific task at hand. But do not become a slave to those techniques. Although you may wish you had more instruments, more space, and especially more time to do justice to the lighting, you should realize that the final criteria for video lighting is not how faithfully you observe the standards as outlined in a book, but how it looks on the monitor and, especially, how to get it done on time.

Let's take a look at some of the lighting basics: (1) operation of lights, (2) studio lighting, (3) field lighting, and (4) measuring illumination.

Operation of Lights

Lighting presents some obvious hazards: ordinary household current is powerful enough to kill; the lamps, barn doors, and sometimes the instruments themselves get so hot that they can cause serious burns. If placed too close to combustible material, lighting instruments can cause fires. The lighting instruments with barn doors are suspended far above studio areas and, if not properly secured, can come crashing down. Staring into a bright, high-intensity light beam can cause temporary vision problems. Even so, you don't need to be scared and give up lighting before getting started. You can easily eliminate these hazards by observing a few safety rules.

CHECKLIST: LIGHTING SAFETY

☑ *Electricity*   Don't ever handle an instrument with wet hands, even if it is unplugged. Do not "hot-plug" the instrument: Switch off the power before connecting or disconnecting the power cables or patch cords. Patch cords connect selected lighting instruments to specific dimmers. *Wear gloves.* Use wood or fiberglass safety ladders rather than metal ones. Do not touch any metal while working with a power cable. If you need an adapter to connect a power cable or plug it in, tape the connection with electrician's tape. Do not waste electric energy.

Use only those instruments that are absolutely necessary. Turn off the studio lights and use house lights for the basic blocking rehearsals. Turning off the lights will keep the studio cooler and will also extend the life of the expensive bulbs.

☑ *Heat*   The quartz lamps (quartz housing and a tungsten-halogen filament) get extremely hot. They heat up the barn doors and even the housing of the lighting instrument itself. Never touch the barn doors or the instrument with your bare hands once it is turned on. Use gloves or a lighting pole to adjust the barn doors or the instrument.

Keep the instruments away from combustible materials, such as curtains, cloth, books, or wood paneling. If you need to place a lighting instrument close to such materials, insulate the materials with a sheet of aluminum foil.

Let the bulbs cool down before replacing them. Do not touch quartz lamps with your fingers. Fingerprints or any other stuff clinging to the lamp will cause it to overheat at these points and burn out. Use a tissue or, in case of emergency, your sweater or shirttail when exchanging the bulbs. Be sure the power is shut off before reaching into the instrument. If you can, let the larger instruments "warm up" through reduced power before bringing the dimmer up full.

☑ **Placing and securing the instruments**   Before lowering movable battens, make sure that the studio floor is clear of people, equipment, and scenery. Give a warning before actually lowering the batten, such as "Batten 5C coming down!" Wait for an "all-clear" signal before lowering the batten, and have someone watch the studio floor while you do so. Tighten all necessary bolts on the *C-clamp*. **SEE 7.26** Secure the instrument to the batten, and the barn doors to the instrument, with a safety chain or cable. Check the power connections for obviously worn or loose plugs and cables.

7.26

C-CLAMP

Use the C-clamp to fasten heavy lighting instruments to the lighting battens. Even when tightly fastened to the batten, the C-clamp allows the lighting instrument to be turned.

Whenever moving a ladder, watch for obstacles below and above. Don't leave your lighting wrench or other tools on top of the ladder. Don't take any unnecessary chances by leaning way out to reach an instrument. Whenever possible, have somebody steady the ladder for you.

☑ *Eyes*   When adjusting an instrument, try not to look directly into the light. Work from behind, rather than in front of, the instrument. This way you look *with* the beam, rather than into it. If you have to look into the light, do it very briefly and wear dark glasses.

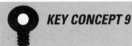

KEY CONCEPT 9   **Do not abandon safety for expediency.**

Studio Lighting

Now you are ready to do some actual lighting assignments. Although you may find yourself struggling with lighting at remote locations more often than doing fancy studio work, you will find that learning to light is easier in the studio than in the field. As the Triple-I LD tells you, the art of lighting is neither mysterious nor complicated if you keep in mind its basic functions: (1) to reveal the basic shape of the object or person; (2) to lighten or darken the shadows; (3) to show where the object is relative to the background; and (4) to give some sparkle to the object or person.

The photographic, or triangle, lighting principle   Still photographers have taught us that all these functions can be accomplished with three lights: (1) the *key light*, which reveals the basic shape; (2) the *fill light*, which fills in the shadows if they are too dense; and (3) the *back light*, which separates the object from the background and provides some sparkle. The various lighting techniques for video and motion pictures are firmly rooted in this basic principle of still photography, called the *photographic principle* or *triangle lighting*. **SEE 7.27**

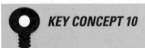

KEY CONCEPT 10   **The basic photographic principle, or triangle lighting, consists of a key light, a fill light, and a back light.**

Applying the lighting triangle   In the studio Fresnel spots are normally used for key lights. Fresnels let you aim the beam at the object without too much spill into other set areas. By focusing or flooding the light beam or by using the barn doors, you can further control its spread. But you can also use other instruments

7.27

BASIC PHOTOGRAPHIC PRINCIPLE

The basic photographic principle uses a key light, a fill light, and a back light. They are arranged in a triangle, with the back light at its apex, opposite the camera.

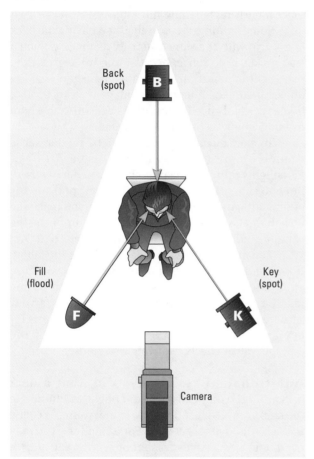

7.28

KEY LIGHT

The key light is the principal light source. It reveals the basic shape of the object. A spotlight is generally used as a key.

for a key light, such as an Omni light, a scoop, or even a softlight. As you can see, the *key light* is not defined by the instrument used, but by its function: to reveal the basic shape of the object. The key light is usually placed above and to the right or left of the front of the object. **SEE 7.28** Note that the key light produces fast falloff (a dense attached shadow).

To outline the subject more clearly against the background, and especially to give the hair—and with it the whole picture—some sparkle and luster, you need a *back light*. Some lighting people think that it is especially the back light that gives the lighting its professional polish. **SEE 7.29**

7.29

BACK LIGHT

The back light outlines the subject against the background and provides sparkle. Focused spots are used as back lights.

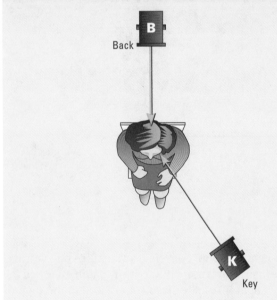

As the name suggests, the back light falls on the back of the subject's head. You place it opposite the camera directly in back of, and above, the subject. Because the area to be illuminated by the back light is rather limited, you use Fresnel spots. To keep the back light from shining into the camera or being in the shot, place it fairly high behind the subject.

Some lighting directors insist on having the back light burn with the same intensity as the key. Such a rule makes little sense, because the intensity of the back light depends on the relative reflectance of the object or subject. A blond woman who wears a white blouse certainly needs a less intense beam than a man in a dark suit who has black, curly hair.

To slow down falloff and thereby render dense shadows more transparent, you use a *fill light*. Floodlights rather than spotlights are generally used. But you can, of course, also use Fresnel spots (or any other spotlight) as fill lights. Obviously, you place the fill light on the other side of the key light, opposite the camera, and aim it toward the shadow area. **SEE 7.30**

The more fill light you use, the slower the falloff. If the fill light is as strong as the key light, you have eliminated the attached shadow and, with it, any falloff; the pictures look flat. Many news or interview sets are lighted flat (with equally strong softlights for key and fill) to show the close-up faces of the newspeople or guests relatively wrinkle-free.

Additional lights Unless you want a dark background, you need additional light to illuminate the background or set. This additional source is called *background light* or *set light*. For a small set, you may need only a single Fresnel spot or scoop. **SEE 7.31** A large set may require a few more instruments, each of which illuminates a specific area. To keep the attached shadows of the background on the same side as the foreground shadows, you must place the background light on the same camera side as the key light.

You can also use the background light to provide some visual interest to an otherwise dull background. You can either produce a slice of light, or a prominent cast shadow, that cuts across the background. To suggest nighttime when lighting an interior set, keep the background generally dark and illuminate only small portions of it. If you want to evoke daylight, illuminate the background evenly. You can colorize a neutral gray or white background simply by putting color gels (color media) in front of the background lights. Colored lights can save you a lot of painting. **READY ZVL 8**

7.30
FILL LIGHT

The fill light slows down falloff and renders shadows more transparent. Floodlights are generally used to fill in the dense shadows.

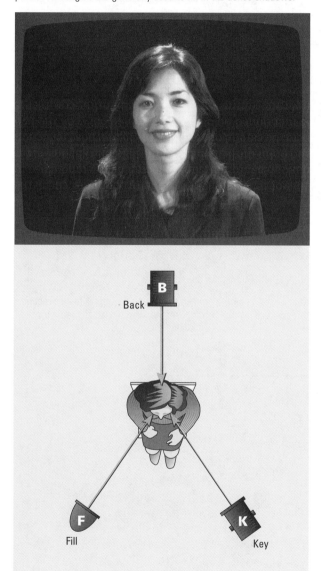

7.31
BACKGROUND LIGHT

The background, or set, light illuminates the background and various set areas. Spots or floodlights are used on the same side as the key.

Designing multiple triangles   What if you have two people sitting next to, or facing, each other? Do you need a key, fill, and back for each one? Yes, if you have enough instruments and time available. But you should always try to accomplish a lighting setup with as few instruments as possible. If the people sit opposite each other, the key light for one person may serve as the other's back light, or a single softlight can serve as fill light for more than one person. Sometimes the key light will spill over onto the background and thus eliminate the need for a set light.

When designing illumination keep in mind that you *light for the camera.* Knowing the principal camera positions is essential for effectively applying the lighting triangle. If, for instance, you arc the camera around a person so that the key light is opposite the camera, the key light now functions as a back light.

Whenever possible, put up the set where the lights are rather than move the lights to the set location. If, for example, you have to put up and light a simple two-person interview set, look up at the lighting grid and find a key, fill, and back light triangle and place the chair in the middle of it. Even if you can't find another lighting triangle (key, fill, back) for the other chair, you are still ahead: half of the lighting is already done.

Light plot   For more-complicated shows, you need to prepare a ***light plot***. Once you have a detailed floor plan, which shows the scenery, the major action areas, and the principal camera positions, you can go to the studio and note the position, type, and functions of the lighting instruments needed. Arrows will indicate the approximate directions of the beams. **SEE 7.32**

7.32

LIGHT PLOT FOR TWO-PERSON INTERVIEW

The light plot shows the type and position of the lighting instruments used and the approximate direction of the beams. Sometimes light plots also indicate the size (wattage) of the instruments. Note that there are two overlapping lighting triangles—one for person A and the other for person B.

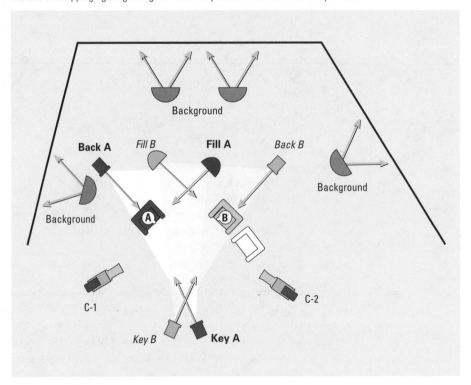

Other lighting techniques   When you are called upon to do some last-minute lighting, do not whine about artistic integrity or lack of assigned time. Simply turn on as many floodlights as possible and then try to place some back lights to give the scene some polish. This is not the time to fret about triangle principles or falloff. Every so often such emergency techniques will result in surprisingly good lighting.

Even under normal circumstances, don't be a slave to the photographic principle. Sometimes you will find that a single Fresnel aimed at the windshield of a car is all you need to produce a convincing nighttime effect; at other times you may need four or five carefully placed instruments to re-create the effect of a single candle. The effectiveness of the lighting is determined not by how faithfully you observe the traditional lighting rules, but by how the scene looks on the monitor.

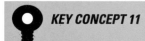

KEY CONCEPT 11   **The major criterion for good lighting is how it looks on the monitor.**

Field Lighting

Whereas studio lighting is done exclusively with various types of instruments, field lighting often extends to the control or augmentation of available light. When shooting outdoors, you are pretty much dependent on available light. Your lighting job is to manipulate sunlight so that it yields, at least to some extent, to the basic lighting principles. When shooting indoors you can apply all studio lighting principles, except on a smaller scale. Windows always present a problem because the light entering from outside is usually brighter than the indoor light and has a much higher color temperature than the lights used indoors.

Outdoors—overcast   An overcast or foggy day is ideal for outdoor shooting. The clouds and fog act as giant diffusion filters: The giant and brutally bright spotlight of the sun becomes a huge but gentle softlight. The highly diffused light produces slow falloff and transparent shadows. The camera likes such low-contrast lighting and produces crisp and true colors throughout the scene. The scene is basically illuminated by high-intensity baselight.

Bright sunlight   The bright sun acts like a giant high-intensity spotlight. The key side is very bright and the falloff appropriately fast; the shadows are very dense, and the contrast between light and shadow sides is extremely high.

This extreme contrast presents a formidable exposure problem. If you close down the iris to compensate for the bright light (high *f*-stop setting), the shadow areas will turn uniformly dark and dense and will show no detail. If you open up the iris to see some detail in the shadow area, you will overexpose the bright areas in the picture. The automatic aperture in a camcorder is of no help in this situation; it simply adjusts to the brightest spot in the scene and renders all shadow areas equally dark. Even the most sophisticated camera cannot adjust itself to these conditions.

What you must do, therefore, is provide enough fill light to slow down the falloff, reduce the contrast, and make the attached shadows more transparent

7.33

USE OF A REFLECTOR

The reflector acts like a fill light: It bounces some light back toward the dense shadow areas and slows down falloff.

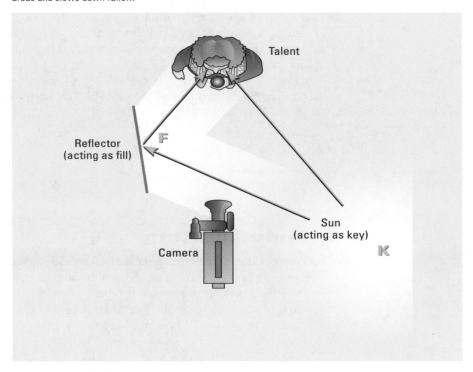

without overexposing the bright areas. But where in the field can you get a fill light strong enough to offset the sun?

In expensive and elaborate productions, high-intensity spotlights (usually HMI lights), which burn at 5,600°K, are used as outdoor fill lights. Fortunately, you can also use the sun to serve simultaneously as key and fill lights—all you need is a reflector to bounce some of the sunlight back toward the shadow area. **SEE 7.33** You can use a sheet of foam core or a white card as a reflector, or use crumpled aluminum foil taped to a stiff backing. You can also use a number of commercially available reflectors that fold up and prove effective over considerable distances. The closer you hold the reflector to the object, the more intense the fill light will be. Some LDs or DPs (directors of photography) use multiple reflectors to reflect light into areas that face away from the light source. In this case, the reflector becomes the principal light source. With good reflectors you can even guide sunlight indoors to light up a room or hallway without any lighting instruments.

7.34

REFLECTOR USED INDOORS

To achieve effective triangle lighting with two lights, use one for the key and the other for the back light. The fill light is provided by a reflector.

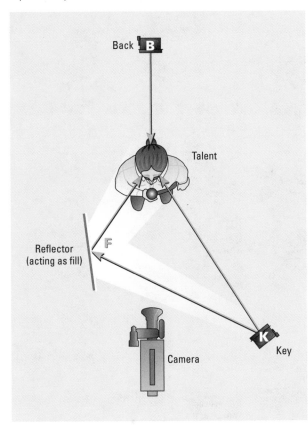

Avoid shooting against any bright background, such as a sun-drenched white wall, the ocean, or a lake. Anyone standing in front of it will be rendered a silhouette, unless you use huge reflectors or other high-intensity fill lights. Whenever possible find some shade in which to position the subject. A beach umbrella will not only provide some visual interest, but also make your lighting job considerably easier.

Indoors without windows If the room is adequately illuminated, try to shoot with available light and see how it looks. If it looks good to you, there is no need for additional lights. Remember to white-balance the camera to the available light before starting to videotape. Most indoor lighting can be easily improved by placing some back lights in the appropriate areas. Potential problems include light stands that show up on-camera, or a back light that cannot be placed high enough to keep out of camera range. In this case, place the instrument somewhat to the side, or use some 1 × 2 lumber to create a temporary support for the back light. Move the back light close enough to the subject to keep it out of camera view.

When lighting a person who remains stationary in a room, as in an interview, you use the same photographic principle as in the studio except that you now have to place portable lights on stands. Try to have the key or fill light double as the background light. To avoid the infamous reddish hot spot on the object and to make the light look generally softer, attach scrims (spun-glass material) on all three instruments. You can use wood clothespins to attach the scrims to the barn doors. Because the useful lamp life is limited in portable instruments, keep the instruments turned off as much as possible (this will also keep the room cooler). Just in case, bring along some spare light bulbs.

If you have only two lights with which to light a person indoors, you can use one as the key, the other as the back, and then use a reflector to act as the fill light. **SEE 7.34**

If you have just one lighting instrument, such as an Omni light, you can use it as a key, with the reflector acting as the fill. In such a setup, you must necessarily sacrifice the back light. If the subject remains in one place, and if you shoot fairly tightly, try using the single light source as a back light and bounce it onto the face of the subject with a large reflector. The reflector will act as key and fill lights.

INTERIOR LIGHTING

To achieve even baselight in an interior, small portable floodlights are further diffused by light-diffusing umbrellas.

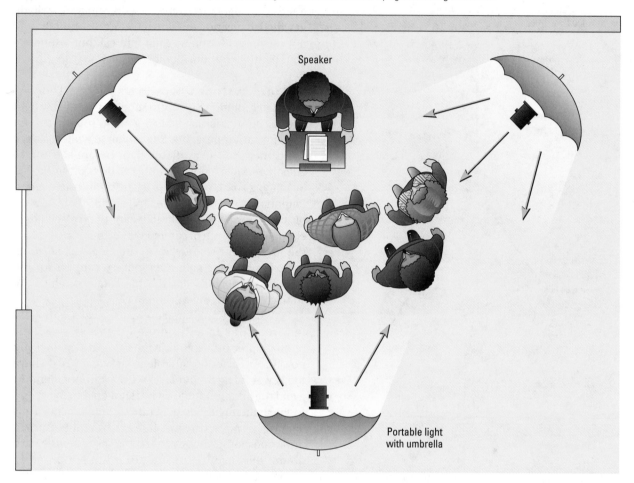

Speaker

Portable light
with umbrella

To light an ordinary-sized room so that you can follow somebody walking through it, use the portable lights in the flood position and reflect them off the ceiling or walls, or diffuse their beams with scrims. If available, use light-diffusing umbrellas. Aim the instrument into the umbrella, with the opening of the umbrella toward the scene, or at reflectors rather than directly toward the action area. You can apply the same technique for lighting a large interior, except that you need more or higher-powered instruments. The idea is to get as much baselight as possible with a minimum of instruments. **SEE 7.35**

Interiors with windows As mentioned before, windows are always a problem. Even if you don't shoot against them, they admit a great amount of high-color-temperature light, which is hard to match with ordinary lighting instruments. If you try to augment the bluish 5,600°K outdoor light with the normal indoor 3,200°K lights, the camera will have trouble finding the correct white balance. You need to raise the color temperature of the indoor lights to match that of the outdoor light (from 3,200°K to 5,600°K). You do this by attaching a blue filter or light-blue color medium to the lighting instruments; or you can affix commercially available (but expensive) light-orange filter material onto the windows to lower the outdoor light to the indoor color temperature of 3,200°K.

If you must include a window in the shot, you will notice that the window is by far the highest-intensity light source. Rather than raise the intensity of the portable lights to match that of the window (usually a futile effort), you can cut down the intensity of the outdoor light by covering it with a plastic neutral density (ND) sheet, which is similar to the color-correction sheets. Such an ND filter will lower the intensity of the light without changing its color temperature.

The best way to cope with windows is to avoid them. Draw the curtains or persuade the subject to sit opposite, or at least sideways to, the window. Remember that if you use additional lights to slow down the window-light falloff, you need to correct the fill lights for the proper outdoor color temperature (by attaching a light-blue color medium or the appropriate filter). In this case, a reflector is the simplest way to slow down falloff. See the guidelines for simple field lighting that follow. **READY ZVL 9**

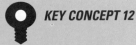

KEY CONCEPT 12   **In the field, light for visibility rather than artistic impact.**

GUIDELINES: FIELD LIGHTING

☑ *Scout ahead* Scout the location and determine the lighting requirements *before* the actual shooting date. Check the available power, the person who can give you access to the breaker box (name, address, home and work phone numbers), the nature of the outlets, and the extension cords needed. Have adapters available that fit the various outlets.

☑ *Be prepared* Always take with you a few rolls of gaffer's tape, a roll of aluminum foil, gloves, a small wrench, some wood clothespins (plastic ones will melt), and a small fire extinguisher.

☑ *Don't overload circuits* Once on location, don't overload the circuit. Although a normal 15-amp household outlet will accommodate 1,500 watts of lighting instruments, do not plug more than 1,000 watts into a single circuit. Realize that several outlets may be on the same circuit, even if they are in different corners of the room. To test which outlets are on the same circuit, plug the light into various outlets and turn off the breaker. If the light goes out, you are on the designated circuit. If the light stays on, the outlet is connected to another circuit. Keep in mind that even long extension cables can add to the circuit load.

☑ ***Don't waste bulb life*** As mentioned before, turn on the lights only as needed. The light bulbs for portable lighting instruments have a limited life span. Turning off the lights as much as possible will preserve energy, extend the life of the bulb, and reduce the heat in the performance areas.

☑ ***Secure the light stands*** Be especially careful when placing lighting instruments on portable stands. Secure all light stands with sandbags so they won't tip over when somebody brushes against them. Place extension cords out of the main traffic pattern. If you have to string them across a hallway or threshold, tape them securely in place (here is where the gaffer's tape comes in handy) and/or put a rubber doormat over them.

☑ ***Move cords carefully*** Don't pull on an extension cord that is connected to a lighting instrument; light stands tip over easily, especially when the stand is fully extended.

Measuring Illumination

In critical lighting setups, you may want to check whether there is enough baselight and whether the contrast between light and dark areas falls within the acceptable limits (normally 40:1) before turning on the cameras. You can check this with the help of a light meter. A light meter simply measures the amount of foot-candles or lux emitted by the lighting instruments—the *incident light*—or reflected off an object—the *reflected light*.

Incident light An incident-light reading gives you some idea of the baselight level in a given area, which translates into how much light the camera receives from a particular location on the set. To measure general incident light, you must stand next to, or in front of, the illuminated person or object and point the light meter *toward the camera lens.* Such a quick reading of incident light is especially helpful when checking the prevailing light levels at a remote location.

If you want a more specific reading of the intensity of light coming from specific instruments, you point the light meter *into the lights.* To check the relative evenness of the incident light, point the light meter toward the major camera positions while walking around the set. If the needle or digital read-out stays approximately at the same intensity level, the lighting is fairly even. If the needle or read-out dips way down, the lighting setup has *holes* (unlighted or underlighted areas).

Reflected light The reading of reflected light is done primarily to check the contrast between light and dark areas. To measure reflected light, stand close to the lighted object or person and point the light meter at the light and shadow areas from the direction of the camera. Be careful not to block the light whose reflection you are trying to measure. As mentioned before, the difference between the two readings will indicate the *lighting contrast.* Note that the lighting contrast is determined not only by how much light falls on the object, but also by how much light the object reflects back into the camera. The more reflective the object, the higher the reflected-light reading will be. A mirror reflects almost all the light falling into it; a black velour cloth will reflect only a small portion.

Don't become a slave to the light meter. After all, the best way to tell whether the lighting is right is to look at the video monitor. 💿 *READY ZVL 10*

ONCE AGAIN, REMEMBER...

◼ Types of Light and Light Intensity

The two basic types of light are directional and diffused. Directional light is focused and causes harsh shadows; diffused light is spread out and creates soft shadows. Light intensity is measured in European lux or American foot-candles. There are approximately 10 lux per foot-candle.

◼ Shadows

Shadows are classified into attached and cast shadows. Attached shadows are affixed to the object; they cannot be seen independent of the object. Cast shadows can be seen independent of the object that causes them. Falloff indicates the change from light to shadow and the contrast between light and shadow areas. Fast falloff means that the light area changes abruptly into dense shadow areas; the contrast is high. Slow falloff means that the light turns gradually into the shadow side; the contrast is low.

◼ Colors

Colors are generated through additive color mixing. All colors are mixed by adding the primary light colors—red, green, and blue—in various proportions. Color temperature refers to the relative reddishness or bluishness of white light. White-balancing adjusts the camera to the color temperature of the prevailing illumination so that the camera will reproduce a white object as white on the video screen.

◼ Lighting Instruments

Lights are usually classified into spotlights and floodlights, and studio and portable lights. Spotlights produce a sharp, focused beam; floodlights produce highly diffused, nondirectional illumination. Studio lights are normally suspended from the ceiling. Portable lights are supported by collapsible light stands.

◼ The Photographic Principle, or Triangle Lighting

Lighting functions can usually be achieved with a key light (principal light source), a fill light (fills in dense shadows), and a back light (separates subject from background and gives it sparkle). Reflectors frequently substitute for fill lights. The background light is an additional light used for lighting the background and set area. In field lighting, it is often more important to provide sufficient illumi-nation than careful triangle lighting. In the field, floodlights are used more often than spotlights.

Measuring Light

When measuring incident light (the light falling on the object) you point the light meter from the position of the illuminated object at the camera lens or into the lights. When measuring reflected light, you stand close to the object and point the meter at the object from the camera position.

Z E T T L ' S   V I D E O   L A B   2 . 1

*Let's go to our virtual studio and do some lighting. There you can not only watch some of the lighting effects that Mary, the LD, is demonstrating, but also do some lighting yourself. Click on the **lights** monitor and play tape 1 **Meet Mary**.*

RUN ZVL 1
Load tape 2 **Light and Shadow** and play the introduction. Mary's opening remarks give you some idea about the quality of light and the functions of shadows. She confirms that the art of lighting consists mostly of shadow control rather than mere illumination. What she tells you in module 1 **Light** about directional and diffused light sources (spotlights and floodlights) is one of the most important lighting principles.

RUN ZVL 2
Load tape 4 **Measurement** and play the introduction. Mary introduces you to two important lighting concepts: baselight and contrast. Module 1 **Meters** shows you the difference between the American and European units of measuring light intensity. Both units are used interchangeably by most LDs. Now click on module 2 **Baselight** and see how the light meter is used to measure the intensity of the overall baselight level. Note that the LD points his meter toward the camera lens and into the lights themselves to measure baselight. Now click on the next two modules, **Contrast** and **Quiz**, and move the light meter into the brightest and darkest spots in the picture. As you can see, your measurement of the contrast between light and dark shows up as a ratio of 60:1. Is this acceptable for most cameras?

RUN ZVL 3
Go back to tape 2 **Light and Shadow** and play module 2 **Attached**. You can see again how important attached shadows are in revealing form and texture. Note how much denser and more dramatic the attached shadows are when using directional light as opposed to diffused light, which renders the shadows much more transparent. To see another example of how the reversal of attached shadows can cause unusual effects, load tape 8 **Design** and play module 4 **Horror**.

RUN ZVL 4   Go back to tape 2 **Light and Shadow** and play module 3 **Cast.** Mary uses a pencil to show the various functions of cast shadows. Watch how the cast shadow is blurred when the pencil is relatively far away from the paper, but sharp and defined when the pencil touches the paper, and how it appears blurred again when diffused instead of directional light is used. As you can see, the cast shadows in the photo of the Gothic cloister aisle provide visual interest and drama.

RUN ZVL 5   Load tape 3 **Falloff.** In her introduction Mary points out two ways of describing falloff: the relative contrast between light and shadow side, and the relative speed with which light turns into shadow. In module 1 **Fast,** note how directional light sources (including the sun) produce fast falloff. Watch the lighting diagram on the right and note how the spotlight produces fast falloff. Module 2 **Slow** shows that diffused light (in this case, the scoop in the lighting diagram) produces slow falloff and that it can be used to lighten up shadows. Slowly push up the intensity slider. Notice how the fast falloff on Mary's face becomes progressively lighter until falloff is practically eliminated. By pushing the lever down, the falloff becomes faster again. Remember this falloff control when you do some triangle lighting later on. Module 3 **None** shows you how to eliminate falloff by having the lights coming from camera-right and camera-left burn at equal intensity. This is the same effect as you got by pushing the intensity lever all the way up.

RUN ZVL 6   Load tape 5 **Color Temperature** and listen once again to Mary's introduction to color temperature. The important point she makes is that color temperature has nothing to do with the physical temperature of the lamps, but rather with the relative reddishness or bluishness of white light. Modules 2 and 3 tell you what color temperatures are and how to adjust them for effective white-balancing. Click on module 2 **Light sources.** Compare the light illustrated in the diagram on the left with its corresponding color temperature scale on the right. Now you can see that the bluish light has a high color temperature and the reddish light a low one. Module 3 **Controlling** is important for proper white-balancing. Mary is right in insisting on matching the color temperatures of all light sources falling on a scene *before* balancing the camera. Believe her: Raising the color temperature of an indoor light to the 5,600°K outdoor standard is much simpler than trying to lower the outdoor light to the 3,200°K indoor standard.

RUN ZVL 7   Load tape 6 **Instruments** and play the introduction, where Mary introduces you to spotlights and floodlights. In module 1 **Studio,** pay particular attention to the direction you need to move the lamp-reflector unit ("bulb-reflector assembly") to adjust the spread of the beam. Watch the diagram on the left and how the beam width changes when you push the assembly toward the lens or pull it away. Also note her pronunciation of "Fresnel." In module 2 **Field,** you can see the diffusing effect of the umbrella and how the intensity of the light drops noticeably when moving it just a little farther away from the subject.

RUN ZVL 8 Load tape 7 **Triangle Lighting** and play the introduction. Watch the effects when you turn on the key, fill, back, and background lights. In module 1 **Key**, watch how the focused, high-intensity key light produces fast falloff, and how you can control the falloff by turning on the fill light to low or high intensity. Now play module 2 **Back** and turn on the backlight. Note how it separates the model's hair from the dark background and gives the hair some much-needed sparkle. Now turn on the fill light in module 3 **Fill**. When you turn up its intensity, the fill light practically eliminates all the shadows on the model's face. The falloff increases when you click the *Low-intensity* button. By turning on the background light in module 4 **Background**, you see how the background light helps make the whole scene brighter and less dramatic. What if you were now to turn off all lights except the background light? Or only the key? Or the key and background together? What effects would you get? Go to module 5 **Try It** and experiment with the various combinations.

RUN ZVL 9 Yes, you have seen it before. But because windows are a constant hazard in shooting interior scenes, load tape 5 **Color Temperature** once more and click on module 3 **Controlling**. If you can afford it, it is better to lower the color temperature of the light coming through the windows to the indoor 3,200°K by putting orange gels over the windows. Regardless of where you are in the room, you will not be bothered by the high-color-temperature outdoor light. The more economical way is to gel the indoor lights with a light-blue filter to raise their color temperature to the 5,600°K outdoor standard.

RUN ZVL 10 If you are still unsure of how to read incident and reflected light, load tape 4 **Measurement** and view again the first three modules: **Meters**, **Baselight**, and **Contrast**.

KEY CONCEPTS

- Lighting means deliberate illumination and shadow control.

- Attached shadows reveal form and texture.

- Cast shadows help tell us where things are and when events take place.

- Falloff defines the contrast between light and dark areas and how quickly light turns into shadow.

- The additive primary light colors are red, green, and blue.

- Color temperature measures the relative reddishness or bluishness of white light. Reddish white light has a low color temperature; bluish white light has a high color temperature.

- Spotlights produce a sharp, directional light beam. They cause fast falloff.

- Floodlights produce general, nondirectional illumination. They cause slow falloff.

- Do not abandon safety for expediency.

- The basic photographic principle, or triangle lighting, consists of a key light, a fill light, and a back light.

- The major criterion for good lighting is how it looks on the monitor.

- In the field, light for visibility rather than artistic impact.

KEY TERMS

ATR Stands for audiotape recorder.

cardioid A unidirectional microphone pickup pattern.

condenser microphone High-quality, sensitive microphone for critical sound pickup. Used mostly indoors.

DAT Stands for digital audiotape.

DVD Stands for digital versatile disc. It can store 4.7 gigabytes of video and/or audio information. Also called *digital videodisc*.

dynamic microphone A relatively rugged microphone. Good for outdoor use.

fader A volume control that works by sliding a button horizontally along a specific scale. Identical in function to a pot. Also called *slide-fader*.

hypercardioid A microphone with a very narrow pickup pattern that has a long reach. It can also hear sounds coming directly from the back.

jack A socket or receptacle for a connector.

lavaliere A small microphone that is clipped onto clothing.

mini disc A small optical disc that can store one hour of CD-quality audio.

mini plug Tiny connector used for some consumer audio equipment.

omnidirectional Pickup pattern with which the microphone can hear equally well from all directions.

pickup pattern The territory around the microphone within which the mic can hear well.

polar pattern The two-dimensional representation of the pickup pattern.

RCA phono plug Small connector used for most consumer video and audio equipment.

ribbon microphone High-quality, highly sensitive microphone for critical sound pickup. Produces warm sound.

sweetening The manipulation of recorded sound in postproduction.

unidirectional Pickup pattern with which the microphone can hear best from the front.

VU meter A volume-unit meter; measures volume units, the relative loudness of amplified sound.

windscreen Acoustic foam rubber that is put over the microphone to cut down wind noise.

XLR connector A professional three-wire connector for audio cables.

Audio and Sound Control

YOU have probably heard over and over again that television is primarily visual. You have also often heard that the worst sin you can commit in video production is showing "talking heads." The Triple-I director you previously met at the MTV shoot thinks that this "talking head" idea is a total misconception and reveals that many people still don't seem to understand the true nature of the video medium. She tells you that video programs rely on the sound portion much more than film. According to her, the audio portion not only conveys information, but also gives sequences added energy and structure. "There is nothing wrong with talking heads," she tells you, "so long as they talk well and have something worthwhile to say."

In fact, much of the information in television and video programs is conveyed by somebody talking. You can do a simple experiment to prove this point: First, turn off the video portion of the program and try to follow what is going on; second, turn on the video again, but turn off the audio. You will probably have little trouble following the story by hearing only the sound track, but you will, in most cases, have a difficult time knowing what is going on by seeing only the pictures. Even if you can follow the story by watching the pictures, the lack of sound leaves the message strangely incomplete.

You will find that most amateur video is characterized not just by the madly moving camera and fast zooms but by bad audio as well. Even professional video productions tend to suffer more from bad sound than bad pictures. Why? At first glance the production of sound seems much easier to achieve than the corresponding video portion. When working your camcorder, you are probably concentrating so hard on getting good pictures that you don't pay much attention to the sounds that surround you. You simply assume that the built-in microphone will do the job of picking up the necessary audio.

Even experienced video production people are confronted by the audio issue. In simple productions, such as an interview with a company executive, the pickup of sound is, indeed, relatively simple compared with the video requirements (lighting and camera handling). If the sound production is a little more challenging, such as doing an interview on a noisy street corner or mixing music and sound effects with dialogue, the audio portion requires at least as much attention and skill as the video, and often more. When videotaping a musical number, audio is obviously the most demanding part of the production. However simple or complex the production may be, sticking a microphone into a scene at the last moment is not the way to go. You need to consider the audio requirements from the very beginning of the technical production planning, when you're considering the medium requirements. **READY ZVL 1**

This chapter examines the various tools and techniques of producing good audio for video.

■ SOUND PICKUP PRINCIPLE
How microphones change sound waves into sound signals

■ MICROPHONES
How they can hear, how they are made, and how they are used

■ SOUND CONTROL
Working the audio mixer and audio console

■ SOUND RECORDING
Analog and digital recording equipment and other audio recording devices

■ SYNTHESIZED SOUND
Computer-generated sounds

■ SOUND AESTHETICS
Environment, figure-ground, perspective, continuity, and energy

SOUND PICKUP PRINCIPLE

Like the translation process in video, in which the lens image of the object is translated into the video signal, the sounds we actually hear are transduced (transformed) into electric energy—the audio signal. This signal is made audible again through the loudspeaker. The basic sound pickup tool is the microphone, or *mic* (pronounced "mike").

You can also create sounds synthetically, by electronically generating and recording certain sound frequencies, a process similar to creating computer-generated video images. We focus first on microphone-generated sounds and then turn briefly to synthesized sounds.

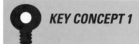

KEY CONCEPT 1   Microphones transduce (transform) sound waves into electric energy—the audio signal.

MICROPHONES

Although all microphones fulfill the same basic function of translating sounds into audio signals, they do so in different ways and for different purposes. Good audio requires that you know how to choose the right mic for a specific sound pickup— not an easy task when faced with the great variety of mics available. Despite all the various brand names and numbers, you will find that you can make some sense out of the different microphones by classifying them by (1) how well they can hear, (2) how they are made, and (3) how they are used.

How Well They Can Hear: Sound Pickup

Not all microphones hear sounds in the same way. Some are built to hear sounds from all directions equally well; others favor sounds that come from a specific direction.

In general, you will find that most microphones used in video production are omnidirectional or unidirectional. The directional characteristic—the zone within which a microphone can hear well—is specified by its *pickup pattern*, the two-dimensional representation of which is called the *polar pattern*.

The *omnidirectional* mic hears equally well from all directions. Visualize the omnidirectional mic at the center of a sphere. The sphere itself represents the pickup pattern. **SEE** **8.1** The *unidirectional* mic is designed to hear especially well in one

8.1

OMNIDIRECTIONAL
PICKUP PATTERN

The omnidirectional microphone hears equally well from all directions.

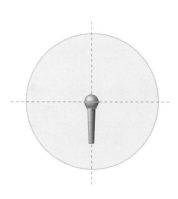

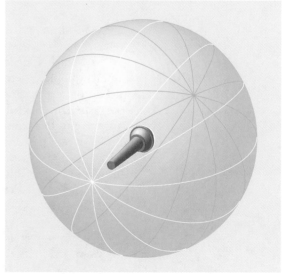

8.2

CARDIOID PICKUP PATTERN

The unidirectional microphone favors sounds that are in front of it. Its pickup pattern is heart-shaped, which is why it is called *cardioid*.

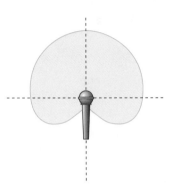

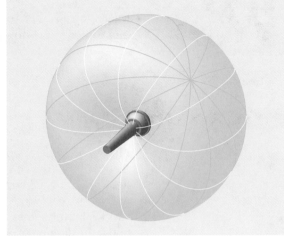

8.3

HYPERCARDIOID PICKUP PATTERN

The hypercardioid pickup pattern is narrower than the cardioid and has a longer reach. Hypercardioid mics can also hear sounds coming from the back of the mic.

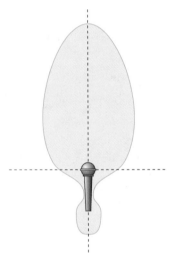

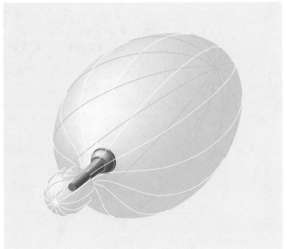

direction—from the front of the mic. Because the pickup pattern of a unidirectional mic is roughly heart-shaped, it is also called *cardioid*. **SEE 8.2**

When this "heart" (pickup pattern) gets progressively thinner, we speak of supercardioid, hypercardioid, or ultracardioid mics. The "heart" of the cardioid pickup pattern has now been stretched to the shape of a watermelon. **SEE 8.3** The *hypercardioid* and ultracardioid mics have a "long reach," which means that you can produce sounds that seem to come from fairly close by, although they may be quite far away. Hyper- and supercardioid mics are also sensitive to sounds that come directly from behind. Because these microphones are usually fairly long and are aimed at the direction of the sound source, they are commonly called *shotgun mics*. 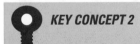 *READY ZVL 2*

KEY CONCEPT 2 The pickup pattern indicates the zone in which a microphone can hear well—its directionality.

▨ How They Are Made

When selecting a mic for a particular audio task, you need to consider both its specific pickup pattern and its basic mechanics—its *sound-generating element.* When classifying microphones by how they are made, there are three types: (1) dynamic, (2) condenser, and (3) ribbon.

The *dynamic mic* uses a small coil that moves within a magnetic field when activated by sound. The movement of the coil produces the varying sound signal. The *condenser mic* has a movable plate that oscillates against a fixed one to produce the sound signal. The *ribbon mic* has a small ribbon, rather than a coil, that moves in a magnetic field. But don't worry too much about exactly how these sound elements work; it is more important to know how these mics differ in their use.

Dynamic   *Dynamic microphones* are the most rugged. You can take them outside in all kinds of weather, and they can even withstand occasional rough handling. You can work with them close to extremely loud sounds without distorting the sound too much or causing damage to the mic. Many dynamic microphones have a built-in *pop filter,* which eliminates the breath pops that occur when someone speaks into the mic at very close range. **SEE 8.4**

Condenser   These microphones are much more sensitive to physical shock and temperatures than are dynamic mics, but they produce higher-quality sounds. *Condenser microphones* are generally used indoors for critical sound pickup. They are especially prominent in music recording. Unlike dynamic mics, condenser microphones need a small power supply to activate the sound-generating device inside the microphone. Some need a small battery that is inserted in the microphone housing. **SEE 8.5** Others get their power supply through the cable from the audio console (usually called *phantom power*). If you use a battery, make sure that it is inserted properly (with the + and – poles as indicated in the housing) and that the battery

8.4

DYNAMIC MICROPHONE WITH POP FILTER

Dynamic microphones are the most rugged. They can withstand rough handling and extreme temperatures. The built-in pop filter reduces breath pops.

8.5

POWER SUPPLY FOR CONDENSER MICROPHONE

Most condenser microphones use a battery to charge the condenser plates. When fed to the microphone from the audio console, the power is called phantom power.

8.6

WINDSCREEN ON SHOTGUN MICROPHONE

The windscreen, made of porous material, protects the microphone from excessive wind noise.

8.7

WINDSOCK PULLED OVER WINDSCREEN

The windsock is used on top of the windscreen to further reduce wind noise.

is not run-down. Always have a spare battery handy when using a condenser mic.

If you use a condenser shotgun mic (or, for that matter, any shotgun mic) outdoors, you need to protect the whole microphone from wind noise by covering it entirely with a ***windscreen***. **SEE 8.6** Windscreens are made of acoustic foam rubber or other synthetic material, which lets normal sound frequencies enter the mic but keeps most of the lower wind rumbles out. For ENG/EFP microphones that are used primarily outdoors, you may want to add a *windsock,* also called *wind jammer*—a ragged cloth resembling a mop that can be pulled over the windscreen. **SEE 8.7**

Ribbon *Ribbon microphones* (sometimes called *velocity mics*) are similar to condenser mics in high pickup quality and sensitivity. **SEE 8.8** Ribbon mics produce a warm, rich sound, but they do not like rough handling, extreme temperatures, or very close and loud sound blasts. In fact, a loud sound burst close to the ribbon mic can cause permanent damage. The hero of a television western learned an impressive lesson about the ribbon mic's sensitivity quite accidentally during a live television promo for his series: When he punctuated his quick-draw skills by firing a blank close to the mic, he blew the delicate ribbon clear out of the microphone. Only a lip reader could follow his subsequent pitch. *READY ZVL 3*

KEY CONCEPT 3   **Treat all microphones gently, even when turned off.**

8.8

RIBBON MICROPHONE FOR HIGH-QUALITY SOUND PICKUP

The delicate ribbon microphone is often used by singers because it produces high-quality, rich sounds.

(*Note:* Beyer Dynamic is a trade name—not the type of microphone. The mic pictured here is a ribbon microphone.)

How They Are Used

Now that you know the basic types of microphones, you need to learn how to use them effectively. Even the most sophisticated and expensive mic will not guarantee good sound unless it is placed in an optimum pickup position. In fact, the proper positioning of the mic relative to the sound source is often more important than its sound-generating element. In video production, microphones are, therefore, often identified by the way they are used rather than how they are made: (1) lavaliere microphones, (2) hand microphones, (3) boom microphones, (4) desk and stand microphones, (5) headset microphones, and (6) wireless, or radio, microphones.

Lavaliere microphones   The *lavaliere* mic, or *lav* for short, is a very small, rugged, omnidirectional microphone (dynamic or condenser) that is used principally for voice pickup. The quality of even the smallest one, which is about the size of a fingernail, is amazingly good. The combination of small size, ruggedness, and high quality have made the lavaliere indispensable in video production. It is usually clipped on top of the clothing, such as the lapel of a jacket or the front of a shirt, 6 to 8 inches below the chin. **SEE 8.9** Although primarily intended for voice pickup, you can also use the lavaliere for a variety of music pickups. Sound people have used the lavaliere successfully on violins and string

8.9

CLIP-ON LAVALIERE MICROPHONE

The small lavaliere microphone is usually clipped onto the clothing of the performer. It is normally used for voice pickup.

basses. Don't be overly influenced by the normal use of such microphones. Try them out in a variety of ways and listen to the sound they deliver. If it sounds good to you, you've got the right mic.

The obvious advantage of the lavaliere is that the talent has both hands free when he or she wears it. There are other important advantages to using a lavaliere mic:

▶ Because the distance from mic to sound source does not change once the mic is properly attached, you do not have to "ride gain" (adjust the volume) as much as with a hand mic or a boom mic.

▶ Unlike lighting for the boom mic, which must be done in such a way that the boom shadows are hidden from camera view, the lavaliere mic needs no special lighting considerations.

▶ Although the talent's action radius is somewhat limited by the microphone cable, the lavaliere lets him or her move more quickly than with a boom mic or even a hand mic. For greater mobility you can plug the talent's lavaliere microphone into a belt-pack transmitter and use it as a wireless or radio mic.

Unfortunately, there are also some disadvantages to using a lavaliere mic:

▶ If the environment is very noisy, you cannot move the mic closer to the talent's mouth. Consequently, the surrounding (ambient) noise is easily picked up.

▶ You need a separate mic for each sound source. In a two-person interview, for example, you need separate lavaliere mics for the host and guest. In a five-person panel show, you obviously need five mics.

▶ Because it is attached to clothing, the microphone may pick up rubbing noises, especially if the talent moves around a great deal. You may also get occasional popping noises from static electricity generated by the clothing.

▶ If the microphone must be concealed under clothing, the sound often takes on a muffled character and the danger of rubbing noises is greatly increased.

▶ Once the lav is attached, its distance to the mouth does not change. Hence, the sounds do not seem to come from a closer distance on a close-up or from farther away on a long shot.

Here are some points to consider when using a lavaliere microphone:

▶ Be sure to put it on. As obvious as this sounds, on the opening cue many a performer has been found sitting on the mic instead of wearing it.

▶ To put on the microphone, bring it up underneath the shirt or jacket and attach it securely on the outside. Do not put the mic next to jewelry or buttons. If you have to conceal the mic, don't bury it under layers of clothing; try to keep the top of the mic as exposed as possible. Tuck the microphone cable into the talent's belt or clothing so that the cable cannot pull the mic sideways or, worse, completely off. To further avoid pops and rumbles, put a small loop in the cable just below the mic clip, or try putting a loose knot in the small mic cable where it leaves the mic. Wedging a small piece of foam rubber between mic and clothing will further reduce rubbing noises.

▷ Once the microphone is attached to the mic cable but not yet to the talent, watch that you do not pull the mic off a table or chair and drop it on the floor. Although the lavaliere is fairly rugged, it does not bear up well to mistreatment. If you accidentally drop the mic during the setup or strike (clearing the production space), test it immediately to see whether it is still functioning properly. Once the mic is attached, ask the talent to avoid hitting it with his or her hand or some object that might be demonstrated on-camera.

▷ When used outdoors, attach the little windscreen that slips over the top of the mic.

▷ After the show watch that the talent does not get up and walk off the set without first removing the microphone.

Hand microphones   As the name implies, *hand microphones* are handled by the talent. You use a hand mic in situations in which you need to exercise some control over the sound pickup.

A reporter can move a hand mic closer to his or her mouth when working in noisy surroundings, thereby eliminating much distracting ambience; the reporter can also point it toward the person he or she is interviewing. Because the talent can point the microphone toward whoever is doing the talking, you need only a single microphone for an interview with one or even several guests. Performers who do audience participation shows like the hand microphone because it allows them to approach people and to talk to them spontaneously without any elaborate multiple-microphone setup.

A singer can control the intimacy of the sound (its presence) by holding the unidirectional hand mic very close to his or her mouth during an especially tender passage, and pulling it farther away when the song gets louder and more external. Experienced singers use the hand mic as an important visual element; they work the mic during a song by switching it from one hand to the other to signal—visually—a new song segment or a change of pace or simply to supply additional visual interest. **SEE 8.10**

8.10

USE OF DIRECTIONAL MICROPHONE BY SINGER

To emphasize the richness of her voice, the singer holds the directional hand mic close to her mouth.

When the hand mic is used outdoors for numerous production tasks and under a great variety of weather conditions, you need a rugged mic that bears up well under rough handling and extreme conditions. Dynamic hand mics with built-in pop filters are a popular mic for such productions. Singers, on the other hand, demand much more sound quality than a field reporter and prefer high-quality condenser or ribbon hand microphones. But these sensitive hand mics would not fare well under the extreme weather and handling conditions of some field productions and consequently are mostly confined to indoor use.

The major disadvantage of the hand mic is what we have just mentioned as one of its advantages: the control of the mic by the talent. Inexperienced talent often block their own and their guests' faces; this no-no becomes especially apparent when the mic has a large, colored pop filter attached to it. Also, in the excitement of the interview, an inexperienced reporter may aim the microphone toward the guest when asking the question, and then toward himself or herself when listening to the answer. As humorous as this unintentional comedy routine may seem to the bystander, it certainly is not funny to the production people who see their efforts being ruined by this maneuver.

Other disadvantages of using a hand mic are that the talent's hands are not free to do other things, such as demonstrate a product. And, unless it is a wireless hand mic, pulling the cable while working a hand mic is not always easy to do.

Here are some hints for the talent using a hand microphone:

▶ During rehearsal, check the action radius of the mic cable. Also see that the cable has free travel and will not catch on furniture or scenery. Checking the reach of the cable is especially important when the mic is connected to a camcorder.

▶ Check out the microphone before the videotaping or live transmission. Say a few of the opening lines so that the audio engineer or camcorder operator can adjust the volume of the audio signal. When there are several microphones in the immediate vicinity and you need to find out which one is turned on, do not blow or whistle into it—or, worse, whack it—rather, lightly scratch the pop filter. This scratching noise will enable the audio engineer to identify your microphone and separate it from all others.

▶ When using a hand mic in the field under normal conditions (the environment is not excessively loud, and there is little or no wind), hold the microphone at chest level and speak across rather than into it. **SEE 8.11** In noisy and windy conditions, hold the mic closer to your mouth. **SEE 8.12**

▶ When using a directional hand microphone, you must hold it close to your mouth and speak or sing directly into it, as shown in figure 8.10.

▶ When using a hand mic to interview a child, do not remain standing; squat down so that you are at the child's level. This way you establish more-personal contact with the child, and the camera can get a good two-shot. **SEE 8.13**

▶ If the microphone cable gets tangled during a take, do not panic and yank on it. Stop where you are and continue your performance while trying to get the attention of the floor manager or somebody else who can untangle it for you.

8.11

NORMAL POSITION OF HAND MICROPHONE

In a fairly quiet environment, the hand mic should be held at chest height. The performer speaks across the mic rather than into it.

8.12

POSITION OF HAND MICROPHONE IN NOISY SURROUNDINGS

In noisy surroundings the performer holds the mic closer to the mouth and speaks into the mic rather than across it.

8.13

INTERVIEWING A CHILD

When interviewing a child, you should squat down when holding the mic toward the child. The child is now more aware of you than the mic, and the camera operator can include both faces in the shot.

▶ If you need to use your hands while holding a hand mic, tuck it temporarily under your arm so that it can still pick up your voice.

▶ When the hand mic is directly connected to a camcorder, the camera operator should also turn on the camera mic (built-in or attached). The camera mic will then supply the second audio track on the videotape with the surrounding (ambient) sounds without interfering with the hand mic, which is supplying the major audio. In fact, you should always have the camera mic turned on, even if you do not intend to use such sounds. Most likely, you will make use of the ambient sound during postproduction editing.

KEY CONCEPT 4   **Test the hand mic you are using before going on the air.**

Boom microphones   Whenever the microphone is to be kept out of the picture, hypercardioid or supercardioid *shotgun mics* are used. As you recall, such highly directional microphones can pick up sounds over a fairly great distance and make them seem to come from close by. You can aim the mic toward the principal sound source while eliminating or greatly reducing all other sounds that lie outside its narrow pickup pattern. Note, however, that it is equally efficient at picking up extraneous noise that lies in its pickup path.

When used for an elaborate studio production, such as the videotaping of a soap opera, shotgun mics are suspended from a large boom, called a *studio boom* or *perambulator boom*. A boom operator, who stands on the boom platform, can extend or retract the boom, tilt it up and down, pan it sideways, rotate the microphone toward the sound source, and even have the whole boom assembly moved. This is all to move the microphone as close to the sound source as possible while keeping it out of the camera's view.

The problem with using a studio boom is that it is quite large and takes up a lot of studio operating space. Furthermore, you will discover that operating a boom is at least as difficult as running a camera. Because of its size, the big boom cannot be used in field productions. This is why shotguns are more commonly suspended from fishpoles—or simply handheld—in field or studio productions that are taped in short segments.

A *fishpole* is a sturdy, lightweight metal pole that can be extended. The shotgun mic is attached to the pole with a *shock mount*, which absorbs the vibrations of the pole and the rubbing noises of the mic cable. Always test a shock mount before each take to see whether the mic can be moved about without transferring the handling noise or pole vibrations. Even the best shotgun mic is rendered useless by a noisy pole or shock mount.

8.14

SHORT FISHPOLE USED FROM ABOVE

The short fishpole is normally held high and dipped into the scene as needed.

If a scene is shot fairly tightly (with tight medium shots and close-ups), you can use a short fishpole—which is much easier to handle than a long one. You can hold it to pick up the sound either from above or below. If the sound pickup is from above the source, hold the boom in your outstretched arms and dip it into the scene as needed. **SEE 8.14** If the sound pickup is from below the source, turn the pole so that the mic is pointing up toward the people speaking. **SEE 8.15**

When the shots are wider and you need to keep farther away from the scene, you must change to a long fishpole. Because the long fishpole is heavier and more difficult to handle, you should anchor it in your belt and raise and lower it as you would an

8.15

SHORT FISHPOLE USED FROM BELOW

The short fishpole can also be held low with the mic pointed up for good sound pickup.

8.16

LONG FISHPOLE

The long fishpole can be anchored in the belt and raised and lowered much like an actual fishing pole.

actual fishing pole. The long fishpole is usually held above the sound source. **SEE 8.16**

Here are some additional hints for operating a shotgun mic mounted on a fishpole:

▶ With a fishpole it is especially important that you check the reach of the microphone cable. Because you must concentrate on the position of the mic during the pickup, you will not be able to monitor the cable at the same time.

▶ Make sure that the cable is properly fastened to the pole and that it does not tug on the microphone.

▶ If the performers walk while speaking, you need to walk with them, holding the mic in front of them. If the camera shoots straight-on (along the z-axis), you need to walk slightly ahead and to the side of them, holding the mic in front of them. If the blocking is lateral (from one side of the screen to the other along the x-axis), you need to stay in front of them, walking backward. Because you must keep your eyes on the performers and the mic, you need to be careful not to bump into obstacles. Rehearse the walk a few times before the actual take. If possible, have a floor person guide you during the take.

▶ If you operate a long fishpole, anchor it in your belt and raise and lower it into the scene as needed.

▶ Always wear a headset so that you can hear what the mic is picking up (including unwanted sounds, such as the drone of an airplane during a Civil War scene). Listen especially for the low rumble of wind, which is easy to miss when concentrating on dialogue.

8.17

HANDHELD SHOTGUN MICROPHONE

The shotgun mic should be held only by its shock mount. When used outdoors, the windscreen is a must.

Handholding a shotgun mic is as simple as it is effective. You become the boom—and a very flexible one at that. The advantage of holding the shotgun mic is that you can walk up to the scene as close as the camera allows, moving and aiming the mic quickly and easily in various directions. **SEE 8.17** Some audio people insist on covering the handheld shotgun with a windscreen even if shooting indoors, but it is a must when shooting outdoors. Hold the microphone only by its shock mount—never directly. This minimizes the handling noises and also prevents covering up the microphone *ports*—the openings in the mic barrel that keep the mic directional.

Desk and stand microphones   *Desk microphones* are hand mics mounted on a small stand. You use them for panel shows, public hearings, speeches, or news conferences. Because the people using them are usually more concerned with what they are saying than with the quality of the audio, they frequently (and unintentionally) bang on the table or kick it while moving in their chairs, and sometimes even turn away from the microphone while speaking. Considering all these hazards, which microphones would you suggest for a desk mic? If you suggested an omnidirectional dynamic mic, you are right. This type of microphone is best suited to handle abuse. If you need more-precise sound separation, use a unidirectional dynamic mic.

When placing the microphones, you can use a single mic for each performer or to serve two people simultaneously. Because microphones can cancel each other's frequencies when positioned too close together, you should place the individual mics at least three times as far apart as any mic is from its user. **SEE 8.18**

Despite your careful placement of the multiple desk mics, inexperienced—and even experienced—users sometimes feel compelled to grab the desk mic and pull it toward them as soon as they are seated. To save your nerves and optimize sound pickup, simply tape the microphone stands to the table.

Stand mics are hand microphones that are clipped onto a sturdy microphone stand. They are used for singers, speakers, musical instruments, or any other sound source that has a fixed position. The quality of mics used on stands ranges from rugged dynamic mics for news conferences or speeches to high-quality microphones for singers and instrumental pickups.

8.18

SETUP FOR MULTIPLE DESK MICROPHONES

When using several desk mics for a panel show, place them at least three times as far apart as any mic is from its user.

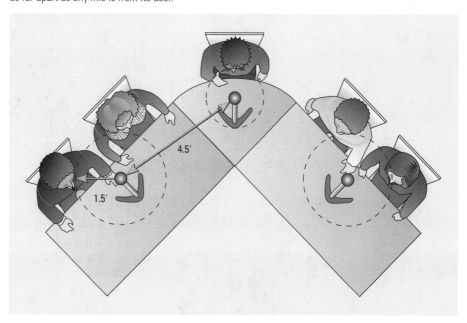

8.19

HEADSET MICROPHONE

The headset mic is a good-quality microphone attached to earphones. The earphones carry a split audio feed, with one earphone carrying the program sound and the other carrying instructions from various production people.

Mic

For some performers, such as rock singers, the microphone stand serves as an important prop. They tilt it back and forth, hold themselves up by it, lift it, and even swing it through the air like a swordsman (not recommended, by the way—especially if the microphone is still attached to it).

When setting up a stand microphone for a singer with an acoustic guitar, a single stand may support two microphones: one at the midpoint for the guitar pickup and another at the top for the voice. The 3:1 spacing rule of placing multiple desk mics also applies to this situation. *READY ZVL 4*

Headset microphones Sportscasters and other performers who are announcing an event often use a headset microphone. **SEE 8.19** This type of mic basically consists of an earphone headset with a good-quality microphone. The earphones can carry a split audio feed, which means that the talent can hear the program sound (including his or her own voice) in one ear and instructions from various production people in the other. Note that a headset has a microphone attached to it; a headphone is for listening only.

8.20

WIRELESS LAVALIERE MICROPHONE WITH RECEIVER

Wireless lavalieres are connected to a small transformer worn by the talent. The receiving station picks up the signal and sends it by cable to the audio console.

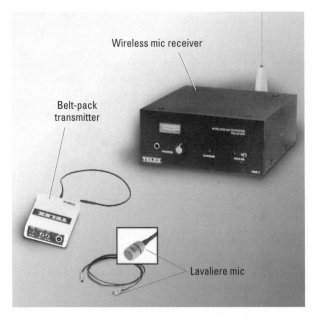

Wireless mic receiver

Belt-pack transmitter

Lavaliere mic

Wireless, or radio, microphones *Wireless microphones* are also called *radio mics* because they actually broadcast the audio signal from a small microphone transmitter to a receiver, which in turn is connected to the mixer or audio console.

The most popular wireless microphones are hand mics used by singers. These high-quality microphones have a small transmitter and antenna built into their housing. The performer is totally unrestricted and can move about without having to worry about a microphone cable. The wireless microphone receiver is connected by cable to the audio console for sound control and mixing. Because each wireless mic has its own frequency, you can use several simultaneously without signal interference.

Another popular radio mic is the wireless lavaliere, which is often used in news and interviews, in EFP, and occasionally in sports. If, for example, you are asked to pick up the groans of a bicyclist during a race, or the breathing of a skier and the clatter of the skis during a downhill run, a wireless lav is the obvious choice. Also, wireless lavs are sometimes used for dramatic studio productions instead of the boom microphone.

The wireless lavaliere is plugged into a small transmitter that is worn by the talent. Normally, you simply put the transmitter into the performer's pocket or tape it to the body and string the short antenna wire along the pants, skirt, or shirt sleeve or around the waist. The receiver is similar to that used with wireless hand mics. **SEE 8.20** Actually, any microphone can become a semiwireless mic by connecting it to a compatible transmitter and plugging its receiver into the audio console.

Unfortunately, wireless mics are not without problems, especially when used outdoors. The signal pickup depends on where the talent is relative to the transmitter. If the talent walks beyond the transmitter's range, the signal will first become intermittent, and then be lost altogether. Also, if the talent moves behind a tall building, or if near high-voltage lines, X-ray machines, or strong radio transmitters, the audio may become distorted or totally overpowered by the extraneous signals. Even the talent's perspiration can influence the transmitter and reduce signal strength. Although wireless equipment has an assigned frequency that is purposely different from police and fire transmissions, you may occasionally pick up a police or fire call instead of your talent's comments.

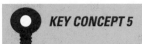

KEY CONCEPT 5   **Wireless, or radio, microphones are subject to interference.**

The microphone table on the facing page gives an overview of some of the most popular microphones. Realize, however, that new microphones are developed all the time and that the model numbers change accordingly. **SEE 8.21**

8.21

TABLE OF MICROPHONES

MICROPHONE	TYPE AND PICKUP PATTERN	USE
Sennheiser MKH-70	Condenser Supercardioid	Studio boom, fishpole. Good for EFP and sports.
Sony ECM-672	Condenser Supercardioid	Fishpole. Excellent for indoors.
Electro-Voice RE-50	Dynamic Omnidirectional	Rugged hand mic. Good for all-weather ENG.
Shure SM63L	Dynamic Omnidirectional	Fairly rugged. Excellent for ENG.
Electro-Voice RE-16	Dynamic Supercardioid	All-purpose hand mic. Good outdoors (ENG/EFP).
Shure SM58	Dynamic Cardioid	Hand mic for singer. Crisp, lively sound.
Beyer M 500	Ribbon Hypercardioid	Classic hand mic for singer. Warm sound.
Sony ECM-55	Condenser Omnidirectional	Lavaliere. Good voice pickup. Good studio mic.
Sony ECM-77	Condenser Omnidirectional	Lavaliere. Good voice pickup. Mixes well with boom mics.
Professional Sound Corp. PSC MilliMic	Condenser Omnidirectional	Extremely small lavaliere mic. Mostly used as concealed mic.

SOUND CONTROL

When you use a small camcorder to record a friend's birthday party, you are probably unconcerned about the various steps of audio control. All you need to do is make sure that the built-in microphone is turned on and is in the *AGC* (automatic gain control) mode. The AGC automatically adjusts the volume of the various sounds to normal levels, eliminating the need for any volume adjustment on your part. But if the audio requirement is more demanding, such as controlling the volume during an interview or mixing two or more sound sources, you need to use audio control equipment. This equipment consists of (1) the audio mixer, (2) the audio console, and (3) the patch panel.

The Audio Mixer

The *audio mixer* amplifies the weak signals that come from the microphones and/ or other sound sources. It lets you control the sound volume and mix (combine) two or more sounds. Actually, what you control and mix are not the sounds themselves but the signals, which are then translated back into actual sounds by the loudspeaker.

A normal monophonic audio mixer has three or four *inputs* and one *output* of the manipulated signal. A stereo mixer has two outputs, one for the left channel and another for the right. There is a rotary *pot* (for *potentiometer*), also called a *fader*, for each input; one *master pot* or *fader* (two for stereo mixers); and a monitor *jack* (outlet) for your earphones so that you can hear the outgoing signal. A *VU meter*, which measures volume units, helps you visually monitor the volume of each incoming source and the final *line-out* signal that leaves the mixer. **SEE 8.22**

8.22

AUDIO MIXER

The audio mixer allows you to control the volume of a limited number of sound inputs and mix them into a single output signal.

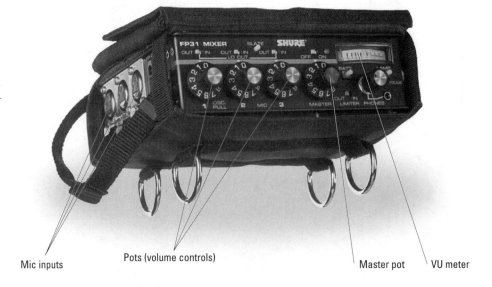

Mic inputs

Pots (volume controls)

Master pot

VU meter

8.23

VOLUME UNIT (VU) METER

The VU meter indicates the relative loudness of sound. The scale is given in volume units, ranging from −20 to +3 (upper scale), and percentages, ranging from 0 to 100 (lower scale).

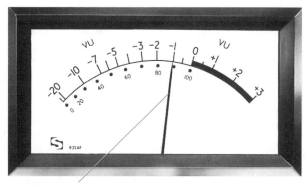

Adjust peak levels to fall near 0

Controlling the volume　Controlling sound volume—or, as it is often called, *riding the gain*—is not only to make weak sounds louder and loud sounds softer, but also to keep the sounds to a level where they do not get distorted. To increase the loudness of a sound, you turn the pot clockwise or push the horizontal fader up, away from you. To reduce the sound volume, you turn a pot counterclockwise or pull the fader down, toward you. The VU meter reflects your gain adjustment by oscillating along a calibrated scale. **SEE 8.23**

If the volume is very low and the needle barely moves from the extreme left, you are riding the audio "in the mud." When loud sounds make the needle hit the right side of the meter, you are "bending the needle" and should turn the volume down to avoid sound distortion. Always try to keep the needle between 60 and 100 percent of the lower scale (or −5 and 0 on the upper scale). Don't worry if the needle spills occasionally into the red, but keep it from oscillating entirely in this overload zone. When working with digital audio, you need to keep especially close watch on proper levels. Overloading the volume not only results in distorted sound but adds considerable noise to the recording.

Some larger audio consoles have VU meters with LED (light-emitting diode) displays instead of oscillating needles, or meters that react to various aspects of loudness. All of them indicate visually whether there is sound coming through and how loud the sound is relative to a given volume scale.

Live field mixing　*Mixing* means combining two or more sounds. You don't need a mixer if you simply interview somebody in the field. You plug the interviewer's hand mic into the appropriate input on the camcorder, turn on the camera mic for ambience, and start the recording. But if you have a complicated audio assignment that requires more than two inputs or more-precise volume control for all inputs than the AGC or the pots on the camcorder can give you, a small mixer will come in handy.

The following guidelines will help you cope with some of the field-mixing tasks.

▶　Even if you have only a few inputs, label each one for what it controls: mic for the host and guest, ambience mic, and so forth.

▶　Double-check all inputs from wireless microphone systems. For some reason, they have a habit of malfunctioning just before the start of an event.

▶ Always send a test tone at 0 VU (100 percent) to the videotape before the actual recording. Adjust the VU meter on the videotape recorder (either the recorder part of the camcorder or a separate videotape recorder) so that it also reads 0 VU. You have now calibrated the output from the mixer with the input of the recorder.

▶ Most professional mixers and consoles give you a choice between mic-level inputs or line-level inputs. Mic-level inputs are for relatively weak audio signals, such as microphones. Line-level inputs are for relatively high-level inputs, such as a CD player. If you set the input level to *mic-level* and plug in a high-output audio source, the resulting sounds will be grossly distorted. On the other hand, if you plug in a microphone into the audio input set at *line-level*, you will barely hear the resulting audio. Many a field production has been ruined by somebody not paying attention to the correct input setting. The audio mixer output is usually line-level; if you connect the line-out with a camcorder or separate videotape recorder (VTR), the audio input must be line-level also.

▶ When working a mixer, set the master pot at 0, and then adjust the volume of the various inputs for the proper mix. Watch the VU meter of the master pot (line-out). If it spills into the red zone, readjust the volume of the various inputs, but leave the master pot at 0.

▶ Try to separate the inputs as much as possible. If you record sound for postproduction on an audiotape, try to put distinctly different sound sources on separate audio tracks. Even when recording sound on videotape, try to keep the primary sound source on one track and the ambient sounds on the other. You can then mix the two sounds more carefully in postproduction.

▶ If you have to do a complicated sound pickup in the field, protect yourself by feeding it not only to the VTR but also to a separate audiotape recorder as well.

The Audio Console

Although large audio consoles are rarely used for simple video productions, they are standard equipment in the audio control rooms and audio production rooms of television stations, large corporate production centers, and major postproduction houses. Even if the many buttons and levers of a large audio console resemble an exotic control panel in a science-fiction spaceship, there is no reason to be intimidated; even the largest audio console operates similarly to the small mixers. Like the mixer, the audio console has inputs, volume controls, loudness meters, mixing circuits, and outputs for the manipulated signal. Unlike the mixer, however, the console has slide faders instead of rotary pots, and a variety of additional quality controls as well as assignment and on/off switches.

The audio console is relatively large because, instead of the four inputs of the small mixer, it may have twenty-four or more. Each input has a separate slide fader, VU meter or some other loudness meter, and an array of quality controls and switches. The console has additional subgroup faders that control the mix of various inputs before it gets to the master fader, and two master faders that control the two channels of the outgoing stereo signal. **SEE 8.24**

8.24

AUDIO CONSOLE

The audio console has many inputs (twenty-four or more for large video productions), each of which has its own slide fader volume control, a variety of quality controls, various on/off and assignment switches, and a volume meter.

An audio console lets you control the volume of all inputs, mix some or all of the input signals in various ways, and manipulate the sound signals of each input channel for the final mix. For example, with the quality controls you can add reverberation (echo) to the incoming sounds; reduce unwanted frequencies such as a hum or squeal; boost or attenuate (reduce) the high, middle, or low frequencies of each sound; and move a sound to a specific horizontal position between the two stereo speakers. Some controls allow you to adjust the strength of the signal input before it is amplified, or to turn off all other inputs except the one you want to hear. You can also group some inputs together into subgroups that can then be further mixed with other inputs or subgroups.

Why so many inputs? Because even a simple six-person panel discussion may use up to nine inputs: six for the microphones (assuming that each panel member has his or her own microphone), one for the CD that contains the opening and closing theme music, and two more for the two VTRs that play back program segments during the discussion.

Considering the many microphones and other sound equipment used in a rock concert, even twenty-four inputs seem modest. Professional recording studios have even larger consoles. To ensure maximum flexibility, some of the larger "in-line" consoles have a separate output for each input. *READY ZVL 5*

■ Cables and Patch Panel

Audio cables provide an essential link between the sound sources and the audio console or other recording equipment, such as the VTR. Because cables do not have any moving parts or complicated circuitry, we tend to consider them indestructible. Nothing could be farther from the truth. An audio cable, especially at the connectors, is vulnerable and must be treated with care. Avoid kinking it, stepping

8.25

AUDIO CONNECTORS

All professional microphones use the three-wire cables and XLR connectors. Other audio connectors include the phone plug, the RCA phono plug, and the mini plug.

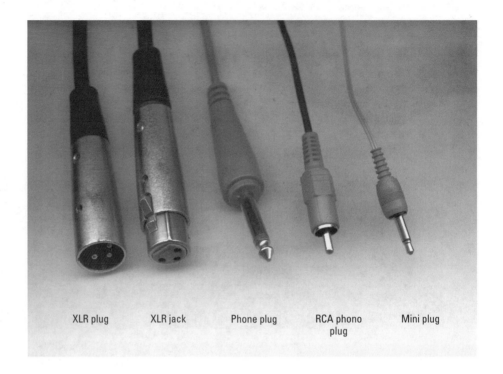

| XLR plug | XLR jack | Phone plug | RCA phono plug | Mini plug |

on it, or rolling a camera pedestal over it. Even if you have a perfectly good cable, it may pick up electrical interference from lighting instruments and produce a hum in the audio—another reason for checking out the audio system before the director calls for a rehearsal.

Another potential problem comes from the various connectors that terminate the cables. All professional microphones and camcorders use three-conductor cables (called *balanced* cables) with three-conductor ***XLR connectors***. They are relatively immune to outside interference from unwanted frequencies. With an XLR jack (input plug) in a camcorder, you can use any professional audio cable to connect high-quality microphones to the camera. Most consumer microphones and camcorders use the smaller ***RCA phono plug*** or the ***mini plug*** for their (unbalanced) cables. Some audio cables terminate with the larger *phone plug,* which is often used for short cable runs to connect various musical instruments, such as electric guitars. **SEE 8.25**

Adapters make it possible to hook up cables with different connectors. Although you should have such connectors readily available, avoid them as much as possible. Any adapter is, at best, a makeshift solution and is always a potential trouble spot. *READY ZVL 6*

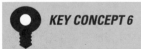 *KEY CONCEPT 6*   **Always check that the connectors on the cable fit the microphone output and the inputs at the other end (such as camcorder, mixer, or some recording device).**

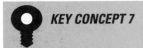

KEY CONCEPT 7   **Keep cable connections and adapters to a minimum; each one is a potential trouble spot.**

Patching will make your life easier by bringing the various sound inputs (microphones, cassette players, remote inputs, audio tracks of VTRs) into a desired order on the audio console. For instance, if the various audio sources appear in widely dispersed faders on the console (such as the lavaliere mic of the interviewer at fader 1, the audiocassette at fader 2, the video playback at fader 3, and the second lavaliere at fader 4), you may want to move the two lavalieres to adjacent faders, with the video playback in position 3 and the audiocassette in position 4. Rather than change the cables to different inputs, you simply patch these sound sources so that they appear in the desired order on the console.

Patching can be done in two ways. The old (highly reliable) way is to physically connect the incoming signals (called *outputs* because they are carrying the audio signals that are to be connected with the audio console) to the various faders on the audio console (called *inputs*). **SEE 8.26** The new way is to have a

8.26

PATCHING

The four audio sources (lav 1, audiocassette, videotape playback, lav 2) are rerouted through patching (lav 1, lav 2, videotape playback, audiocassette).

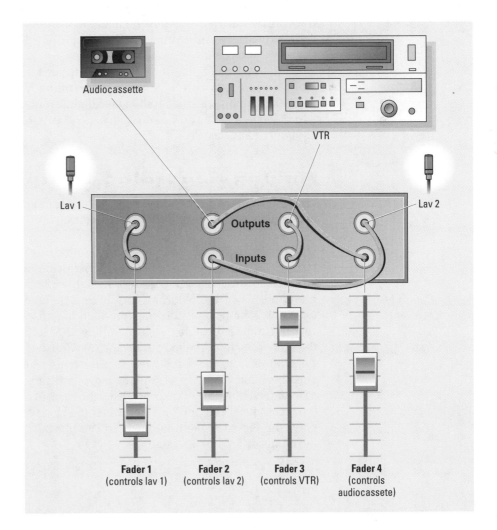

computer take over the signal routing, which accomplishes the same task faster and without many additional cables and connectors. Some of the more common connections are hardwired, which in audio lingo is called *normaled.* A normaled circuit does not have to be patched, but you may need a patch to undo the hardwired connection.

SOUND RECORDING

Sound, like video, can be recorded as analog or digital signals. Despite the inherent difference between analog and digital equipment, there is relatively little difference in the operation of these two types. The recording is only as good as the signal you feed into the recorder. Careful attention to the pickup of sounds will often save you many frustrating hours of postproduction. But even the best sound pickup will not do you any good if you don't record it properly.

In most video productions, sound is recorded on the audio tracks of the videotape simultaneously with the video (see chapter 10). Some more ambitious projects, however, require *audio postproduction,* which means that you try to eliminate some of the unwanted sounds or add something to the existing audio track on the videotape—a process called ***sweetening****.* In audio postproduction you can also create an entirely new audio track and add it to the video that has already been shot and edited.

Although the operation of analog and digital audio equipment is usually similar, we organize this section into analog and digital categories. This grouping emphasizes that analog and digital sound tracks are not compatible, which means that you cannot play back an analog recording with digital equipment and vice versa.

Analog Recording Equipment

The surviving—and still widely used—analog audio recording equipment consists of audiotape recorders and cassette machines.

Open-reel audiotape machines For home use, the open-reel *ATR (audiotape recorder)* is almost extinct. Even for most professional applications—such as audio-recording interviews—small, highly portable cassette machines are preferred. Yet in the recording studio and the audio postproduction room of television stations and video postproduction houses, the reel-to-reel ATR is still very much alive. Despite the great variety of ATRs available, they all operate on the same principle. The magnetic tape (in widths of ¼-inch, ½-inch, 1-inch, and 2-inch) moves from a *supply reel* to a *takeup reel* over at least three *heads:* the erase head, the record head, and the playback head. **SEE 8.27** When you use the ATR for recording, the erase head clears the track of all previous recordings so that the record head can put the new audio on a clean tape. The playback head then plays the recorded material back. In the playback mode, the erase head and record heads are not activated.

8.27

ANALOG HEAD ASSEMBLY

In a reel-to-reel audiotape recorder, the tape moves from a supply reel over the head assembly to the takeup reel.

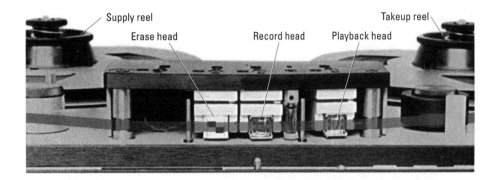

Supply reel   Takeup reel

Erase head   Record head   Playback head

Multitrack machines Simple stereo audiotape recorders use only two channels or tracks, one for the left channel and the other for the right channel on a ¼-inch tape. More-complex recorders have twenty-four or even more tracks on a 2-inch tape. Because each track needs its own erase, record, and playback heads, the twenty-four-track recorder has, indeed, twenty-four of each in the head assembly. Additionally, each track requires its own VU meter so you can see whether the sound is within its volume limits. This means that there are twenty-four VU meters in a twenty-four-channel ATR. **SEE 8.28**

Analog audiocassette machines The audiocassette has two small reels encased in a plastic housing. One of the reels acts as the supply reel, the other as the takeup reel. When the cassette is switched from its A side to its B side, the takeup reel becomes the supply reel and the supply reel becomes the takeup reel.

8.28

TWENTY-FOUR-CHANNEL ATR

This twenty-four-channel audiotape recorder uses a 2-inch-wide audiotape to accommodate the twenty-four separate audio tracks. Each channel has its own erase head, record head, playback head, and VU meter.

8.29

ANALOG AUDIOCASSETTE

The encased reel-to-reel audiocassette is highly reliable and facilitates operational ease.

Supply reel   Takeup reel

Analog cassette

8.30

OPERATIONAL CONTROLS ON AUDIOTAPE RECORDER

The standard operational controls on ATRs are record, play, stop, rewind, and fast-forward.

The major advantages of the cassette system over the reel-to-reel, or open-reel, system are that the cassette is smaller, it can hold more continuous information (up to 180 minutes for some cassettes), and the recorders are much more portable than are open-reel machines. Analog cassettes are the familiar type you use in your home or car. **SEE 8.29**

Operational controls Despite their great variety, almost all audio recorders (including digital ones) have the same five operational controls: (1) stop, (2) play, (3) record, (4) rewind, and (5) fast-forward. **SEE 8.30**

Digital Recording Equipment

The major digital recording and playback equipment used in video production includes: (1) digital audiotape recorders, (2) digital multitrack recorders, (3) computer disks, (4) CDs, DVDs, and mini discs, and (5) digital cart systems.

8.31

DIGITAL AUDIOTAPE (DAT) CASSETTE

The DAT cassette is slightly smaller than the analog audio cassette, yet delivers higher-quality sound.

DAT cassette

Digital audiotape recorders Recorders for digital audiotape—or *DAT*—can be open-reel recorders or, more common, cassette recorders. They look similar to their analog cousins and have similar operational controls. The advantage is that the recording and playback is relatively noise-free and more easily stored and synchronized with digital video recordings. The DAT cassettes are even smaller than analog cassettes, yet deliver much higher quality audio. **SEE 8.31**

Multitrack recorders Modular digital multitrack recorders—or *MDMs*—use videotape systems (such as the ½-inch S-VHS system) to record up to eight tracks of high-quality audio.

Computer disks Computer hard drives with large-capacity disks, such as the Iomega Jaz or Zip cartridges, are popular and useful audio-recording devices. Assuming that your desktop computer has the necessary audio processing capability, you can store and exchange a great variety of audio files without the need for special equipment. Digital audio workstations (DAWs) have very large capacity disks and software that visualizes audio signals for accurate sound manipulation. But even relatively inexpensive audio software programs for desktop computers are powerful tools for matching audio with video in postproduction editing or for manipulating the audio source material.

Once you have learned to "read" the sound image on the computer screen, you can select certain sound portions with great precision and put them into any sequence. To match the new sound track with the video, the computer provides each video frame and the accompanying (very brief) sound portion with a corresponding address. The most widely used address system is called the *SMPTE time code* (see chapter 10). The displayed time code reads out hours, minutes, seconds, and frames (30 frames per second), keeps the ATR and VTR running at exactly the same speed, locates specific "addresses" (frames), and ensures that the right sound portion is matched with each corresponding video frame. This process is called *audio synchronization.* **SEE 8.32**

CDs, DVDs, and mini discs　As you know, the professional optical *compact disc (CD)* is a popular digital playback device. The CD player uses a laser beam for optically sensing the digital information that is compacted on a small (about

8.32

DIGITAL AUDIO WORKSTATION (DAW) DISPLAY

Various computer programs visualize sounds and their progression. They are especially useful for sound editing and synchronizing with video.

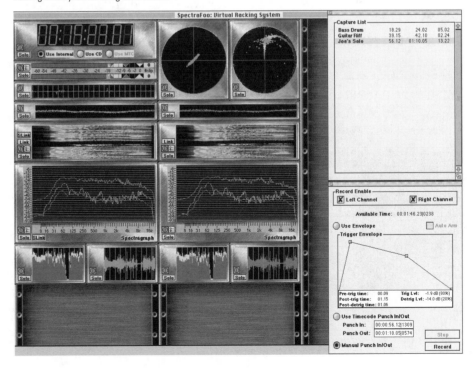

8.33

CD OPERATIONAL DISPLAY

The standard CD display consists of seven basic controls: (1) play (2) pause, (3) stop, (4) down button, (5) up button, (6) fast-forward, and (7) fast-rewind. The down button leads to the beginning of the present track and to previous tracks. The up button leads to the end of the present track and to subsequent tracks.

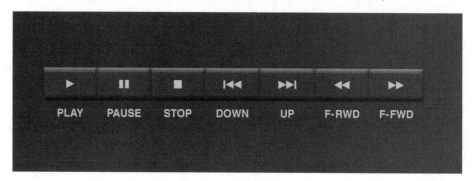

5-inch) disc. The advantage of the CD is that it reproduces almost noise-free sound (assuming that the recording was relatively noise-free in the first place). A highly accurate LED read-out system, which functions much like a counter, allows you to select a precise starting point, regardless of how deeply the segment may be buried in the disc. The standard CD display consists of seven basic controls: (1) play (2) pause, (3) stop, (4) down button, (5) up button, (6) fast-forward, and (7) fast-rewind. Pressing the down button takes you to the beginning of the track; repeated pressing skips to previous tracks. The up button takes you to the end of the track; repeated pressing selects the tracks ahead of the one you are playing. Fast-rewind moves the laser back until you release the button. Fast-forward moves the laser forward until you release the button. You can hear the audio in the fast-forward mode. **SEE 8.33**

There are writable CDs that allow you to record new material as you would with audiotape or computer disks. The *DVD*, which stands for *digital versatile disc* or, its original name, *digital video disc*, can hold many times more video and audio information than can the standard CD. The *mini disc* is also an optical disc, but designed for small applications. About half the size of a floppy disk, it can store an hour of high-quality audio.

Digital cart systems These systems use high-density read/write (play/record) removable computer disks. The digital cart system operates much like a home CD player. You can select a particular audio segment and start the audio track instantly. **SEE 8.34**

8.34

DIGITAL CART SYSTEM

This digital cart recorder/player uses a removable high-density read/write computer disk (such as a 100 megabyte Zip disk) and allows random and instant cuing and playback via remote control.

SYNTHESIZED SOUND

The computer can also be used to grab brief portions of a regular sound, such as a telephone ring, translate it into digital form, store it, and make it available for all sorts of manipulations. Through a digital device called a *sampler*, or with the help of sampling software, you can repeat the telephone ring as often as you want, transform it into a shrill beat, speed it up or slow it down, play it backward, have it overlap, or distort it in any other way so that you can no longer recognize the original sound.

If we can translate sound into digital information and manipulate it, could we not have the computer create digital information that can be translated into actual sound? Yes. The *audio synthesizer*, commonly called a *keyboard*, can generate a great variety of complex frequencies that we perceive as sounds produced by various instruments. A single key can give you the sound of a piano, electric or acoustic guitar, organ, or trumpet. A synthesizer, which you can easily carry under your arm, offers more sounds than a large rock band and symphony orchestra combined. **SEE 8.35**

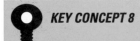 **KEY CONCEPT 8**   **Sounds and sound mixes can be entirely computer-generated.**

8.35

ELECTRONIC KEYBOARD

The electronic keyboard is a sound synthesizer that can simulate a variety of instruments and drum beats.

SOUND AESTHETICS

Even the most sophisticated digital sound equipment is of little use if you cannot use your ears—that is, exercise some aesthetic judgment. Sounds can make us feel about pictures in a certain way. You can make the same scene appear happy or sad by simply putting some happy or sad sounds behind it.

There are five basic aesthetic factors that can help you achieve an effective audio/video relationship: (1) environment, (2) figure-ground, (3) perspective, (4) continuity, and (5) energy.

Environment

In most studio sound-recording sessions, we try to eliminate as much of the background (ambient) sounds as possible. In the field, however, ambient sounds are often as important as the principal ones: They help establish the general environment of the event. If you shoot a scene at a busy downtown intersection, the sounds of cars, car horns, streetcars, and buses; people talking, laughing, and moving about; the doorman's whistle for a taxi; and the occasional police siren are important clues to where you are, even if you don't show all these events in the video portion.

Think of recording a small orchestra. If you do a studio recording, the coughing of one of the crew members or musicians during an especially soft passage would certainly prompt a retake. Not so in a live concert. We have learned to interpret the occasional coughing and other such environmental sounds as proof of the live quality of the event.

As pointed out previously, in normal field recording you should try to use one mic and audio track for the main sound source, such as a reporter standing at a street corner, and another mic (usually the one attached to the camcorder) and the second audio track for recording environmental sounds. Separating the sounds on different videotape tracks makes it easier to mix the two in the proper proportion later in postproduction editing. *READY ZVL 7*

Figure-Ground

One important perceptual factor is the *figure-ground* principle. This refers to our tendency to organize our environment into a relatively mobile figure (a person, a car) and a relatively stable background (wall, houses, mountains). If we expand this principle a little, we can say that we can single out an event that is important to us and assign it the role of the figure, while relegating all other events to the background or, as we just called it, the environment.

For example, if you are waiting for your friend and finally see her in a crowd of people, she immediately becomes the focus of your attention—the foreground—while the rest of the people become the background. The same happens with sound. We have the ability to perceive, within limits, the sounds we want or need to hear as the figure, while pushing all other sounds into the background. When re-creating such a figure-ground relationship with sound, we usually make the "figure" somewhat louder or give it a distinct quality in relation to the background sounds. In the same way, we can easily bring a background sound up in volume to become the figure and relegate the other sounds to the ground.

As you can see, separating the principal sound source (figure) from the ambient sounds (ground) during recording gives you more flexibility in postproduction to emphasize the figure-ground relationship.

 **KEY CONCEPT 9** **The figure-ground principle in audio means to make a specific sound or group of sounds (figure) louder and more distinct than the ambient sounds (ground).**

Perspective

Sound perspective means that close-up pictures are matched with relatively "close" sounds, and long shots are matched with sounds that seem to come from farther away. Close sounds have more presence than far sounds—a sound quality that makes us feel as though we are near the sound source. Far sounds seem to be more distant from us.

This desirable variation of sound presence is virtually eliminated when using lavaliere mics. Because the distance between mic and mouth remains the same, regardless of whether the performer is seen in a close-up or a long shot, the sound has the same presence. This is why you should use boom mics when altering sound presence is important. The boom mic can be moved close to an actor or performer during a close-up and somewhat farther away during a long shot—a simple solution to a potential audio problem.

 KEY CONCEPT 10 **Close-ups need closer sound presence than do long shots.**

Continuity

Sound continuity is especially important in postproduction. You may have noticed the sound quality of a reporter's voice change depending on whether he or she was speaking on- or off-camera. In this case, the reporter used one type of microphone when on-camera and another when off-camera. Also, the reporter changed environments from on-location to the studio. This change in microphones and locations gives speech a distinctly different quality. Although this difference may not be too noticeable when you are doing the actual recording, it becomes readily apparent when the audio is edited together in the final show.

What should you do to avoid such continuity problems? Use identical microphones for the on- and off-camera narration and, if necessary, mix the off-camera narration with some of the separately recorded ambient sounds. You can feed the ambient sounds to the reporter through earphones while he or she is doing the voice-over narration, which will help the reporter re-create the on-site energy.

Sound is also one of the chief elements for establishing visual continuity. A rhythmically precise piece of music can help a series of pictures that otherwise do not cut together very well achieve continuity. Music and sound are often the important connecting link between abruptly changing shots and scenes.

 KEY CONCEPT 11 **Sound is an important factor in providing shot continuity.**

 ## Energy

Good audio depends a great deal on your ability to sense the general energy of video sequences and adjust the volume and presence of the sound accordingly. No volume meter in the world can substitute for your aesthetic judgment. Unless you want to achieve a special effect through contradiction, you should match the general energy of the pictures with a similar energy of sound. *Energy* refers to all the factors in a scene that communicate a certain degree of aesthetic force and power. Obviously, high-energy scenes, such as a series of close-ups of a rock band in action, can stand higher-energy sounds than a more tranquil scene, such as lovers walking through a field of flowers. Also, as you have just learned, close-ups should have more sound presence and energy than should long shots.

 KEY CONCEPT 12 **High-energy pictures should be matched with high-energy sounds; low-energy pictures, with low-energy sounds.**

Although you might not be quite ready to place the microphones and work a large audio console for the complicated videotaping of a rock concert, you are certainly qualified to undertake somewhat simpler audio jobs, such as placing the mics for an interview or panel show and watching the audio levels during the performance. In any case, the Triple-I people will certainly be pleased with your understanding of the importance of sound in video production and your knowledge of various audio equipment and aesthetic requirements.

 # ONCE AGAIN, REMEMBER...

Sound Pickup Principle

Microphones transduce (transform) the sounds we hear into electric energy—the audio signal.

Microphones

Microphones are classified by how well they can hear (their directional pickup characteristics), how they are made, and how they are used.

Directional Characteristics

Omnidirectional mics can hear equally well from all directions; unidirectional, or cardioid, mics can best hear sounds that come from the front. Hyper- and supercardioid mics cancel sounds coming from the sides and make far sounds that lie in the directional pattern appear close to the mic.

Mechanics

Classified by how they are made, there are three types of mics: dynamic (the most rugged), condenser (high-quality but sensitive), and ribbon (high-quality and very sensitive).

Use

Classified by how they are used, there are four types of mics: small lavaliere microphones, which are clipped onto the clothing of the performer; hand mics, which are carried by the performer; boom mics, which are suspended from a small fishpole or studio boom assembly; and desk and stand mics, which are mounted on a small desk stand or fairly heavy adjustable stand.

Audio Mixer and Console

The mixer amplifies the incoming sound signals, controls the volume of each sound, and mixes (combines and balances) them in specific ways. A field mixer is small and normally has a maximum of four inputs. The audio console is much larger; it has many more inputs, each of which has a volume control and various quality and sound selection controls.

Analog Recording and Playback

High-quality reel-to-reel audiotape recorders (ATRs) use various tape widths, depending on the number of audio tracks recorded on them. Twenty-four-channel ATRs normally use 2-inch tape. Analog cassette machines are still popular in video production.

Digital Recording and Playback

Digital recording and playback equipment includes digital audiotape (DAT) recorders; modular digital multitrack (MDM) recorders; computer disks and workstations; compact discs (including read/write CDs), digital versatile discs (DVDs), and mini discs; and digital cart systems.

Synthesized Sound

Once sounds are in digital form, the computer can manipulate them. Computerized sound equipment, such as the keyboard, can create—synthesize—its own sounds.

Sound Aesthetics

The five basic aesthetic factors that can help you achieve an effective audio/video relationship are environment, figure-ground, perspective, continuity, and energy.

Z E T T L ' S   V I D E O   L A B   2 . 1

*To emphasize again the importance of audio in video production, listen to what Phil, our audio expert, has to say. Clicking on the **audio** monitor will give you the opportunity to work with a variety of audio equipment. You will be able to choose and use specific mics, plug in cables, and even do some mixing.*

R U N   Z V L   1

But first, load tape 1 **Meet Phil** and play the introduction.The various audio problems Phil demonstrates in his opening remarks are, unfortunately, all too common. Watching and listening to the tapes and modules will help you achieve good audio and avoid most of the common audio mistakes.

R U N   Z V L   2

Load tape 3 **Microphones**. Listen to Phil's introduction and then click on module 3 **Pickup patterns**. Now you can not only see the pickup pattern of various mics, but also hear them. Click the *Omni* [directional], *Cardioid,* and *Hypercardioid* buttons at screen-left and listen how the mics with various pickup patterns differ in how they hear the four people sitting around the table. Press the *Hypercardioid* button again and listen carefully. Although its pattern is designed primarily to pick up faraway sounds from the front, it can hear fairly well from the back too.

R U N   Z V L   3

Click on module 2 **Transducer**. Phil confirms that the three major sound-generating elements, more technically called transducers, differ greatly in how sensitive they are to physical shock and handling. But now listen carefully to the quality differences of the three types of microphones. Click the *Dynamic* button on the left. How would you describe the characteristic of the sound of this dynamic hand mic? Relatively thin? Rich? Warm? Now listen to the condenser mic and the ribbon mic. Can you hear the difference? If you can't hear it right away, turn up the volume on your computer by clicking on the speaker icon in the lower-right corner of the screen.

R U N   Z V L   4

Play the rest of the mic modules: module 1 **Mic choice**, module 4 **Mic types**, and module 5 **Placement**. Pay particular attention to Phil's criteria for choosing a mic in module 1 **Mic Choice**. In module 4 **Mic types**, click the buttons on the left and observe how the various mics can and should be used. Pointing the hand mic to whoever is speaking seems obvious, but in the excitement of an on-location interview, such mistakes are more likely to occur. Observe also how the fishpole boom mic can be pointed at the sound source from above or below. Pay particular attention to how the lavaliere mic should be placed for optimal sound pickup. Phil seems to tell you the obvious in module 5 **Placement**: that you should point the mic toward the sound you want to pick up. But placement affects not only how well you can hear the sound, but also the sound quality.

R U N   Z V L   5

Load tape 5 **Mixers**; module 1 **Parts** and module 2 **Signals** give you detailed information about mixers that you can apply directly to consoles. Module 3 **Calibration** provides an opportunity to calibrate audio systems, that is, to adjust the audio input of a VTR to the mixer or console output (0 VU).

R U N   Z V L   6

Pay particular attention to the various connectors and their use when playing tape 4 **Connectors**. Missing the proper connector can delay or even ruin an otherwise carefully prepared video production.

RUN ZVL 7 Before playing tape 6 **Aesthetics**, replay the introduction on tape 1 **Meet Phil**. Notice how the music and the appropriate props (plate with hors d'oeuvres and flowers) create the illusion of a specific environment or mood. Now load tape 6 **Aesthetics**. As you can see and hear, module 2 **Environment** creates a hospital environment by having Phil wear a green surgeon's gown and a stethoscope, but especially by playing the well-known sound effects of a hospital environment (paging of doctors). Phil makes another important point in module 1 **Continuity**. Even if the various shots do not cut together too well (although they do in this segment), continuity in sound can easily compensate for video problems and make the viewer perceive a smooth shot sequence.

K E Y   C O N C E P T S

- Microphones transduce (transform) sound waves into electric energy—the audio signal.

- The pickup pattern indicates the zone in which a microphone can hear well—its directionality.

- Treat all microphones gently, even when turned off.

- Test the hand mic you are using before going on the air.

- Wireless, or radio, microphones are subject to interference.

- Always check that the connectors on the cable fit the microphone output and the inputs at the other end (such as camcorder, mixer, or some recording device).

- Keep cable connections and adapters to a minimum; each one is a potential trouble spot.

- Sounds and sound mixes can be entirely computer-generated.

- The figure-ground principle in audio means to make a specific sound or group of sounds (figure) louder and more distinct than the ambient sounds (ground).

- Close-ups need more sound presence than do long shots.

- Sound is an important factor in providing shot continuity.

- High-energy pictures should be matched with high-energy sounds; low-energy pictures, with low-energy sounds.

C.G. (character generator) A small computer dedicated to the creation of letters and numbers in various fonts. Its output can be directly integrated into video images.

chroma key Special key effect that uses a color (usually blue) for the key source background. All blue areas are replaced by the base picture during the keying.

digital video effects (DVE) Video effects generated by a computer with high-capacity hard drives and special graphics software. The computer system dedicated to DVE is called a *graphics generator*.

ESS system Stands for electronic still store system. Stores many still video frames in digital form for easy access.

key An electronic effect in which the keyed image (figure—usually letters) blocks out portions of the base picture (background) and, therefore, appears to be layered on top of it.

matte key The key (usually letters) is filled with gray or a specific color.

morphing Short for *metamorphosis*. Using a computer to animate the gradual transformation of one image into another (boy into old man, cat into lion).

super Short for *superimposition*. The simultaneous overlay of two pictures on the same screen.

wipe A transition in which one image seems to "wipe off" (replace) the other from the screen.

Visual Effects

**OW that you know what a video camera does** and how to give lens-generated images effective composition, you can expand your creative efforts to synthetic video—images that are electronically manipulated or totally computer-generated. These synthetic images can be as simple as electronically generated titles that appear over a background image, or a computer-generated landscape that changes with your point of view. Although the camera still supplies the majority of video images, synthetic images are becoming more and more important to video production.

 KEY CONCEPT 1   **Video consists of lens-generated and computer-generated images.**

A visit to Triple-I's "Pixel Room" (formerly the art department) seems to substantiate this claim. Instead of the usual drafting boards and messy tables full of drawing pads, paints, and cans holding various brushes and pencils, you see a variety of computers, large color monitors, high-capacity hard drives, electronic drawing tablets, computer printers, fax machines, modems, and lots of cables. The art director tells you that video graphics "have moved from pencil to pixel" and that the entire video production scene "is a new ball game." You certainly get the feeling that computer-manipulated or computer-generated images have become an essential element in every phase of video production.

This chapter explains analog and digital image manipulation and the major aspects of synthetic image creation.

■ **STANDARD ELECTRONIC VIDEO EFFECTS**
   Superimposition, key, chroma key, and wipe

■ **DIGITAL EFFECTS**
   Digital image manipulation equipment, common digital video effects, synthetic image creation, and animation

STANDARD ELECTRONIC VIDEO EFFECTS

The standard electronic effects are achieved with an electronic switcher (see chapter 11) and a special-effects generator (SEG) that normally is built into, or connected to, the switcher. Many special effects have become so commonplace that they are no longer "special" but are part of the normal video vocabulary: (1) the superimposition, or super, (2) the key, (3) the chroma key, and (4) the wipe.

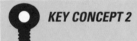 Superimposition

The *superimposition* (or *super* for short) shows two images at the same time, as in a double exposure. In a super you can see both complete images at the same time. **SEE 9.1** (Chapter 11 explains how to do a superimposition with the switcher.) A super is simply a dissolve at about midpoint. Stopping the dissolve a little before the midpoint gives you a superimposition that favors the image from which you were dissolving; stopping a little after the midpoint gives you a super that favors the image to which you were dissolving.

Supers are mainly used to show inner events—thoughts and dreams—or to make an image more complex. You are certainly familiar with the (overused) example of the close-up of a face over which various dream sequences are superimposed. You could, for instance, superimpose two slightly different camera pictures of a ballet dancer, thereby revealing the complexity of the movement and its grace. This synthetic image now generates its own meaning. As you can see, you are no longer simply photographing a dance, but helping to create it. *READY ZVL 1*

KEY CONCEPT 2   **The superimposition is a simultaneous overlay of two pictures.**

9.1

SUPERIMPOSITION

The superimposition, or *super* for short, shows two images simultaneously, as in a double exposure.

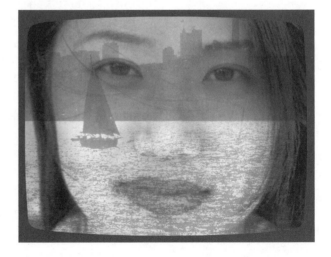

Key

The *key* is another method of combining two video images electronically. But unlike a super, where you can see the base picture through the superimposed image, the keyed image (figure) blocks out portions of the base picture (ground) and, therefore, appears to be layered on top of it. Paradoxically, there are keys that are partially transparent, to reveal the background image.

To understand how a key works, consider the white lettering of a name that appears over the image of a scene. The *C.G. (character generator)* supplies the white title against a black background; the studio camera supplies the picture of a scene. The C.G. title is called the *key source,* and the camera picture of the scene constitutes the *base picture,* or *background.* During the key, the key source cuts itself into the base picture. The base picture replaces all the dark areas around the title, but does not overlap the lettering itself. The effect is that the letters appear layered over the scene. **SEE 9.2** Instead of using the C.G., you can also paint the white title on a black card and have a second camera take a picture of it. The camera focused on the title card, rather than the C.G., is now the key source.

Instead of lettering, you can, of course, key any other electronic image into a base picture, such as lines that divide the screen into different areas, or boxes that highlight specific images.

Because the keying process can have some technical variations, there are different—and often confusing—names for them. You may hear the terms *key, matte, matte key,* or *chroma key* used interchangeably. We group them here by the way they are commonly used: (1) the normal key, (2) the matte key, and (3) the chroma key.

Normal key   In a normal key, there are only two video sources: the base picture and the key source. The normal key simply replaces all dark areas around the title, thus making the title appear to be layered on top of the base picture.

Matte key   In this key you add a third video source, which is either generated by the switcher or by an external video source. Most often a *matte key* refers to the

9.2

KEYED TITLE

The keyed letters seem pasted on top of the background image.

THE MORNING SHOW

9.3

NORMAL MATTE KEY

In the normal matte key, the letters are filled with gray or a specific color.

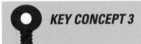

Letter filled with color

9.4

EDGE MODE

In the edge mode, the matte key puts a black border around the letters. This separation from the background makes them more readable.

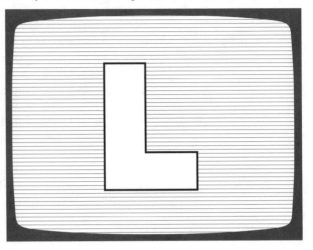

letters of a title that are filled with various colors or grays or that have different borders. **SEE 9.3** The matte keys that create various borders around the letters are subdivided into the *edge mode*, the *drop-shadow mode*, and the *outline mode*. **SEE 9.4–9.6**

> **KEY CONCEPT 3**   **The key source cuts into the base picture, making the key seem layered on top of the base picture.**

Chroma key   When using a *chroma key*, the subject or object to be keyed is placed in front of a plain colored background. The usual colors are blue or green, mainly because these colors are notably absent in skin tones. A typical example of chroma keying is the weathercaster who seems to stand in front of a large weather map. All he actually does is stand in front of a plain chroma blue (an even, saturated medium-dark blue) background. The weather map is usually computer-generated. During the key the weather map replaces the blue background areas, making the weathercaster appear to be standing in front of it. When he turns to point to various areas of the map, he actually sees only a plain blue background. To coordinate his gestures with the "background" weather map, he must watch a monitor that shows the entire key effect. **SEE COLOR PLATE 6**

Because everything that is blue will be replaced by the weather map in our example, the weathercaster cannot wear anything blue that comes close to the color of the background drop. For example, if the weathercaster wore a blue sweater, you would see only his head and hands during the chroma key. His sweater would

9.5

DROP-SHADOW MODE

The attached (drop) shadow gives the letters an added dimension and further separates them from the background.

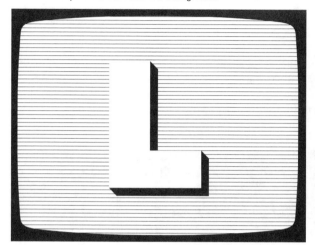

9.6

OUTLINE MODE

In the outline mode, you see only the contour of the letters. The outline mode needs a relatively simple background.

act like the chroma-key background and be replaced by the weather map. As a matter of fact, chroma keying can be used in such a way to achieve special effects. If, for instance, you cover a dancer's upper body and head with a chroma-key blue material and have her move in front of the blue background, the key will show only her legs dancing.

You can also use the chroma-key technique to simulate a variety of backgrounds. You could, for example, simulate a spectacular view from an office window by simply placing the desk and chair in front of a chroma-key background and using a photo of the actual view as the background source. During the chroma key, the person behind the desk would appear to be sitting in front of a picture window. The advantage of such a key effect is that you would avoid the formidable lighting problem of having the person silhouetted against the bright window (see chapter 7).

Chroma keying, which in film production is also called the *blue-screen technique,* is extensively used for creating motion picture effects. In this case, the effect is first produced on videotape by high-quality electronic machinery (either photographed by a high-definition television [HDTV] camera or computer-generated) and later transferred to film.

You can also use other colors for chroma keying, such as green. As stated, the reason why blue and green are so popular in chroma keying is that they are relatively absent in skin or hair colors. But what about blue and green eyes? Wouldn't they let the background show through during a key? Yes, they may do just that in an extreme close-up, in which case you need to have the talent wear different-colored contact lenses. Fortunately, even blue or green eyes normally reflect so many other colors that they reject the background signal. **READY ZVL 2**

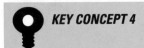

KEY CONCEPT 4 **In a chroma key, all blue or green background areas are replaced by the keyed background image.**

Wipe

In a *wipe* a portion of or a complete video image is gradually replaced by another. Wipes come in a great variety of configurations and are usually displayed as icons (graphic representations of what the wipe looks like) on the switcher buttons with which you can preset a particular wipe. **SEE 9.7**

9.7

WIPE PATTERNS

A group of buttons on the switcher shows the various wipe patterns available. Elaborate systems offer up to 100 different patterns.

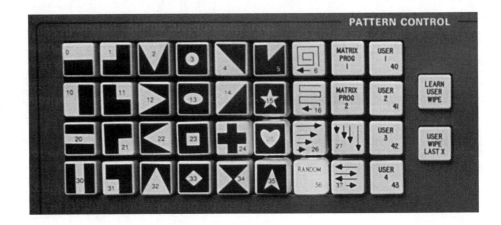

Some of the most common wipes are the horizontal and vertical wipes. In a *horizontal wipe*, the second image gradually replaces the base picture from the side. **SEE 9.8** A *split screen* is simply a horizontal wipe that is stopped in the middle. More often split screens are generated by digital effects, which give more control over the size of the split image than does the analog wipe. In a *vertical wipe*, the base picture is gradually replaced by the second image from the top down or from the bottom up. **SEE 9.9**

Other popular wipes are *corner wipes*, whereby the second image originates from one corner of the base image, or *diamond wipes*, in which the second image originates in the center of the base image and spreads as an expanding diamond-shaped cutout. **SEE 9.10 AND 9.11** In a *soft wipe*, the demarcation line between the two images is purposely blurred.

Don't go overboard with wipes simply because they are so easily done. All wipes are highly visible and obvious transitions that need to fit the character and mood of the specific video material. Using a diamond wipe during a news program to reveal a more detailed shot of a murder scene is hardly appropriate; but it is quite acceptable when changing from a medium shot of a new computer model to a CU (close-up) of its high-capacity hard drive. Be especially careful when using wipes for the 16 × 9 HDTV aspect ratio. Even on a relatively small screen, the wipe

9.8

HORIZONTAL WIPE

In a horizontal wipe, the base picture (A) is gradually replaced by another from the side (B).

9.9

VERTICAL WIPE

In a vertical wipe, the base picture is gradually replaced by another from the bottom up or from the top down.

9.10

CORNER WIPE

In a corner wipe, the base picture is gradually replaced by another that starts from a screen corner.

9.11

DIAMOND WIPE

In a diamond wipe, the base picture is gradually replaced by the second image in an expanding diamond-shaped cutout.

seems to travel a long distance and, therefore, becomes especially noticeable and sometimes even intrusive. 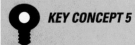 *READY ZVL 3*

KEY CONCEPT 5   Use special effects only if they help clarify or intensify the intended message.

DIGITAL EFFECTS

The computer has greatly expanded the range of possibilities for manipulation of the lens-generated image; it can even create still or animated images that rival high-quality lens-generated images in every respect. *Digital video effects (DVE)* change the normal analog video signal into digital data to create a variety of special effects. Basically, the DVE equipment can grab a video frame from any source (live camera or videotape), change it into digital information, store it, manipulate it according to the effects programs available, and retrieve the effect on command. To keep this topic manageable, we give only a brief overview of three major aspects of digital image manipulation and image creation: (1) digital image manipulation equipment, (2) common digital video effects, (3) synthetic image creation, and (4) animation.

Digital Image Manipulation Equipment

All desktop computers with a generous amount of RAM (random-access memory) and storage capacity are capable of manipulating video images—all you need is the proper software. There are three types of systems that will facilitate image manipulation: (1) electronic still store systems, (2) frame store synchronizers, and (3) desktop computers.

Electronic still store (ESS) system   With an *ESS system,* you can grab any video frame, digitize it, and store it on a disk. These ESS systems—which can store thousands of frames—perform like a superfast slide projector. You can call up and display any stored image in a fraction of a second. Once in digital form, the still image can be changed in size, shrunk, expanded, and used in combination with other images. The familiar box above the newscaster's shoulder is usually a digitized frame that is keyed into the base picture of the news set.

Frame store synchronizer   Even with relatively simple DVE equipment, you can perform more effects than normally needed for good storytelling. The primary function of the digital *frame store synchronizer* is to stabilize a picture and synchronize two different video sources so that they don't roll when switching from one to the other. But some can also be used for simple DVE. With the frame store synchronizer, you can freeze a moving image similar to a photo snapshot, change it into a mosaic, advance it frame by frame at different rates—a process called *jogging*—or solarize it (mix the positive image with its negative one). **SEE 9.12 AND 9.13**

9.12

MOSAIC EFFECT

With the mosaic effect, the image is changed into equal-sized squares, resembling mosaic tiles. In an electronic mosaic, the size of the "tiles" can be manipulated.

9.13

SOLARIZATION

Solarization is a combination of a positive and a negative image of the same subject. The black lines indicate where the two images meet.

Desktop computers As mentioned, any desktop computer with enough RAM and hard drive capacity can perform the most amazing and varied digital image manipulations. All you need is the appropriate software, which is readily available. Professional equipment, usually called a *graphics generator,* simply has higher storage capacity and higher processing speeds, but often relies on the same software (such as Adobe Photoshop and Aftereffects) that you can buy in any computer store.

■ Common Digital Video Effects

To understand the analog-to-digital translating process, try to visualize how a photo is transformed into a mosaic, as shown in figure 9.12. The video frame (complete picture) represents the analog video signal; it shows a continuous change of shape, color, and brightness. As a mosaic the same image is seen as a series of tiles, each representing a discrete picture element—a *pixel.* Because each pixel can be identified separately by the computer, you can now tell the computer which ones to take out, move, or replace with a different color. Once satisfied with the manipulation, you can store the image in the computer for later use.

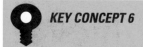

KEY CONCEPT 6 **Analog video must be digitized before any digital manipulation can take place.**

More-sophisticated DVE equipment can change the size of the image (lettering or an actual scene), squeeze or stretch it, paste it on a cube, have it tumble, flip, spin, bounce, and fly through the screen space. **SEE 9.14–9.17**

9.14

STRETCHING

Stretching changes the format of the frame and the image within it.

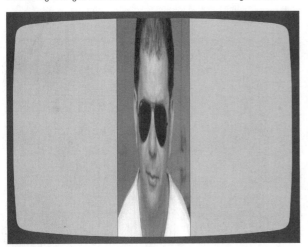

9.15

CUBE

In the cube effect, the images seem glued to the sides of a rotating cube.

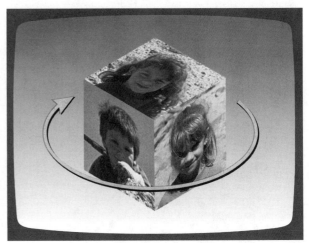

9.16

ROTATION

The image can tumble, flip, or spin. According to the normal x-, y-, and z-axes of three-dimensional space, rotation around the x-axis (horizontal axis) is a tumble; around the y-axis (vertical axis), a flip; and around the z-axis (depth axis), a spin.

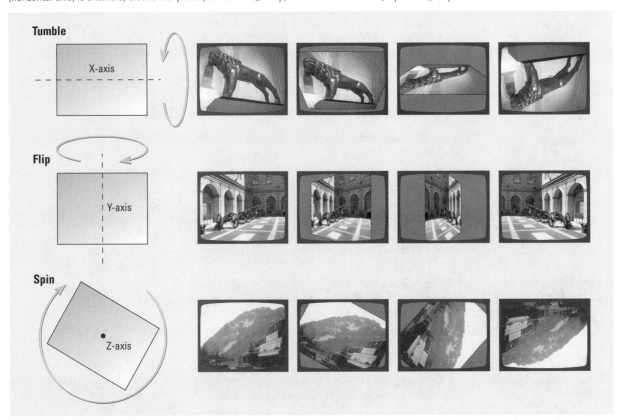

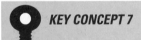

FLY

In the fly mode, the image zooms from a certain spot to a full image or recedes into another screen position.

Synthetic Image Creation

In addition to manipulating lens-generated images, the computer can create a great variety of images on its own, independent of the video camera. Such *synthetic images* range from simple lettering to complex motion sequences that rival well-shot and edited videotaped footage. Numerous software programs can help you generate a great variety of still or moving images. As you may recall, the people from Triple-I had several small and larger computer systems in the Pixel Room that were specially dedicated to the creation of synthetic images. Such systems are generally classified by their primary function: (1) *character generators* and (2) the more complex *graphics generators.*

KEY CONCEPT 7   **Synthetic images are entirely computer-generated.**

Character generator   The *C.G. (character generator)* is designed to produce letters and numbers of different fonts (styles and sizes) and colors. It looks and works like a personal computer and is run by simplified word processing software. A typical C.G. program offers a menu from which you select the font and color of the letters and numbers. You then type the copy on the keyboard, colorize the letters, center them or move them to a specific spot on the display screen, insert or delete words, scroll the copy up or down the screen, or have it crawl sideways—all with a few simple commands. **SEE 9.18** Through the switcher you can key the copy directly into the video of the program in progress, or save and store it on a floppy disk for later retrieval.

The C.G. adds speed and flexibility to creating titles. For instance, if you don't like a particular font or color, you can change it to something else with a single computer command before keying it into the base picture. The C.G. is used extensively in telecasts of sporting events. During such live telecasts, the C.G.

VIDEO CREATED BY CHARACTER GENERATOR

The C.G. is designed to generate specific titles.

operator is fully occupied with typing names of players and statistics (or accessing them from a disk). More-elaborate C.G.s can create small graphic displays, such as block diagrams or sales curves. Each complete screen display constitutes a *page*, which can be accessed randomly. *Random access* means that you do not have to pass through pages 1, 2, 3, and 4 to get to page 5—you can call up page 5 directly.

Graphics generator   As you just learned, graphics generators are high-speed computer systems that are used primarily for the manipulation and especially for the creation of graphic images. Graphics software is usually divided into drawing and painting programs.

Drawing software is designed to create technical illustrations, such as floor plans, line drawings, or other two-dimensional graphics. **SEE 9.19** Most weather charts and diagrams that visualize some progress or regress are produced with the help of drawing software. Some of the more-elaborate drawing programs let you rotate the generated picture, stretch it, cut-and-paste other images onto it (very much like keying), show its mirror image, and duplicate it as many times as you want.

Painting software offers a rich color palette and almost as many options as the drawing pad or canvas. The menu provides a wide choice of pen, crayon lines, or brush strokes, thousands of colors, subtle shades, and anything from soft watercolor effects to bright, highly reflecting color areas. If you don't like a particular shape, color, or texture, you can erase your creation and substitute it with a new one with a stroke of the stylus. If you like the first version better after all, you can quickly retrieve the original via a few simple commands. **SEE COLOR PLATE 7**

You can also simulate three-dimensional images that seem to occupy 3-D screen space. These images resemble lens-generated images and exhibit the same

9.19

IMAGE CREATED BY DRAWING PROGRAM

The drawing program facilitates technical drawings or two-dimensional images.

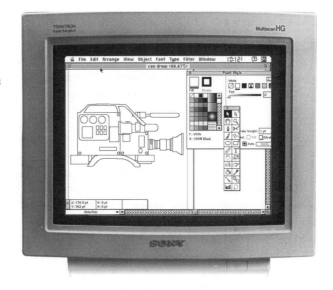

characteristics: assumed volume, attached and cast shadows, texture, and perspective that shows the object from a specific point of view. Chapter 15 further explores using computers for creating virtual indoor and outdoor settings.

Rotating the image changes the perspective from which you view the object, enabling you to see the object from below, from above, or from any angle you choose that has been built into the graphics program. You can also change the direction and intensity of the key light, and with it the attached and cast shadows. **SEE 9.20** For example, you could change the key from its above-eye-level position to a below-eye-level position, or increase the intensity of light and thereby the speed of falloff.

With some algorithms, called *fractals,* you can even "paint" free-form images, such as trees, mountains, or colorful patterns. **SEE COLOR PLATE 8**

9.20

CHANGE IN PERSPECTIVE AND LIGHT

3-D images can be rotated from various points. The principal light source (key light), and with it the shadows, can also be moved into various positions.

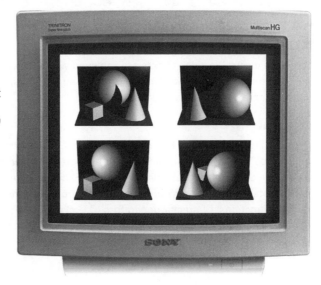

Animation

Certain software programs enable you to animate a sequence by filling in all missing frames between a start and a stop position of the intended motion sequence. You can then have the sequence run as slowly or as quickly as you like. Such programs also let you sketch in the background images or combine foreground and background motions. You can also link appropriate sounds with these animated sequences. Other software programs (such as QuickTime) let you run moving videotape or film sequences that can be combined with still images and text.

One popular animation technique is morphing. *Morphing*, which comes from the word *metamorphosis* (meaning the change or transformation of form, shape, and structure), lets you transform continuously and gradually one image into another. For example, you can *morph* the picture of a young boy into one that shows him as a ninety-year-old man, and then have this old man slowly transform into a lion. Morphing has been used extensively in monster movies, where people suddenly turn into wild beasts right before your eyes. **SEE COLOR PLATE 9**

Synthetic image creation is becoming more and more common even in relatively simple video production processes and interactive video programs. Such computer-generated images and their applications are explored further in chapters 10 and 15.

You should feel less intimidated now when going back to the Pixel Room of Triple-I, and you may even enjoy creating some graphic images on the computer. But don't get carried away by all this digital wizardry. After all, the content of the package is still more important than its wrapping. Even the best DVE treatment will not change a basically insignificant message into a significant one. On the other hand, properly used effects can clarify and intensify the screen event, supply additional meaning and, like music, increase the energy of the event.

 ONCE   AGAIN,   REMEMBER...

Standard Electronic Video Effects

Standard electronic video effects are achieved with an electronic switcher and special-effects generator (SEG). They include superimpositions, normal keys, matte keys, chroma keys, and various wipes.

Digital Effects

Digital images and effects can be stored via an ESS (electronic still store) system and can be further manipulated by a frame store synchronizer or a desktop computer. Common digital video effects (DVE) change the analog video signal into digital data. Systems for synthetic image creation are generally classified by their primary functions. Character generators (C.G.s) are used to create titles; graphics generators are high-end computer systems that can create and manipulate still and animated images.

Z E T T L ' S   V I D E O   L A B   2 . 1

This time your virtual studio will demonstrate some of the effects you've been reading about in this chapter. Although the examples are brief and highly selective, Veronica, the expert editor, gives you a pretty good idea of what electronic effects are and how they are perceived.

RUN ZVL 1 Click on the **editing** monitor and load tape 6 **Transitions & Keys**. Listen to Veronica's precise introduction to transition effects and then play module 2 **Dissolve**. Note that a superimposition is simply a dissolve at about midpoint. Stopping the dissolve a little before the midpoint gives you a super that favors the image from which you were dissolving; stopping a little after the midpoint gives you a super that favors the image to which you were dissolving.

RUN ZVL 2 Jump to module 5 **Key**. As you can see, this demonstration involves the chroma key. You can clearly see now why you should not wear anything blue in front of the chroma-key background, especially if you use blue as the key color. The chroma key of Veronica at the windy beach is made even more realistic by her hair blowing in the wind. A strong fan and the sound effects of surf and wind did the trick.

RUN ZVL 3 Select module 3 **Wipe**. What you see here are some simple wipe configurations. Notice that even the simplest wipes show up so prominently that they are usually classified as special effects. Similar to the dissolve that becomes a super when stopped at about the midpoint, the horizontal wipe becomes a split screen when stopped midway. Veronica seems to enjoy talking to herself from one screen half to the other.

K E Y   C O N C E P T S

- **Video consists of lens-generated and computer-generated images**

- **The superimposition is a simultaneous overlay of two pictures.**

- **The key source cuts into the base picture, making the key seem to be layered on top of the base picture.**

- **In a chroma key, all blue or green background areas are replaced by the keyed background image.**

- **Use special effects only if they help clarify or intensify the intended message.**

- **Analog video must be digitized before any digital manipulation can take place.**

- **Synthetic images are entirely computer-generated.**

C O N T E N T S

CHAPTER 10

Video Recording

CHAPTER 11

Switching and Postproduction Editing

CHAPTER 12

Editing Principles

Video Recording, Switching, and Editing

EVERY time something goes wrong during a production, the Triple-I production people resort to the standard joke: "Don't worry—we'll fix it in post." But then they usually go back and do another take to fix whatever went wrong right then and there. Fixing even minor flaws in postproduction is usually difficult, time-consuming, and costly. Postproduction should not be seen as a convenient rescue operation for a sloppy production, but as an organic extension of the production process in which the various segments are given form and order. Postproduction is a time to build a program that has clarity and impact.

Because postproduction is usually the most time-consuming aspect of the whole production process, you can fine-tune it only by knowing the basics of video recording, storage, and sequencing. Part III deals with these processes, including chapters on the various video-recording and storage systems, on switching, and on postproduction editing.

KEY TERMS

audio track The area of the videotape used for recording the audio information.

composite video A system that combines the Y (black-and-white) and C (red, green, and blue) video information into a single signal. Also called *NTSC*.

control track The area of the videotape used for recording synchronizing information.

field log A record of each take during the videotaping.

interactive video A computer-driven program that gives the viewer some control over what to see and how to see it. It is often used as a training device.

multimedia Computer display of text, still and moving images, and sound. Usually recorded on CD-ROM or DVD (digital versatile disc).

nonlinear storage system Storage of video and audio material in digital form on a hard drive or read/write optical disc. Each single frame can be directly accessed by the computer.

NTSC Stands for National Television System Committee. Normally designates the composite video signal, consisting of combined chroma information (red, green, and blue signals) and luminance information (black-and-white signal).

RGB component video A system in which all three color signals are kept separate. The three signals are recorded separately on videotape. Often called *RGB system*.

time base corrector (TBC) An electronic accessory to videotape recorders that helps make videotape playbacks electronically stable. It keeps slightly different scanning cycles in step.

video track The area of the videotape used for recording the video information.

Y/C component video A system that keeps the Y (luminance, black-and-white) and C (color, red-green-blue) signals separate. Y and C are combined again when recorded on tape. Often called *Y/C system* or *S-video*.

Y/color difference component video Analog system in which three signals—the luminance (Y) signal, the red minus its luminance (R−Y) signal, and the blue minus its luminance (B−Y) signal are kept separate. All three signals are recorded separately on videotape. Similar to the RGB system.

Video Recording

ALL Triple-I postproduction people seem to have their own language. You hear them complain about a composite recording that should have been recorded in component form for extensive postproduction, or an RGB signal that needs three wires to be transported and, therefore, requires an entirely new editing system. But they are certainly surprised that you already know all about digital processes, lossy compression, and the digitizing of analog audio and video signals.

This chapter will help you understand basic video-recording systems, recording processes, and how to use and store video recordings.

■ **VIDEOTAPE-RECORDING SYSTEMS**
Tape and disk-based recording systems, basic videotape tracks, composite and component recording systems, types of videotape recorders, time base corrector, and tape formats

■ **VIDEOTAPE-RECORDING PROCESS**
The necessary checklists: before, during, and after

■ **NONLINEAR STORAGE SYSTEMS**
Computer disks, the ESS system, read/write optical discs, and CD-ROMs and DVDs

■ **USE OF VIDEO RECORDING**
Interactive video and multimedia

VIDEOTAPE-RECORDING SYSTEMS

All videotape-recording systems operate on the same basic principle: The video and audio signals are recorded and stored in analog or digital form on magnetic tape and converted again into pictures and sound during playback. These systems vary greatly in how the signals are put on the videotape. Some videotape recorders, called *VTRs,* are designed for operational ease, such as the ones built into consumer camcorders or the popular *VCR* (videocassette recorder). Others are designed for high-quality recordings whose pictures and sound will maintain their quality even after several dubbings during postproduction.

To make some sense out of the various systems, this section takes a closer look at (1) tape and disk-based recording systems, (2) basic videotape tracks, (3) composite and component systems, (4) types of videotape recorders, (5) the time base corrector, and (6) tape formats.

Tape- and Disk-Based Recording Systems

Tape-based systems can record and play back analog or digital video and audio information. Disk-based systems use large-capacity computer disks or read/write (rerecordable) optical discs. They can record digital signals only. The recording and especially the playback of relatively brief program material is done more and more by *video servers*—high-speed, large-capacity computers. Tape-based editing systems are called *linear systems* and disk-based systems are *nonlinear.* You will read more about the important difference between linear and nonlinear systems in chapter 12.

Basic Videotape Tracks

All videotape recorders use separate tracks to record the video and audio as well as various control data. Most videotape recorders put at least four tracks onto a videotape: the ***video track*** containing the picture information, two ***audio tracks*** containing all sound information, and a ***control track*** that controls the synchronization of the frames. **SEE 10.1**

10.1

BASIC VIDEOTAPE TRACK SYSTEM

The basic track system of a videotape consists of a slanted video track, two or more audio tracks, and a control track.

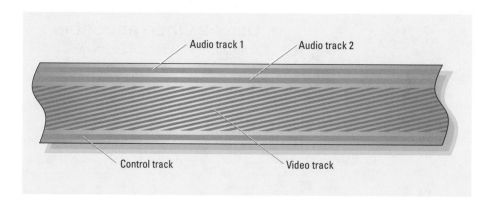

Audio track 1   Audio track 2

Control track   Video track

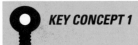

KEY CONCEPT 1   **Videotape recorders record analog or digital video and audio signals and other information necessary for the proper operation of the tape.**

To avoid superfast tape travel when recording the high-frequency video signal onto videotape and to squeeze the maximum amount of information on the tape, all recorders move the tape as well as the video-recording heads. In this way the tape moves in a loop around a head drum, which contains the spinning video-recording heads. The video heads in digital systems spin at very high speeds. **SEE 10.2**

Simple VCRs and camcorders use a stationary head for erasure, and only one set of rotating heads for video recording and playback. More-sophisticated models may use separate spinning heads for erasure, recording, and playback operations. The advantage of a separate erase head, often called a "flying erase head" for consumer camcorders, is that it can precisely erase each recorded field without affecting the adjacent ones (remember, there are sixty fields for every second of video recording). As you will see, such precise erasure is an important prerequisite for stable edits.

The audio tracks—up to four high-fidelity digital tracks in the high-end digital VTRs—usually run lengthwise near the edges of the videotape. The control

10.2

VIDEO-RECORDING HEAD

The videotape moves past the spinning head drum (or spinning heads inside the drum) at an angle, creating a slanted video track.

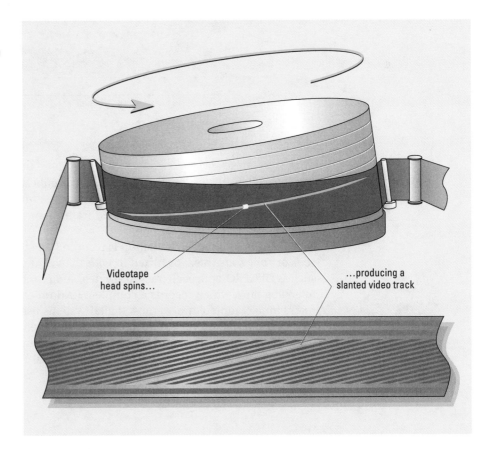

Videotape
head spins...

...producing a
slanted video track

10.3

CONTROL TRACK WITH SYNC PULSES

The control track consists of equally spaced sync pulses. Thirty such pulses indicate one second of video.

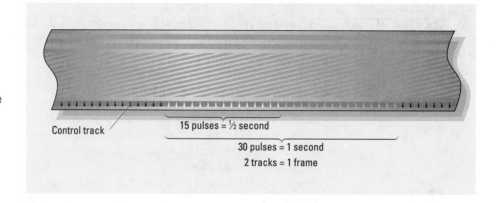

Control track

15 pulses = ½ second

30 pulses = 1 second

2 tracks = 1 frame

10.4

DVCPRO TRACKS

This digital system uses ten tracks for a single frame. Each track has specific video, audio, and code information.

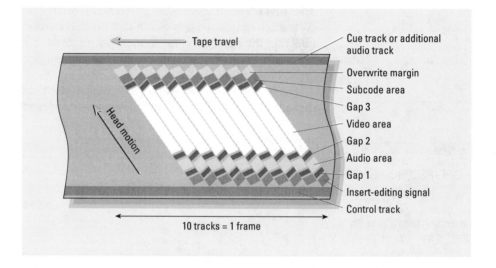

Tape travel

Head motion

Cue track or additional audio track

Overwrite margin

Subcode area

Gap 3

Video area

Gap 2

Audio area

Gap 1

Insert-editing signal

Control track

10 tracks = 1 frame

track, which also runs lengthwise, contains evenly spaced blips or spikes, called *sync pulses*, which keep the scanning in step, control the speed of the head drum, and mark each complete video frame—an important feature in video-tape editing. **SEE 10.3**

The *address code* information is recorded on still another track, the *address code* or *time code* track, or mixed in with the video signal. Some digital systems, such as DVCPRO, split each track into video, audio, and code information. Contrary to analog tape, which records a complete field on each track and takes only two tracks for a complete frame, most digital systems use more tracks for a complete frame. The DVCPRO system, for instance, needs ten tracks to complete a single frame. **SEE 10.4** Hi8 recorders similarly incorporate video, audio, and code information in each track. (See chapter 11 for details.) *READY ZVL 1*

Composite, Y/C Component, and RGB Component Systems

Composite, Y/C component, and RGB component systems refer to how the video signals are transported inside, and recorded by, the videotape recorder. The *composite* system is the one used in standard video and broadcast television equipment. The *Y/C component* and the *RGB component* systems are designed to produce higher picture quality than the composite system and to resist deterioration in multiple videotape generations.

Composite system   The signal for *composite video* combines the color, or *C signal*, with the luminance (brightness), or *Y signal*. The C or RGB (red, green, blue) signals and black-and-white information of the Y signal form a single signal that is transported inside and outside the VTR by a single wire. **SEE COLOR PLATE 10** This signal is also called the *NTSC signal*, or simply *NTSC*, because the configuration was adopted by the NTSC (National Television System Committee) as the standard for all normal video and broadcast television equipment. The advantage of this system is that regardless of the relative electronic sophistication of the VTR or the tape format (width) used, it can be used with other composite equipment, such as monitors or switchers. For instance, you can use the same monitor for displaying images from a top-of-the-line digital VTR or from a consumer VCR, so long as all operate with the composite (NTSC) system.

Not all countries in the world use the NTSC system. Many nations have standardized on other systems (such as PAL or SECAM), which are not compatible with NTSC. For instance, to play a videotape from Italy, which uses the PAL system, you need a standards converter—an electronic device that changes other systems to NTSC. There are videocassette machines available that translate the recording standards automatically.

The disadvantage of composite video is that the picture quality of the original recording is not as high as with other systems and that it tends to deteriorate relatively quickly in multiple generations, unless you use a high-end professional studio VTR. Also, because the color and luminance information are mixed into one signal, they sometimes interfere with each other, creating video interference called *artifacts*.

Y/C component system   You can probably tell now how this system works. In *Y/C component video*, the Y signal, which is the luminance (black-and-white) information of the video picture, and the C signal (the RGB color information) are kept separate until they are recorded on videotape. During the playback the two video channels (Y and C) are separated again. Some technicians call this separation *Y/C component system;* others prefer to call it the *Y/C system* or *S-video* (because the S-VHS recorders use the Y/C component system). In any case, you need two wires to transport the Y/C signal. **SEE COLOR PLATE 11**

The advantage of this separation is that it ensures higher picture quality for the original recording and subsequent generations. To preserve this advantage, you need recorders, video monitors, and editing equipment designed specifically to handle the separate Y/C signals. Some systems use two wires to transport the signals through the videotape recorder, but then combine the signals into one when put on tape; others keep the Y and C signals separate even during the recording. Because of this Y/C separation in S-VHS systems (which stands for super-VHS), you can play back standard VHS cassettes on S-VHS videotape recorders, but you cannot play S-VHS cassettes on a standard VHS recorder. The S-VHS system is, therefore, only downward compatible.

RGB, or Y/color difference, component system   The *RGB component video* system or, simply, *RGB system,* preserves the original RGB (red, green, blue) video signals throughout the recording process. They are recorded as three separate signals on the videotape. As you might have guessed, this system needs three wires to transport the three signals in the videotape recorder and in all associated equipment. Because the three signals are kept separate throughout the transport and recording process, it is a true *component* system.

For technical convenience and to save bandwidth (smaller cars can travel on narrower roads) the original RGB video signals are changed into a *Y/color difference* signal. The RGB signals are split into a Y (luminance) signal and two separate color difference signals: the R–Y (red minus luminance) signal and the B–Y (blue minus luminance) signal. These three signals are kept separate throughout the transport and recording process. As you might have guessed, this *Y/color difference component video* system needs three wires to transport the three signals in the VTR and in all associated equipment. What happened to the green signal? The green signal appears again when the color difference signals are matrixed (remixed) upon leaving the VTR. For all practical purposes, it is probably easier for you to envision the three component signals as RGB throughout the transport and recording process. **SEE COLOR PLATES 12 AND 13**

Confused? Well, it is somewhat confusing, because the terminology is inconsistent. You may simply want to remember that the NTSC one-wire system is composite (all signals are mixed into one). All other systems, which separate luminance from color, or all three individual color signals (RGB), are component.

As with the Y/C system, the RGB or Y/color difference component system requires specific video monitors, switching, and editing equipment to accommodate the three separate video signals. For example, even if you have a high-quality NTSC videotape recorder and color monitor, you cannot play back anything that has been recorded on component equipment, which makes the whole component operation rather expensive. To overcome this dilemma, most high-end component equipment has NTSC composite inputs and outputs. Why, then, use the more cumbersome component systems? Because a component system maintains a high picture quality even through many tape generations. It is therefore used when doing extensive postproduction, such as building complex effects.

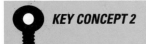

KEY CONCEPT 2   **Videotapes recorded as Y/C component, RGB component, or Y/color difference component signals cannot be played back on composite (NTSC) equipment.**

Types of Videotape Recorders

To make matters even more confusing, each of the three systems (composite, Y/C component, RGB or Y/color difference component) uses various recording methods. Refer to the table of the most commonly used analog VTRs. **SEE 10.5**

As with analog recorders, digital VTRs come in different types and tape formats. Some digital VTRs are designed for docking with ENG/EFP cameras; others are larger high-quality recorders specifically designed for extensive

10.5

TYPES OF ANALOG VIDEOTAPE RECORDERS

TYPE	CHARACTERISTICS
BetacamSP	Uses ½-inch videotape cassette. Y/C component. High quality.
S-VHS	Uses ½-inch cassette. Y/C component signal transport, but composite when actually recorded on tape. Good-quality first generation. Can play back VHS cassettes.
VHS	Uses ½-inch cassette. NTSC composite. Quality not good enough for professional productions, but is used extensively in off-line post-production (product not intended for final release). S-VHS cassettes cannot be played back on VHS recorders.
Hi8	Uses 8mm (a little more than ¼-inch) cassette. Y/C component or composite output. High-quality first generation.
Occasionally still in use:	
1-inch VTR	Reel-to-reel model. Uses 1-inch tape format. NTSC composite. High quality.
U-matic	¾-inch cassette recorder. NTSC composite. Good quality, but bulky.

10.6

DIGITAL BETACAM VTR

This digital Betacam VTR is a high-quality RGB component recording system that uses ½-inch cassettes. The function display shows a variety of video and audio information.

VU meters   Cassette slot

Audio controls

Function display   Editing controls   Operational controls   Shuttle controls

postproduction. **SEE 10.6** Refer to the table on the characteristics of the various commonly used digital VTRs. **SEE 10.7**

If you want to replace a composite analog VTR with a composite digital one, you can simply unplug the analog VTR and connect the digital one to the very same cables. All other equipment, such as monitors and switchers, will perform equally well with either machine. Not so with the Y/C component, or RGB digital (D-1 through D-5) models, which need, as you already know, component switchers, editors, and monitors that can handle the separate signals.

Time Base Corrector

The *time base corrector (TBC)* functions much like the frame store synchronizer, except that it stores only a few lines at a time instead of a whole frame. But just like the *frame store synchronizer*, the main purpose of the TBC is to help make videotape playbacks, dubs, and edits electronically stable. It does so by keeping slightly different scanning cycles in step during the videotape recording and playback and adjusts the sync from various video sources so that they all scan exactly alike. Switching from one source to another will not cause a temporary picture breakup or roll. Most high-end VTRs have a built-in time base corrector. Lower-end equipment, however, needs to be hooked up to a TBC especially during editing.

10.7

TYPES OF DIGITAL VIDEOTAPE RECORDERS

TYPE	CHARACTERISTICS
D-1	Uses 1-inch reel-to-reel tape. RGB component. Superior quality through many generations.
D-2	Uses 19mm (about ¾-inch) cassette. NTSC composite. Superior recording quality. Excellent quality through many generations.
D-3	Uses ½-inch cassette. NTSC composite. Excellent recording quality. Can be docked with ENG/EFP cameras and used with standard NTSC equipment. Digital audio with compact-disc quality.
D-5	Uses ½-inch cassette. RGB component. Superior recording quality. Can be docked with ENG/EFP cameras. Can be used for extensive postproduction without deterioration. Digital audio with compact-disc quality.
D-6	Uses 19mm (about ¾-inch) cassette. RGB component. 10 to 12 digital audio channels. D-6 is especially intended for HDTV, but can also record all lower-numbered D formats.
D-7	SMPTE classification of Panasonic's DVCPRO (see below).
Digital Betacam	Uses ½-inch cassette. RGB component. Superior quality. Can be docked with ENG/EFP cameras. Uses compression.
Digital-S	Uses ½-inch cassette. Y/C component. Very good quality. Uses compression.
DVCPRO	Uses ¼-inch (6.35mm) cassette. RGB component. Despite its small cassette, recording has excellent BetacamSP quality. Uses compression.
DVCAM	Uses ¼-inch (6.35mm) cassette. RGB component. Excellent DVCPRO-like quality. Can stay compressed throughout dubbing and editing, which results in practically no picture deterioration.

Note that there is no D-4. Rumor has it that the number 4, like our number 13, was skipped by the Japanese manufacturer because of superstition.

■ Tape Formats

Historically, *tape format* referred to the width of the videotape. In the early days of videotape recording, format was an important indicator of recording quality: The narrower the tape, the poorer the recording quality. Today the recording method or VTR type, rather than tape width, is a more accurate indicator of the highest-quality system. For example, the ½-inch BetacamSP or D-5 videotape recorders are better than the old 1-inch analog recorders; and the DVCPRO and DVCAM systems, which use a ¼-inch (6.35mm) tape width, are superior to the ½-inch S-VHS system, rivaling or surpassing, in fact, the quality of the BetacamSP. If you are familiar with the basic tape formats, you run less of a risk of taking the wrong tape along for your video recording.

VIDEOTAPE-RECORDING PROCESS

The relative ease with which we can operate a VTR may find us putting videotape recording at the bottom of our production priority list. Such an attitude often leads to disaster. Taking the wrong video cassettes on an EFP shoot is as serious a problem as forgetting the camcorders. Videotape recording requires careful preparation and meticulous attention to detail in the preproduction, production, and postproduction phases.

Like a pilot who goes through a checklist before every flight, you should establish your own "before, during, and after" VTR checklists. You will find that such checklists are especially helpful when doing field productions. The following lists include major production items only. You may need to adapt or add to these lists to meet your specific equipment and recording requirements.

THE "BEFORE" CHECKLIST

☑ ***Schedule*** Is the videotaping equipment actually available for the studio or field production? Most likely, your operation will have more than one type of VTR available. Which VTR do you need? Be reasonable in your request. You will find that VTRs are usually available for the actual production or the remote shoot, but not always for your playback demands. If you need a VTR simply for reviewing the scenes shot on location, or for timing purposes, don't request a digital Betacam, but have the material dubbed down to a regular ½-inch VHS format and watch it on your home VCR. In any case, you need to request a VTR that can actually play back your videotapes. For example, if you shot your material with an S-VHS camcorder, a regular VHS VCR will not produce acceptable images during playback. Most likely, all you will see is a series of picture breakups. Likewise, the digital BetacamSP tape will not play back on an DVCPRO or DVCAM videotape recorder.

☑ ***VTR status*** Does the VTR actually work? Always do a brief test recording and play it back before the actual videotaping. A simple head clog can put even the most expensive VTR out of service. You can detect dirty heads if the picture starts to become progressively noisy or even break up during playback. The heads in some VTRs can be cleaned by simply running a head-cleaning tape. Others need more-direct cleaning procedures, which you had best leave to a professional.

☑ ***Power supply*** If you use a VTR in the field, or if you use a camcorder, do you have enough batteries for the entire shoot? Are they fully charged? If you power the VTR, the camera, and perhaps even the camera light with the same battery, your recording time will be considerably less than if you run each of these pieces on separate power supplies. If you use household current for the power, you will need the appropriate adapter. Check whether the connectors of the power cable fit the plugs of the power supply and camera. Don't try to make a connector fit a jack it isn't designed for. You may blow more than a fuse if you do.

☑ ***Tape***   Do you have the correct tape? Does the cassette match the type and format of the VTR? Although the difference between a ½-inch and an 8mm or ¼-inch cassette is readily apparent, the difference between a normal ½-inch VHS and a ½-inch digital cassette is not so obvious. Check whether the boxes actually contain the correct tapes. Do not rely solely on the box label. Because cassettes can be loaded with various lengths of tape, look at the supply reel in the cassette to verify that it contains the amount of tape indicated on the box. Cassettes with large supply and takeup reels have little tape and, therefore, a short recording time.

Do you have enough tape for the proposed production? Videotape is relatively inexpensive and does not take up much room. Always take along more cassettes than you think you need. Running out of videotape during a field production does not win you any friends.

Are the cassettes in the recording mode? All cassettes have a device to protect the videotape from accidental erasure. For example, Betacam or the much smaller DVCPRO and DVCAM cassettes have a small tab that can be moved into or out of a record-protect position, similar to computer floppy disks. **SEE 10.8** VHS and S-VHS ½-inch cassettes have a tab on the lower left of the back edge. **SEE 10.9** When this tab is in the open position, or broken off, you cannot record anything on the cassette. To restore the cassettes to the record mode, move the tab into the record position; for breakaway tabs, cover the hole in the cassette with a small piece of adhesive tape. Routinely check the status of the tab before using a cassette for videotape recording. The cassette will play back with or without record-protect devices in place.

10.8

DVCPRO CASSETTE TAB

This DVCPRO cassette has a movable tab that prevents accidental erasure, much like a floppy disk. Make sure that the tab is in the closed position (so that it covers the hole) when videotaping. For playback the tab can be in the closed or open position.

Movable record-
protect tab

10.9

VHS CASSETTE TAB REMOVED

To protect VHS and S-VHS cassettes from erasure, you need to break off the tab. To reuse the cassette for recording, you can secure a small piece of tape over the opening.

Tab removed

10.10

CALIBRATING VOLUME LEVELS OF AUDIO CONSOLE AND VTR

Before videotape recording, you must match the audio level of the audio console with that of the VTR.
To calibrate, both VU meters must show a 0 VU (100 percent volume).

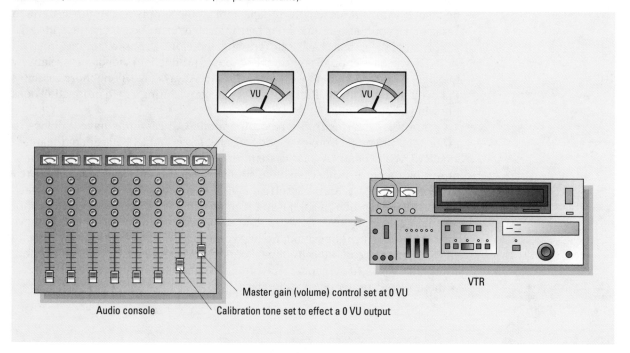

Master gain (volume) control set at 0 VU

Audio console   Calibration tone set to effect a 0 VU output

VTR

☑ *Audio level*   Unless you are using the AGC (automatic gain control), set the audio level before recording. When using a professional camcorder, have the talent deliver the opening lines so that you can adjust the volume controls for optimal audio levels. When using a studio VTR, have the audio engineer feed you a zero-level control tone (with the needle of the VU meter pointing to 0 VU—100 percent volume) from the audio console. You can now adjust the VU meter on the VTR to match the 0 VU reading on the audio console. The line-out signal of the audio console and the input of the VTR are now calibrated. **SEE 10.10**

☑ *Monitor*   In EFP you should play back the various scenes before moving on to the next scene. Watching the playback in the small viewfinder will tell you whether you got the scene on tape, but it will not let you do any critical viewing. To judge the color or the framing, you need a larger monitor that can display the direct feed from the camera. Bring along a monitor that is compatible with the VTR you are using. Also double-check the necessary video cables and power cable connectors. Most low-end recorders have RCA phono connectors that need adaptors for the BNC jacks on monitors or VTRs. When shooting in the field away from any AC power source, you need a monitor that has its own battery as a power supply. Always take a spare monitor battery along.

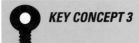 **KEY CONCEPT 3** **Always check that the cassette format matches the VTR and that the cassette tab is in place for recording.**

THE "DURING" CHECKLIST

☑ **Video leader** If possible, start each videotape with a *video leader*. It consists of a 30- to 60-second recording of color bars and a 0 VU test tone, an identification slate, black or leader numbers (from 10 to 2) that flash on the screen every second for eight seconds, and two seconds of black before the first frame of the program video. **SEE 10.11**

The *color bars* can be generated by the ENG/EFP camera you actually use, or, in a studio production, from the CCU (camera control unit). Most consumer camcorders cannot generate color bars. The 0 VU test tone can come from a portable mixer or from the studio console.

During playback you can use the color bars and test tone as important references to match the colors of the playback monitor and the playback volume with those of the videotape recording. Do not copy the video leader from another recording: You would be adjusting your playback equipment to the wrong standard.

10.11

VIDEO LEADER

The video leader helps adjust the playback machine to the video and audio values of the record machine.

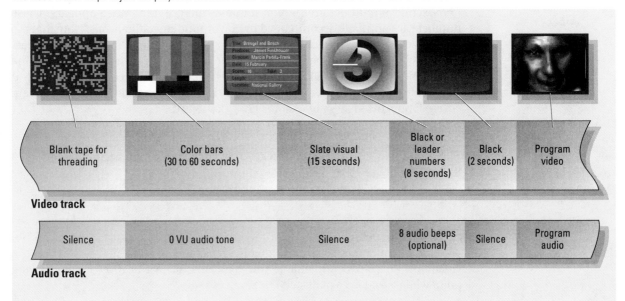

10.12

CHARACTER-GENERATED SLATE

The slate gives vital production information and is recorded at the beginning of each major take.

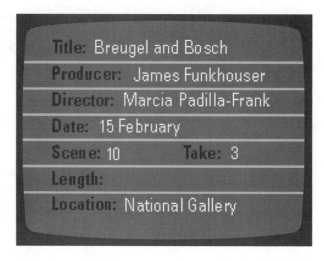

Title:	Breugel and Bosch
Producer:	James Funkhouser
Director:	Marcia Padilla-Frank
Date:	15 February
Scene: 10	**Take:** 3
Length:	
Location:	National Gallery

The video slate shows vital production information, such as the show title; scene and take numbers; date, time, and location of the recording; and the name of the director and producer. The slate is usually done with a C.G. (character generator) or the camcorder's built-in lettering function. **SEE 10.12** In field productions this information is sometimes hand-lettered on a board, also called a slate. Each time you do another take, you need to update the take number on the slate.

The *leader numbers* that show the seconds remaining before the first frame of the program material are also produced by the C.G. These numbers, which were originally developed for film cuing, are used for cuing the videotape during playback. For instance, you can cue the tape at leader number 4, which gives you a four-second preroll before the first frame of the program video appears. These numbers are normally accompanied by corresponding audio beeps. Note that the last two seconds are in black (there are no 2 and 1) and silent. The leader numbers are especially helpful when you need to cue a videotape without the aid of time code. Otherwise, the SMPTE/EBU time code or other address code system lets you cue up the videotape even more precisely. Address systems and how they work are covered more extensively in chapter 11. *READY ZVL 2*

KEY CONCEPT 4 The video leader must be generated by the equipment actually used in the videotape recording.

✓ ***Tape counter*** Even if you record some kind of address system on the videotape, you should reset the mechanical tape counter before starting the videotape. This device will enable you to locate quickly the approximate starting point when asked for a playback.

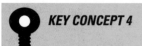

☑ ***Preroll*** When starting a VTR, do not record anything—not even the video leader material—until the VTR has reached operating speed. A certain amount of preroll time is needed to give the transport a chance to stabilize. Most VTRs indicate when they have reached operating speed (by some light signal) and are ready for recording. To avoid temporary video breakup, wait for this signal before starting the actual recording. To alert the director that the VTR has reached operating speed, give a "speed," "locked," or "in-record" cue.

During editing, most VTRs in camcorders back up the tape automatically for the required preroll (see chapter 11). In the playback mode, most high-end VTRs reach operating speed within a fraction of a second; they deliver a stable picture even when you shift directly into play from the pause mode that displays a freeze-frame.

☑ ***Recording levels*** Watch the video and audio recording levels carefully. Many camcorders indicate these levels in the viewfinder display or on small meters on the VTR section. Pay particular attention to the audio portion of the recording. You may get so carried away with the pictures that minor—or even major—audio problems escape your attention.

☑ ***Recording for postproduction*** When recording for postproduction, record enough of each segment so that the action overlaps the preceding and following scenes. Such cushions (or pads) greatly facilitate editing. If you have enough tape, videotape the camera rehearsals. Sometimes you will get a better performance during rehearsal than during the actual take. Record a few seconds of black after each take before stopping the tape. This *run-out* signal acts as a pad during editing or, if you do a live-on-tape recording, as a safety cushion during playback.

☑ ***Retakes*** As the VTR operator, tell the director right away if you feel that another take is necessary for some reason. It is far less expensive to repeat a take than to try to "fix it in post."

☑ ***Recordkeeping*** During the recording keep accurate records of each take. You will be surprised at how quickly you forget just where on the videotape the unforgettable scene is located. A carefully kept *field log* can save you much time in postproduction editing. The field log gives information on the production title, the taping date and location, the names of the producer and director, the scene and take numbers and their sequence, whether the takes are good or not, the tape counter number, and other important production details. **SEE 10.13** If there is only a single column for the take number, circle the good takes.

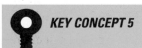

KEY CONCEPT 5   **Keep an accurate field log during the recording session and carefully label all videotapes.**

10.13

FIELD LOG

The field log is kept by the VTR operator during the production. It normally indicates scene and take numbers, the counter number of the VCR or time code, whether the take was good or no good, and what the take was all about. It facilitates locating the various cassettes and shots during post-production previewing.

Production Title: Traffic Safety		Producer/Director: Elan Frank		
Taping Date: 4/15		Location: Intersection of Bonita & Crest Roads		

Scene	Take	OK or No Good	Counter #	Event
1	①	OK	0082	Car running stop sign
	2	NG	0094	VTR problem
	③	OK	0251	Z-axis shot
	④	OK	0463	Camera pans past stop sign
2	1	NG	0513	Pedestrian too far from car
	②	OK	0766	Good Z-axis shot
6	1	NG	0992	Ball too soon in street
	2	NG	1332	Ball too late
	③	OK	1371	Ball rolls ... front of car

THE "AFTER" CHECKLIST

☑ *Recording check*   Before moving on to the next scene or striking the studio set or remote location, verify that you have actually recorded the scene as planned. Rewind the tape to the beginning shot, then fast-forward it two or three times to spot-check the recording. If the tape looks and sounds good, proceed to the next item on the production schedule.

☑ *Labeling*   Label each tape with the tape number and the title and number of the scenes. Label the box with the same information. It is more important to label the tape itself than the box. As obvious as such labeling seems, countless precious hours of postproduction time have been lost because the tape boxes, rather than the tapes, were labeled. Watch that the tape labels match the information of the corresponding field log. Make a photocopy of the field log and keep it in the tape box with the cassette of the corresponding program segments.

☑ *Protection copies*   As soon as possible, dub all source tapes in their entirety so you have a protection (backup) copy of all the material shot.

KEY CONCEPT 6   **Always make protection copies of all the source tapes.**

NONLINEAR STORAGE SYSTEMS

Regardless of whether the video information stored on videotape is analog or digital, you can access it only serially: You need to roll through the first twenty-six shots, for example, before reaching shot 27. Unlike the linear videotape system, ***nonlinear storage systems*** allow random access. When this digital information is stored on a hard drive or some kind of read/write optical disc, you can access shot 27 directly: Instead of having to wait for the tape to roll to the desired frame, you can call it up in a fraction of a second, regardless of where on the disk it is located. Shot 27 and shot 327 are as quickly and easily accessible as shot 1. This random access to each digitized frame has revolutionized postproduction editing, which is explored further in chapter 11.

 KEY CONCEPT 7   **Nonlinear digital storage devices allow random and almost instantaneous access to each video frame.**

The problem with using nonlinear digital video is that high-resolution, full-screen video requires a great amount of storage space, especially when dealing with moving images. New technical breakthroughs and equipment, however, let you squeeze more and more information on smaller and smaller storage devices. The most popular nonlinear digital storage devices are (1) computer disks, (2) the electronic still store system, (3) read/write optical discs, and (4) CD-ROMs and DVDs.

Computer Disks

Because video and audio information can be digitized, you can store it on any type of computer disk. The computer won't know whether the magnetic pulses it stores represent a reproduction of the Mona Lisa or your checkbook balance. So long as the pictures you want to store are still images rather than ones in motion, you can store a great number of video images on a relatively small disk, such as the Iomega Zip disk. Moving images need considerably more storage space. Considering that just one second of video takes thirty individual frames, you can see why, despite high-capacity hard drives, some kind of image compression is necessary for the efficient storage and transport of full-motion video.

Fortunately, various compression methods let you cram more and more information onto ever-smaller disks. Recall from chapter 3 the discussion about lossless and lossy compression and the suitcase example. *Lossless compression* simply finds unused space on the disk and puts the information in the best possible order. *Lossy compression* reduces all nonessential and redundant information, usually borrowing the dropped information from one or two frames that originally carried it and duplicating it when necessary.

Electronic Still Store System

As mentioned in chapter 9, an ESS (electronic still store) system can store a vast array of still images and display any one of the stored frames in a fraction of a second. Even the simplest systems can store up to fifty low-resolution and twenty-five high-resolution still images on a single $2 \times 2\frac{1}{4}$–inch floppy disk. Larger systems can store up to several thousand still frames. In fact, nonlinear editing systems are basically large ESS systems. Such editing systems don't store moving images, but rather a great number of single-frame files.

Read/Write Optical Discs

These optical discs let you "read"—play back—previously recorded material and "write"—record—new material, just like with videotape. Similar to the audio CD or the CD-ROM, read/write optical discs use a laser beam to retrieve the information. They come in various sizes and with varying degrees of sophistication. Even a small read/write optical disc (about 680 megabytes) the size of a regular CD lets you record and play back about seventy minutes of digital audio and a relatively great amount of motion video. Again, the advantage of such an optical disc over videotape is that the disc allows random access, is easier to store, and does not wear out through repeated use.

CD-ROMs and DVDs

As you recall, the optical CD-ROM is a read-only disc. Like an audio CD, it comes with digital audio and video information permanently recorded on it. Unlike read/write optical discs, you cannot erase a CD-ROM and then record some other material on it. It is identical in size to the audio CD (about $4\frac{1}{2}$ inches in diameter) and holds an amazing 650 megabytes of video and audio information. The CD-ROM is designed primarily for use in desktop computers. It holds a vast amount of information, such as an entire encyclopedia with text and illustrations, or a travelogue with maps, or, as in the case of *Zettl's Video Lab 2.1*, more than 620 megabytes of moving video sequences and accompanying sound. Most desktop computers come with built-in CD-ROM drives; others can be hooked up to external drives.

As you learned in chapter 8, the DVD (digital versatile disc or digital videodisc) is a very high density read-only storage device that can hold an astonishing 4.7 gigabytes—all on the same-sized disc as the regular CD-ROM. Once made available as a read/write disc, DVD will be ideal for storage and backup of your video and audio footage.

USE OF VIDEO RECORDING

The original purpose of video recording was to temporarily preserve a live uninterrupted television program for repeated playing or for reference and study. Today, however, we use video recording for the careful construction of a variety of video events through postproduction editing and the creation of computer-generated images.

Video as a field extends far beyond simply producing broadcast or cable television programs. Video recordings have become an important personal communication medium. The popularity of camcorders rivals that of the still camera, and the use of VCRs to record television programs broadcast at an inconvenient time and for watching movies and various other prerecorded program fare at home is commonplace. *Desktop video,* which usually refers to using regular desktop computers and simple editing software in postproduction, has become an important video production tool. (Desktop video is explored further in chapter 11.) This marriage of computers and video has brought about other significant developments: interactive video and multimedia. Although interactive video and multimedia still rely a great deal on basic video production, they have become significant communication media in their own right. The following overview outlines their major characteristics.

Interactive Video

Interactive video is the type over which the viewer has some control of what he or she wants to see and how to see it. The viewer is no longer passive, but has become an active partner in the communication process.

In its simplest form, such interactivity allows you to choose programs from a list of available menus. You can also determine, at least to some extent, how a particular story will end, provided the writer was willing to write two or three different endings. Home shopping and video games are other well-known forms of interactive video.

As a training device, interactive video might show a critical traffic situation. You could then be asked (by the person appearing on-screen or an off-screen announcer) what you, as the driver, would do to avoid an accident. An elaborate interactive program would then show you the consequences of your answer. A simpler program will at least let you know immediately whether your answer was right or wrong. Or, after watching various scenes showing different shoppers in a department store, you may be asked to identify the shoplifter. The computer will then show you the actual culprit.

The most important development in interactive video is the marriage of television and the Internet. Rather than use separate equipment—a television system for watching television, and a desktop computer with modem for accessing information—your television set can now take on many computer functions, and computers can act as little television systems. One distinct advantage of this marriage is the use of existing cable systems for the digital signal transport. Coaxial and fiber-optic cable systems are much better suited for transporting huge amounts of digital data with much greater speeds than was ever possible with the best telephone lines. The advantage of this high-capacity, high-speed transport system is that the Internet is no longer confined to print, still, or crudely moving images, but can expand its database to full-motion video.

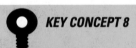

KEY CONCEPT 8   **Interactive video allows the viewer to exercise choice with immediate feedback. It combines the functions of television and the interactivity of the desktop computer.**

Multimedia

Multimedia refers to the display of text, still and moving images, and sound. Multimedia programs come on CD-ROM and DVD and must be played with the appropriate drives on personal computers or with DVD machines. Such programs are used extensively for informational, instructional, and training programs, various types of presentations, and, of course, entertainment. Many movies are available on DVD. The advantage of a DVD recording over a regular VHS tape is not only its superior video quality, but also its superior audio. DVD recordings are especially well suited for large-screen viewing.

Zettl's Video Lab 2.1 CD-ROM is a good example of an interactive multimedia program. If you have been using the program with this book, you know that it presents the material with still and moving images, text, diagrams, narration, music, and various sound effects. It also invites you to make choices and gives you immediate feedback on their relative merit. The interactive program also provides a production laboratory in which you can work different equipment in a variety of production situations without tying up a studio. It is an effective transition between learning production from a book and doing it in the studio and the field.

■ Tape and Disk-Based Recording Systems

Tape-based systems can record and play back analog or digital video and audio information. Disk-based systems can record and play back only digital information.

■ Videotape Tracks

All analog videotape recorders (VTRs) use separate tracks to record the video and audio, as well as various control data. The basic tracks are the video track, which contains the picture information; the audio tracks, which record the sound information; and the control track, which contains the sync pulses. Some videotape recorders use still another track for the address code. Many digital VTRs include video, audio, control, and code information on each track.

■ Composite and Component Systems

The NTSC (National Television System Committee) standard is a composite system that combines the color (C) and the luminance (black-and-white, or Y) part of the video signal into a single composite signal. The Y/C component system separates the color (C) and luminance (Y) information and is sometimes referred to as the Y/C system. The RGB component system keeps the RGB channels separate during the entire recording process. A variation of the RGB system is the Y/color difference system, which uses a narrower bandwidth for signal transport and recording.

■ Types of Videotape Recorders

The two major types of videotape recorders are analog and digital. Although both types use videotape as the recording medium, they are not compatible. This means that you cannot play back an analog tape on a digital VTR or a digital tape on an analog VTR. Each category contains VTR models that differ considerably in quality and tape format.

■ Time Base Corrector

The time base corrector (TBC) is needed to make videotape playbacks, dubs, and edits electronically stable. Like the frame store synchronizer, the TBC keeps slightly different scanning cycles in step during videotape recording and playback. Most high-end VTRs have a built-in TBC.

■ Tape Format

Tape format (which historically referred to various tape widths) is not an indicator of recording quality. Some digital recording systems that use a small, ¼-inch tape width can be superior to analog systems that use ½-inch or even wider tape. Not all VTRs use the same videocassettes. The same tape width does not necessarily mean that the cassettes are interchangeable with all systems.

■ Videotape-Recording Process

There are important procedures that must be observed before, during, and after videotape recording.

Nonlinear Storage Systems

Unlike videotape systems (analog or digital), nonlinear systems allow random access of recorded material. When stored on hard drives, on some kind of read/write optical discs, or on a CD-ROM or DVD, each frame can be accessed separately and instantaneously. Electronic still store (ESS) systems can store thousands of still frames that can be quickly accessed for use in a live program or video recording.

Interactive Video and Multimedia

Interactive video refers to the viewer having some control over what is shown on the screen. Interactive learning programs give the user multiple choices and then either confirm the choice or tell the user why the choice was wrong. Interactive television allows the home viewer to exercise some control over program choice and sometimes even program content. The use of television cable services and the combination of television and computers can provide a new and greatly expanded interactive video experience.

Multimedia refers to the simultaneous display by the computer of text, still and moving images, and sound. Distributed on CD-ROM or DVD, these interactive programs are used extensively for information, instruction, and entertainment.

 Z E T T L' S   V I D E O   L A B   2 . 1

*Although the tapes displayed when you click on the **editing** monitor deal mostly with editing functions, decision making, and editing procedures, Veronica, senior editor of Triple-I, has some important technical information for the video-recording process that will help you later when preparing for, and doing, the actual editing.*

RUN ZVL 1 Click on the **editing** monitor and play tape 1 **Meet Veronica**. Now load tape 3 **Tape Basics** and play module 1 **Tape**. Realize that this track arrangement is a generic one and changes from one system to the next; nevertheless, most videotapes have tracks for the various video, audio, and control signals.

RUN ZVL 2 Skip to module 4 **Leader**. Now you can see the color bars and hear the zero-level control tone. Again you are reminded by Veronica to record bars and tone from the video and audio system you are actually using for the recording and to leave it on for at least thirty seconds. The leader numbers are an important cuing device. The numbers and their beeps are exactly one second apart. Note that the last two seconds of the leader are in black and silent. On this leader even the leader number 3 is silent (as are the last two seconds of black).

K E Y   C O N C E P T S

○ **Videotape recorders record analog or digital video and audio signals and other information necessary for the proper operation of the tape.**

○ **Videotapes recorded as Y/C component, RGB component, or Y/color difference component signals cannot be played back on composite (NTSC) equipment.**

○ **Always check that the cassette format matches the VTR and that the cassette tab is in place for recording.**

○ **The video leader must be generated by the equipment actually used in the videotape recording.**

○ **Keep an accurate field log while recording session and carefully label all videotapes.**

○ **Always make protection copies of all the source tapes.**

○ **Nonlinear digital storage devices allow random and almost instantaneous access to each video frame.**

○ **Interactive video allows the viewer to exercise choice with immediate feedback. It combines the functions of television and the interactivity of the desktop computer.**

assemble editing Adding shots on videotape in a consecutive order without first recording a control track on the edit master tape.

downstream keyer (DSK) A control that allows the title to be keyed (cut in) over the picture (line-out signal) as it leaves the switcher.

edit controller A machine that assists in various editing functions, such as marking edit-in and edit-out points, rolling source and record VTRs, and integrating effects. This is often a desktop computer with a specific software program. Also called *editing control unit*.

EDL Stands for edit decision list. It consists of edit-in and edit-out points, expressed in time code numbers, and the nature of transitions between shots.

effects bus Row of buttons that can select the video sources for a specific effect. Usually the same as a mix bus that has been switched to an effects function.

fader bar A lever on the switcher that activates buses and can produce superimpositions, dissolves, fades, keys, and wipes of different speeds.

insert editing Produces highly stable edits. Requires the prior laying of a continuous control track by recording black on the edit master tape.

key bus A bus (row of buttons) used to select the video source to be inserted into the background image.

linear editing system Uses videotape as the editing medium. It does not allow random access of shots.

M/E bus A single bus that can serve mix or effects functions.

mix bus Rows of buttons that permit the mixing of video sources, as in a dissolve or super. Major buses for on-the-air switching.

nonlinear editing system Allows random access of shots. The video and audio information is stored in digital form on computer disks.

off-line editing Refers to an editing process that will not produce an edit master tape. Equipment is used to produce a rough-cut or an edit decision list.

on-line editing Produces the final high-quality edit master tape. High-quality VTRs are used for on-line editing.

preview bus Row of buttons that can direct an input to the preview monitor at the same time another video source is on the air.

program bus The bus (row of buttons) on the switcher, with inputs that are directly switched to the line-out.

pulse-count system An address code that counts the control track pulses and translates this count into time and frame numbers. Also called *control track system*.

SMPTE time code A specially generated address code that marks each video frame with a specific number (hour, minute, second, and frame). This time code is officially called SMPTE/EBU (for European Broadcasting Union).

window dub A dub of the source tapes to a lower-quality tape format with the address code keyed into each frame.

Switching and Postproduction Editing

JUST **when you have mastered some major terms** of video recording, you are bombarded with another set of terms that deal with switching and postproduction editing: *downstream keyer, linear* and *nonlinear, off-line* and *on-line, EDL, AB-roll editing, window dub,* and *assemble* and *insert editing.*

But don't worry—once you have some practice and actually operate a switcher or do some postproduction editing, these terms will quickly become part of your routine production language. Keep in mind that all these terms and the dazzling variety of editing equipment are created not to make your life more complicated, but to help you achieve aesthetically pleasing and effective picture sequences as discussed in chapter 12. This chapter explains some of the basic sequencing techniques.

◼ SWITCHING, OR INSTANTANEOUS, EDITING

Basic switcher layout, multifunction switchers, and switcher operation

◼ POSTPRODUCTION EDITING

Linear editing systems, assemble and insert editing, nonlinear editing systems and procedures, editing preparations, and off-line and on-line editing procedures

SWITCHING, OR INSTANTANEOUS EDITING

Switching means that you select and join various video sources (such as the pictures supplied by two or more cameras) with various transitions (cuts, dissolves, and wipes) while the production is under way. The production switcher, which is used primarily in multicamera studio productions or in large field productions, makes such instantaneous editing possible. There are also switchers that are used primarily in postproduction, where they function more as transition makers between two shots than as shot selectors.

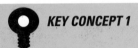

KEY CONCEPT 1 **Switching means instantaneous editing from simultaneously available video sources.**

This section takes a close-up look at (1) basic switcher layout, (2) multifunction switchers, and (3) switcher operation.

Basic Switcher Layout

The *production switcher,* which you will find in production studios and large remote trucks, is specifically designed for instantaneous editing. At first glance the production switcher looks as complex and complicated as a large audio console. But, similar to the audio console, the basic layout principle is relatively simple.

The Triple-I TD feels that the best way to understand the functions of a switcher is to build one—at least theoretically. So he sits down with you and starts drawing the buttons and levers necessary to perform the normal switcher functions.

Program bus To select and connect certain shots, you need several *video inputs.* If all you had were two cameras and you simply wanted to *cut* (instantaneously switch) from one camera to the other, you could get by with only two switcher buttons—one that activates camera 1, and another for camera 2. By pressing the *C-1* (camera 1) button, camera 1 would be put "on the air"—it would go to the line-out and from there to the videotape recorder (VTR) and/or the transmitter.

Because you would probably want to select from additional video sources, which are labeled on the switcher *VTR, CG,* and *rem* (for *remote*), you already have five buttons in the switcher row, called a *bus.* To quickly dump the video and to "cut to black," you need still another button, called the *black (blk) button.* The switcher now has six separate buttons in a single bus. By pressing any one except the black button, the designated video source will be put on the air; the black button takes it off the air (actually, the black button selects a black video signal). This bus, which sends the chosen video source directly to the line-out, is called the *program bus.* **SEE 11.1**

Mix bus If you now want to mix two video sources (as in a dissolve, for example) don't you need two additional buses and some kind of lever to change gradually from one picture to the other? Yes. These are called *mix buses;* the lever that switches from one bus to the other is the *fader bar.* As you can see, this "simple" switcher is getting a little bigger and slightly more complex. You now have a switcher with three

11.1

PROGRAM BUS

Whatever source is punched up on the program bus goes directly to the line-out.

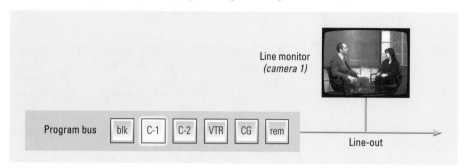

11.2

PROGRAM BUS WITH MIX BUSES AND FADER BAR

The mix buses (A and B) enable the mixing of two video sources, such as in a dissolve or superimposition. The fader bar gradually activates either bus A or bus B when it is moved from one end of travel to the opposite one. The program bus has an additional button *(mix)* that assigns the switching to the mix buses.

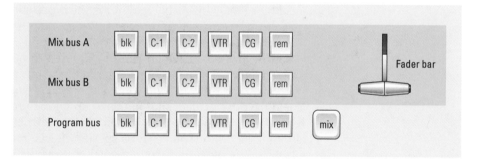

buses: the program bus and two mix buses. Note that the program bus now needs an additional button—*mix*—with which you can transfer the program bus functions to the mix buses. **SEE 11.2**

Preview bus Before putting the selected shots on the air, you will undoubtedly want to see whether the shots cut together properly—whether the sequence fulfills your aesthetic continuity or complexity editing requirements (as discussed in the following chapter). You may also want to see whether a superimposition has the right mix of the two images. Previewing requires more switcher buttons and monitors that let you see the various video choices and what is finally sent to the line-out. To preview the sources, the program bus buttons are simply repeated in an additional bus, appropriately called the ***preview bus.*** **SEE 11.3** As you can readily see, the number of buttons and buses has increased considerably. But because you now know what these buttons are for, they are no longer as bewildering as when you first glanced at an actual switcher.

11.3

PREVIEW BUS

The preview bus lets you preview an upcoming source or effect before it is punched up on the air. The preview bus is identical to the program bus except that its output goes to the preview monitor, not to the line-out.

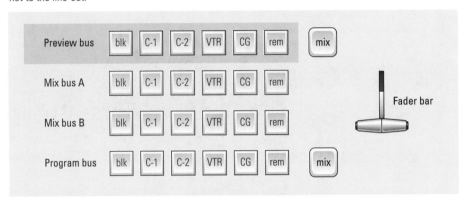

Multifunction Switchers

To keep switchers from getting too large and to keep the number of buses and fader bars to a manageable minimum, the buses and a single fader bar are often made to perform several functions. Rather than have separate mix buses, the program bus and preview bus (here called *preset bus*) are combined in mix/effects buses, or *M/E buses*, which can be assigned to perform both functions. The program bus can also serve as the background bus for a key supplied by the key bus. For example, if you want your name keyed over a particular camera shot, you would have the camera shot punched up on the program bus and the C.G. title (your name) on the key bus. The preset (preview) bus and the program bus can also function as the sources for a specific effects transition, such as a wipe. Take a look at a simple multifunction switcher (Grass Valley 100) as pictured in figure 11.4 and then refer to the illustration to identify the various buses and controls mentioned in the following discussion. **SEE 11.4**

Program bus   For example, the program/background bus of the switcher (shown as the middle bus in figure 11.4) serves four functions: (1) that of a *direct switching bus,* which means that whatever you punch up on the program bus will always go to the line-out, and thus on the air; (2) as temporary *mix bus* A, with the bus below, called the *preset bus,* serving as temporary mix bus B. In this "mix" mode, you can perform fades, dissolves, and supers between the program bus and the preset bus by moving the fader bar from one limit of travel to the other; (3) as temporary *effects bus* A, with the preset bus representing a temporary effects bus B; and (4) as *background* for the key source (such as a title) selected by the key bus above the program bus. In the effects mode, you can use a series of wipes as transitions between the two video sources displayed by the program bus (A) and the preview bus (B).

11.4

MULTIFUNCTION SWITCHER

This multifunction switcher (Grass Valley 100) has only three buses: a preview/preset bus, a program bus, and a key bus. You can delegate the program bus and the preview/preset bus M/E (mix/effects) functions.

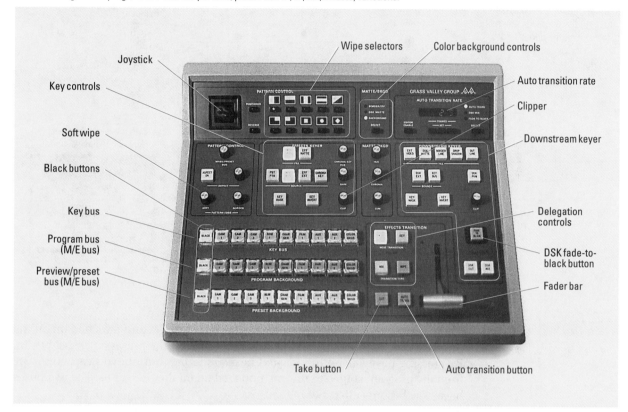

Preset Bus　The preview bus is now called *preset bus,* because whatever you punch up on this bus will appear on the preview monitor and then replace the picture that is on the air (punched up on the program bus) as soon as you press the *take button* or the *auto transition button* next to the preset bus.

Key Bus　The *key bus* is used to select the key source, such as titles from the C.G. The selected source then electronically cuts a hole into the base picture (camera 1's picture of a dancer punched up on the program bus) and then fills it with the hole-cutting video (the white or colored letter *L* supplied by the C.G.) or some other video source (such as a camera picture of a burlap texture). **SEE 11.5**

Delegation controls　The various M/E functions of the program and preset buses are assigned by pressing one of the *delegation buttons* in the effects/transition section of the switcher. For example, by pressing the *mix* button next to the fader bar, you have delegated a mix function to the two M/E buses

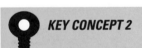

KEYING

In this example the letter *L* is supplied by the C.G. and keyed into the camera 1 video (base picture of the dancer). Camera 2 is focused on the burlap and supplies the signal that fills the cutout letters.

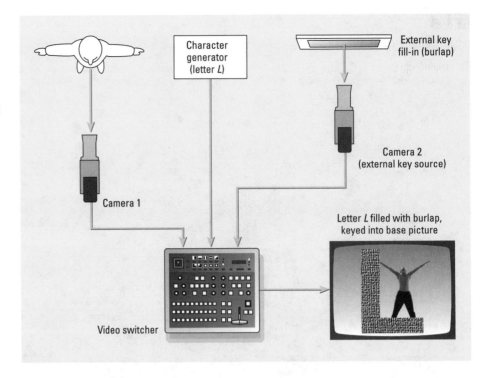

(program and preset). You can now dissolve from the picture punched up on the program bus (M/E bus A) to the one punched up on the preset bus (M/E bus B). By pressing the *wipe* button located next to the *mix* button, you can now wipe from the program source to the one punched up on the preset bus. The two buses have now become effects (wipe) buses.

KEY CONCEPT 2 **Switchers allow the selection of multiple video inputs and the immediate creation of various transitions and effects.**

Switcher Operation

It's time now for you to press a few buttons and learn how to switch—select various video inputs and perform various transitions and effects.

Working the program bus: cuts-only As you recall, the program bus is basically a selector switch of video sources for the line-out. It has this function assigned to it by simply powering up the switcher. If you now want to cut from one video source, let's say C1 (camera 1) to C2 (camera 2), you can simply press the *C-2* button, assuming that C1 is already on the air (the *C-1* button has been

11.6

SWITCHING ON THE PROGRAM BUS

When switching on the program bus, the transitions will be cuts-only. With camera 1 on the air, you can cut to camera 2 by pressing the *C-2* button.

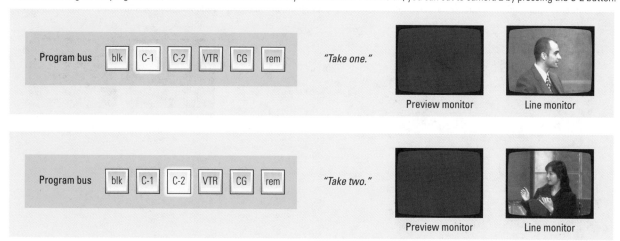

pressed previously). Unfortunately, on the line monitor you will be able to see only what is on the air: C1 before pressing the *C-2* button, and C2 after having pressed it. The preset/preview monitor remains black regardless of the video to which you are switching. **SEE 11.6**

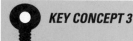

KEY CONCEPT 3   **The program bus sends the selected video inputs directly to the line-out. It is a cuts-only device.**

Working the mix buses: cuts   If you want to preview the upcoming video source, or if you want to dissolve to C2 (mix) instead of cut to it, you first need to delegate a mix function to both buses. You do this on the switcher (Grass Valley 100) by pressing the *background (bkgd)* and *mix* buttons. To cut from camera 1 to camera 2, you need to punch up C2 on the preset bus (which is now M/E bus B) when the director calls, "Ready 2," assuming that camera 1 is already punched up on the program bus. This action will place camera 2's picture on the preview monitor. Camera 1 is still on the line monitor (telling you that C1 is on the air). On the director's "Take 2" command, you press either the *take* button or the auto transition button next to the preset bus. Camera 2 will instantly appear on the line monitor, and C1 will go to the preview monitor. The *C-2* button will light up full, called "high tally" on the program bus, and *C-1* will have "low tally" (lighted halfway) on the preset bus. If you were now to press the *take* button again, C1 would be on the air, and C2 would appear on the preview monitor. **SEE 11.7A AND 11.7B**

11.7A

CUTTING IN THE MIX MODE

When delegated a background and mix function, the program bus becomes M/E bus A, and the preview/preset bus becomes M/E bus B. Here camera 1 is punched up on bus A and on the air. Camera 2 is preset to replace camera 1 as soon as you press the *cut* button.

11.7B

IMAGE CHANGE AFTER CUT

When the cut is completed, the program bus shows camera 2 on the air, while the preview/preset bus switches automatically to camera 1's picture.

Working the mix buses: dissolves   Because you have delegated both buses to the mix mode, you can also perform a dissolve. To dissolve from camera 1 (punched up on the program bus and, therefore, on the air) to camera 2, you need to press the *C-2* button on the preset bus and move the fader bar either up or down to the full extent of travel, or press the auto transition button. On the switcher in figure 11.7, the fader bar is in the down position. You will have to move it all the way up to achieve the dissolve. **SEE 11.8A–11.8C**

Note that when you punch up C2 on the preset bus before the dissolve, the *C-2* button has a low tally, indicating that it is not yet activated. With the fader bar halfway through its travel, both cameras are activated (they show a temporary super on the line monitor). When the fader bar has reached the opposite side of travel (in this case, up), finishing the dissolve from C1 to C2, camera 1 (which was punched up on the program bus) will now be replaced by camera 2 on the program bus, thus freeing the preset bus for the next video source. Note that *C-2* is now high tally on the program bus and *C-1* is low tally on the preset bus.

The preview and line monitors reflect which camera is on the air and which is ready to go on the air. In a multifunction switcher, the program bus always puts the selected image directly on the air, and the mix and wipe effects always move

11.8

DISSOLVE

Once assigned the mix function through the mix delegation control, you can dissolve from camera 1 to camera 2.

A Assuming that camera 1 is on the air on bus A, you need to preset camera 2 on bus B.

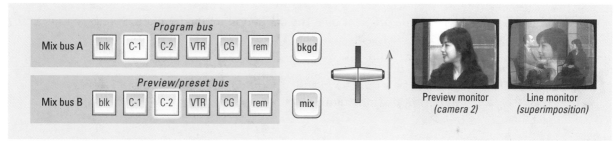

B When the fader bar is stopped midway, you have a super.

C By moving the fader bar to the full limit of travel, you activate the dissolve from camera 1 to camera 2. Once the dissolve is completed, camera 2 will replace camera 1 on the program bus.

from the program bus (background image) *to* the preselected (preset) source. Once the transition is finished, the second source that was punched up on the preset bus (in this case, C2) jumps back up to the program bus and is now the base picture for the new transition or effect.

With camera 2 on the air, how can you now fade to black? You simply press the *blk* (black) button on the preset bus and move the fader bar in the other direction (regardless whether you move it toward or away from the program bus), or press the auto transition button. As soon as the fader bar reaches the opposite end of travel (or the auto transition the end of its run), the black command is transferred

11.9

FADE

When fading to black from camera 2, you need to punch up the *blk* button on bus B (preset/preview) and then dissolve into it by moving the fader bar to its full limit of travel.

	Program bus					
Mix bus A	blk	C-1	C-2	VTR	CG	rem

bkgd

	Preview/preset bus					
Mix bus B	blk	C-1	C-2	VTR	CG	rem

mix

Preview monitor
(black)

Line monitor
(camera 2)

back to the program bus. The *blk* button on the program bus has automatically replaced the *C-2* button. **SEE 11.9**

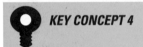

KEY CONCEPT 4   **Mix buses (or buses in the mix mode) let you do cuts, dissolves, superimpositions, and fades.**

Working the effects buses: wipes and keys   With the multifunction switcher, the various *wipe patterns* are accomplished exactly like a dissolve, except that you now need to select a wipe pattern from the wipe selector section of the switcher and press the *bkgd* and *wipe* delegation buttons (instead of background and mix) in the effects/transition section. Moving the fader bar activates the wipe and controls its speed. The auto transition button will accomplish the wipe in the time you specify. Again, once the wipe is accomplished, the second video source wiped to (as selected on the preset bus) will immediately transfer to the program bus.

 Keying is a little more involved. Basically, you select the key source, such as a title from the C.G. and the background picture over which the title is to be keyed (usually the background picture displayed by the line monitor). With the key controls, you can then cut the title into the base picture. With the ***downstream keyer (DSK)***, you can still key an additional title over the complete video image as it leaves the switcher. Note that the downstream keyer is independent of the program bus and puts its title on the air even if the program bus happens to be in black. It simply cuts its title into the black of the program bus. *If you have used the downstream keyer, going to black on the program bus will not get rid of the DSK title.* You need to use the DSK black button to eliminate this type of key.

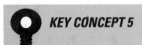

KEY CONCEPT 5   **The effects and key buses can accomplish various wipes, keys, and special effects.**

Almost all production switchers, including digital ones and the effects/ switching software used for desktop computers, operate on this multiple-function principle. Large production switchers have many more special-effects capabilities as well as a high-capacity computer memory that lets you store and recall almost instantly. Large production switchers are especially useful when doing complex digital effects.

POSTPRODUCTION EDITING

Postproduction editing is the third and final stage of the production process. Assuming that your preproduction and production phases went according to plan, you can now select the various video and audio pieces and put them together to give the production its final shape.

Some editors feel that postproduction editing is the most creative aspect of video production. It is an exacting and painstaking activity. We now concentrate on the major operational aspects of this critical postproduction phase: (1) linear editing systems, (2) nonlinear editing systems, (3) editing preparations, and (4) off-line and on-line editing.

Linear Editing Systems

Whenever you use VTRs in the editing process, you have a *linear editing system*, whether the signal on the videotape is analog or digital, or the VTRs are run by a simple edit controller or a complicated computer program. Recall that all videotape-recording systems (analog or digital) are linear, because you cannot access the source material randomly: You cannot directly call up shot 3 without first rolling through shots 1 and 2. For example, if you want to edit shot 14 to shot 3, you must roll through the intervening eleven shots. The basic principle of linear videotape editing is copying various shots from the source tapes to an edit master tape in a desired sequence.

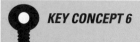

KEY CONCEPT 6　The use of VTRs designates linear editing, whether the recording is analog or digital.

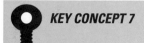

KEY CONCEPT 7　The basic principle of linear editing is copying sections of the source tapes to the edit master tape in the desired sequence.

Single-source linear system　The most basic linear editing system consists of a *source VTR* and a *record VTR*. You use the source VTR to select the various shots and the record VTR to copy the selected shots and join them through cuts. The record VTR performs the actual video and audio edits. Both the source VTR and the record VTR have their own monitors. The source VTR monitor displays the source

11.10

BASIC SINGLE-SOURCE SYSTEM

The source VTR supplies the chosen sections of the original video and feeds it to the record VTR. The record VTR copies the selections and joins them in the desired sequence through cuts. The source monitor displays the video of the source VTR, and the record monitor the video of the record VTR. In this case, the close-up will follow the two-shot.

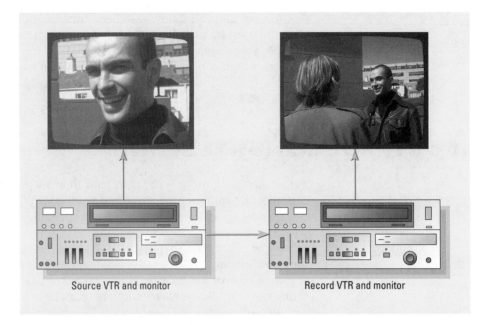

Source VTR and monitor   Record VTR and monitor

material to be edited; the record VTR monitor displays the edited video and audio. **SEE 11.10** Because you have only one source VTR, the single-source VTR editing system is usually limited to cuts-only transitions. There are some systems, called *preread systems,* that allow you to produce dissolves, supers, and wipes with only a single source VTR. In a preread system, the record VTR will not automatically erase its previous footage when the new source video is added, but mixes it according to your instructions.

Edit controller   The *edit controller,* also called the *editing control unit,* will mark and remember frame locations on the source and record tapes, preroll and synchronize the VTRs, allow you to determine whether the audio should be treated with the video or separately, and tell the record VTR when to switch into record mode—thereby performing the edit. Sophisticated edit controllers also activate switchers and audio consoles for various video and audio effects. Usually, the edit controller has separate operational controls for the source and record VTRs (play, fast-forward, rewind, and variable search speeds) and for various common editing functions. **SEE 11.11**

Most edit controllers perform these specific tasks:

▶ Control VTR search modes (variable forward and reverse speeds) separately for the source and record VTRs to locate shots.

▶ Read and display elapsed time and frame numbers from either a pulse-count or an address code system for each VTR. (The address code is discussed later in this chapter.)

▶ Mark and remember precise edit-in and edit-out points.

11.11

EDIT CONTROLLER

The edit controller has separate operational controls for the source VTR and the record VTR, such as search and shuttle controls. The controls in the center activate the preroll and editing functions.

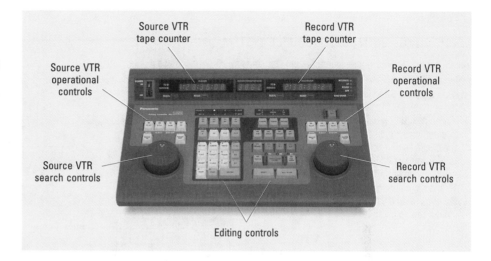

Source VTR tape counter

Record VTR tape counter

Source VTR operational controls

Record VTR operational controls

Source VTR search controls

Record VTR search controls

Editing controls

▷ Back up, or "backspace," both VTRs to exactly the same preroll point. Some edit controllers have a switch that gives several preroll choices, such as a two-second or a five-second preroll. You may recall that prerolling the VTRs ensures that the tapes will achieve the proper speed and synchronization.

▷ Simultaneously start both machines and keep them running in sync.

▷ Run a trial edit so that you can preview it before telling the record VTR to perform the actual edit. This preview edit will appear on the monitor for the record (edit) VTR, although the record VTR has not yet performed the actual edit.

▷ Rewind the record VTR so that you can review the completed edit. The edited shots will appear again on the monitor of the record VTR, but this time the edit has actually been completed. You can now review, instead of preview, the edit.

▷ Allow the user to tell the record VTR to edit either the video or audio track— or both. The actual edits will be performed by the record VTR.

▷ Make the record VTR perform either in the assemble or insert editing mode (discussed later in this chapter).

▷ Permit expansion of the system by interfacing more source VTRs and special-effects equipment.

The diagram on the next page shows how the edit controller fits into the single-source editing system. **SEE 11.12**

KEY CONCEPT 8   **Normally, single-source VTR editing systems are limited to cuts-only transitions.**

11.12

EDIT CONTROLLER IN SINGLE-SOURCE SYSTEM

The edit controller in a single-source system starts and synchronizes the source and record VTRs, locates the in- and out-points for both VTRs, and activates the audio mixer for audio mixing.

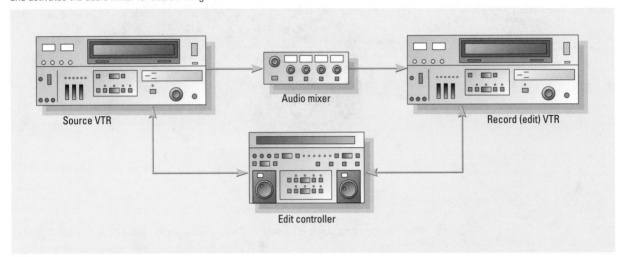

Source VTR

Audio mixer

Record (edit) VTR

Edit controller

Multiple-source linear system This system uses two or more VTRs as source machines, normally labeled with letters *(A VTR, B VTR)*, and a single record VTR.

With a multiple-source VTR system, you can edit the shots from the A and B (and/or C) VTRs without having to change tapes. The big advantage is that you are no longer restricted to cuts-only transitions. You can now perform different transitions between the "A-roll" (the material on the source A VTR) and the "B-roll" (the material on the source B VTR) to dissolves and a great variety of wipes. To accomplish such transitions between the A-roll and the B-roll, you need to feed their video material into a postproduction switcher that will perform the actual switching function. Its line-out is then recorded by the record VTR. You can also use special effects provided by the switcher for a great variety of transitions. *READY ZVL 1*

The edit controllers for such multiple-source systems are usually computer-based. The computer will not only remember your various commands, such as shot selection from A and B rolls, type and length of transition, or special effects, but also make the source VTRs, the switcher, and/or the *SEG (special-effects generator)* perform various feats. Importing an audio mixer—or, in larger productions, an audio console—allows you to control the volume of the different sound tracks and mix in additional sounds. **SEE 11.13**

Note that despite the important part the computer plays, the editing is still linear: It uses videotape instead of some nonlinear storage device, such as a large-capacity hard drive. If you have the feeling that things are getting a bit more complicated than what you expected from a discussion of video "basics," you are

MULTIPLE-SOURCE EDITING SYSTEM

In a multiple-source system, two VTRs (A and B) supply the source material to the single record VTR. The video output of both source machines is routed through the switcher for various transitions, such as dissolves and numerous wipe effects. The audio output of both source VTRs is routed through an audio mixer (or console). Multiple-source systems are usually managed by a computer-driven edit controller.

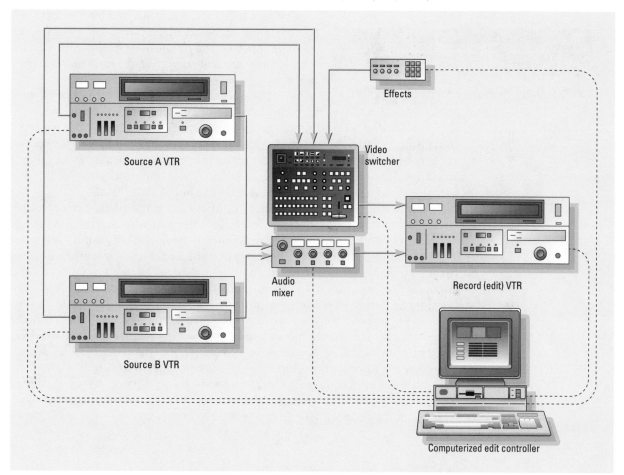

Effects

Source A VTR

Video switcher

Audio mixer

Record (edit) VTR

Source B VTR

Computerized edit controller

right. Postproduction editing is not only a formidable aesthetic challenge, it is also technically complex. Even so, postproduction editing is not unlike operating a desktop computer: Once you have learned how to operate it, its technical complexity helps rather than hinders you in accomplishing many tasks.

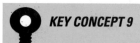 ***KEY CONCEPT 9*** **Dissolves, wipes, and other special-effects transitions are possible with multiple-source editing systems.**

PULSE-COUNT AND ADDRESS CODE DISPLAY

The pulse-count and address code displays show elapsed hours, minutes, seconds, and frames. The frames roll over (to seconds) after twenty-nine, the seconds to minutes and minutes to hours after fifty-nine, and the hours to zero after twenty-four.

| Hours | Minutes | Seconds | Frames |

Pulse-count and address code   When you look at the edit controller, you see number displays for the source tape and the record tape. The displays show hours, minutes, seconds, and frames. **SEE 11.14** They function like the tape counters on a VCR or audiotape recorder, except that they are much more accurate. To perform exact edits, you must be able to locate any given frame on the videotape. Two major systems assist you in this task: the *pulse-count system*, which is also called the *control track system;* and the *time code system*, also called the *address code system.*

The *pulse-count system* uses the control track pulses to count the various frames. Recall that each pulse on the control track designates a video frame, so you can locate a specific spot on the videotape by counting the pulses on the control track. Thirty frames make up one second on the display, so each new second rolls over after the twenty-ninth frame. Each additional minute is generated by the sixtieth second, as is the hour after the sixtieth minute. **SEE 11.15**

You will discover that the pulse-count system is not frame-accurate. This means that you *will not* get the same frame each time you move the tape to a specific pulse-count number. The reason is that some of the pulses are skipped or get lost in the high-speed tape shuttle. For example, if you had to find the tenth house on a street, you would have no trouble. But if you were asked to go to the thirty-six-hundredth house, you would probably have quite a bit more difficulty finding it. Considering that 3,600 pulses constitute only two minutes of videotape recording, you may understand why the counter may be off a few frames when trying to find a specific spot some twenty or more minutes into the tape. Because this system begins to count from whatever starting point you assign, *make sure that you rewind the tape completely and set the counter to zero before logging or editing.*

The advantage of the pulse-count system is its speed. It does not need a device for generating and displaying the address code. For that reason the pulse-count system is still used extensively in analog news editing.

PULSE-COUNT SYSTEM

The pulse-count, or control track, system counts the control track pulses to find a specific spot on the videotape. Thirty pulses make up one second of elapsed tape time.

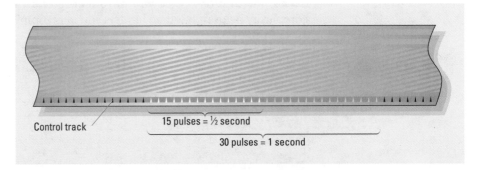

Control track

15 pulses = ½ second

30 pulses = 1 second

11.16

TIME CODE ADDRESS SYSTEM

The time code system marks each frame with a unique address.

··· 00:00:58:25 00:00:58:26 00:00:58:27 00:00:58:28 00:00:58:29 00:00:59:00 00:00:59:01 00:00:59:02 ···

For more-accurate editing, you have to use a *time code,* or *address code, system.* This system marks each frame with a different number and a specific address. With time code the edit controller will guide you precisely to the tenth or thirty-six-hundredth house. To get to the tenth house, the edit controller does not have to start counting from one to ten, but simply looks for the number 10 house. It finds the thirty-six-hundredth house just as easily by looking at its house number.

The most widely accepted address system is the **SMPTE time code** (pronounced "sempty time code"); its full name is *SMPTE/EBU* (Society of Motion Picture and Television Engineers/European Broadcasting Union) *time code.* It gives each frame a specific address, which you can use by looking at the read-out on the edit controller or on the computer display. **SEE 11.16** Although there are similar time code systems, they are not compatible with the SMPTE time code. You must select a specific time code system to use throughout the editing process. Also, you cannot synchronize various video- and/or audiotapes whose frames are marked with different time code systems. 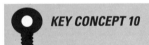 *READY ZVL 2*

KEY CONCEPT 10   **The time code provides a unique address for each frame of recorded video.**

Regardless of where you start the videotape, the time code accurately finds the requested frame. You can use the same time code for your audiotape and have the computer match audio and video frame by frame. The disadvantage of the time code address system is that you need a time code generator to record the time code on a cue or code track on the videotape, or on one of the audiotape tracks. You then need a time code reader to display it. But for accurate editing, you can't do without it.

You can record the time code while videotaping or (as is common in smaller productions and EFP) add it later to one of the cue tracks or audio tracks of the videotape. Because videotape segments rarely exceed one hour, the hour digit is generally reserved to indicate the tape (or reel) number. For example, a time code of 04:17:22:18 would mean that the shot you are seeking is 17 minutes, 22 seconds, and 18 frames into tape (or reel) number 4. This labeling is an added protection so that you can find the right reel even if the physical labels have come off the tape or—more common—were never put on it.

11.17

ASSEMBLE EDITING

In the assemble mode, the record VTR lays down a new control track section based on the sync information for each edited shot. In this illustration the first sync pulse of shot 2 is accurately spaced from the last sync pulse of shot 1 on the edit master tape. The sync pulses from both sections form a continuous track. Any other spacing at the edit point would cause a picture tear.

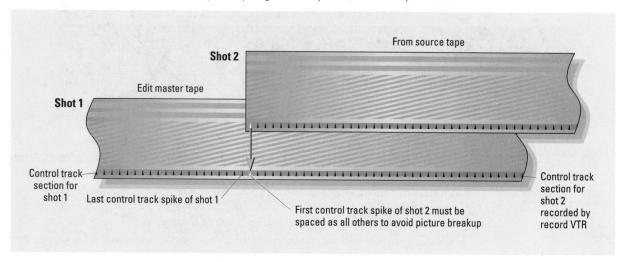

From source tape

Shot 2

Edit master tape

Shot 1

Control track section for shot 1

Last control track spike of shot 1

First control track spike of shot 2 must be spaced as all others to avoid picture breakup

Control track section for shot 2 recorded by record VTR

Assemble editing   All linear editing systems give you the choice between *assemble* or *insert* mode. Generally, assemble editing is faster than insert editing but less electronically stable at the edit points. The major drawback is that assemble editing will not allow you to edit video and audio independently. In *assemble editing,* the record VTR erases everything (video, audio, control, and time code tracks) on the edit master tape to have a clean slate before copying the video and audio material supplied by the source tape. During the transfer everything that is recorded on the selected portion of the source tape is copied to the edit master tape. The record VTR supplies a new control track for the source segment that is copied over to the edit master tape. To achieve a stable edit, the record VTR aligns and spaces the sync pulses of the various source segments so that they form a continuous control track.   **SEE 11.17** Unfortunately, even fairly high quality VTRs do not always succeed in this task. For example, when the record VTR adds the control track of the first frame of shot 2 to the last frame of shot 1, the sync pulses may be just a little farther apart or closer together at the edit point. This slight discrepancy will result in a "tear," which means that during playback the picture will break up or roll momentarily at the edit point.

Because all tracks of the edit master tape are erased prior to copying the new shot from the source tape, you cannot copy the audio track first and then go back to add the corresponding video, or record first the video segments and then match them with the appropriate audio. All you can do is add sections of video and audio together from the source tape to the edit master tape.

The advantage of assemble editing is that you do not have to record a continuous control track (by recording black) for the edit master tape before the actual editing. You can, if necessary, use a tape for the edit master even if it already

11.18

INSERT EDITING

In the insert edit mode, the source material is transferred to the edit master tape without its control track and placed according to the prerecorded control track of the edit master tape.

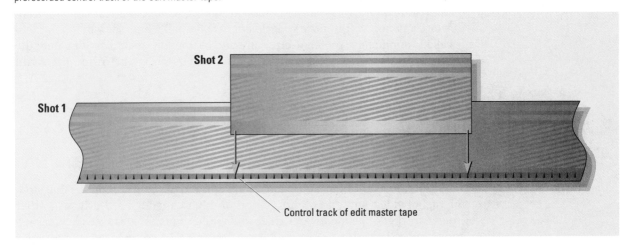

Control track of edit master tape

has some video and audio material recorded on it (although that is not recommended). The flying erase head in your consumer camcorder will erase the video track exactly at the edit point and thus facilitate a tear-free assemble edit—at least most of the time.

Insert editing   Although it requires the previous recording of a continuous control track on the edit master tape, *insert editing* produces highly stable edits. As pointed out earlier, you lay the control track by recording black on the tape. The recording of black happens in real time, which means that you must run the blank edit master tape for thirty minutes to lay a thirty-minute control track. Only then do you have a truly continuous guide for the edit points. **SEE 11.18**

   During insert editing, *the record VTR does not add a new control track,* but places the new shot to fit the existing control track on the edit master tape. All edits are therefore equally spaced. This means that they are highly stable and tear-free, even if you insert a new shot in the middle of the edit master tape.

   Another advantage of insert editing is that you can separate the audio and video tracks. For example, many news and documentary editors prefer to first edit the audio track and then match with the appropriate video what is being said and heard on the audio track. To speed up the editing process, they often have several "blackened" tapes on hand with the control track already recorded on them. These tapes serve as edit master tapes for insert editing. Normally, however, the "blacking" of edit master tapes is part of the editing preparations.

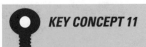 **KEY CONCEPT 11**   **The edit master tape must be prepared for insert editing by first recording black on it.**

Nonlinear Editing Systems

Instead of transferring various shots from source tapes to the edit master tape in a specific order, with a ***nonlinear editing system*** you are concerned with organizing and keeping track of a huge slide library that contains every single frame of your source tapes. The basic nonlinear editing principle is not copying from one tape to another, but *file management*. You probably now see why this system is called "nonlinear": You can select any one of the files, regardless of where the information was located on the source tapes or what other files you have available.

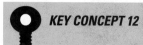 **KEY CONCEPT 12**   **The basic nonlinear editing principle is file management.**

Nonlinear editing systems consist of high-end desktop computers that store the digital video and audio information on high-capacity hard drives or other storage media. To facilitate your video and audio sequencing choices, you need a computer and a high-capacity hard drive. You should also try to get a large, high-quality monitor rather than the standard computer screen. The larger images prevent eye fatigue and also give you a better idea of how the pictures actually look on a television screen. **SEE 11.19** You will find that feeding your edited

11.19

NONLINEAR
VIDEO DISPLAY

Despite a great variety of nonlinear computer systems, most displays show at least the in- and out-numbers for each shot, the last frame of the previous shot and the first frame of the following shot, the logged title of the shot, and some kind of visual representation of the audio track.

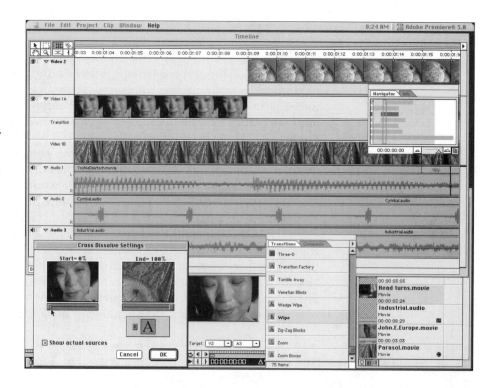

BASIC NONLINEAR EDITING SYSTEM

The basic nonlinear editing system consists of a computer with large-capacity storage devices and editing/effects software. The output of such a system can be an EDL (edit decision list) or broadcast-quality video and audio material.

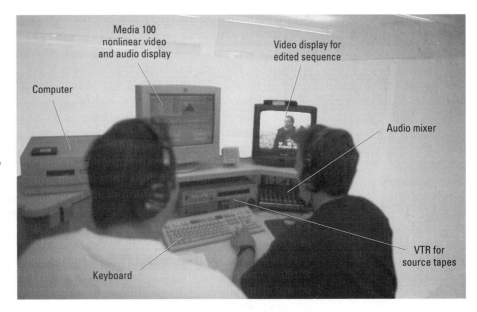

sequence into a second monitor will cause less confusion and will separate your source material from your edited sequences.

The interface for nonlinear systems works with a standard computer keyboard and mouse. In fact, with editing software and the appropriate video and audio hardware, your desktop computer can become a powerful nonlinear editing system. **SEE 11.20**

Nonlinear editing procedures Nonlinear editing is done entirely by computer. Because the video and audio information is no longer stored on tape but compressed on high-capacity hard drives, you can call up any shot directly by its time code address or file name without having to roll the videotape back and forth to locate it. Most systems are capable of displaying a variety of frames and running sequences so that you can preview the edit and see whether the shots cut together well. The computer will also display the in- and out-numbers and the length of the shot. You can hear the sound track when running the sequence and see it displayed visually on the computer screen, as shown in figure 11.19.

Once you have located the desired shot, you do not have to rerecord it. You simply assign it a particular place in the program and put it back in its file on the hard drive. As you can see, the hard drive replaces both the source and record VTRs. Because all shots are equally available for sequencing, you no longer need two source VTRs to create dissolves, wipes, or other such transitions: You simply tell the computer what kind of transition you want between two shots, and the computer will remember and execute it.

Quality　It should be noted that many desktop computer systems do not produce the quality necessary for an edit master tape. In fact, they do not produce an actual video sequence at all, but simply assign a specific order to the selected shots and transitions. The end result of these systems is not an edited videotape but an accurate *edit decision list* (EDL). You will learn more about the importance and use of an EDL later in this chapter. All top-of-the-line editing systems have enough storage capacity to produce high-quality video and audio images that equal or surpass the edit master tapes of a high-end analog videotape-editing system. Their output can be transferred directly to digital videotape or translated back to an analog NTSC edit master tape.

Preview and flexibility　The advantage of nonlinear editing is that you have extremely quick random access to any frame stored on the hard drive. You can display side-by-side the various in- and out-points of the shots to be sequenced, and you can run brief sequences to see whether they fulfill your aesthetic and storytelling requirements. Much like word processing, you can easily eliminate some frames, add others, or shift entire sequences from one location to another. When practicing editing with *Zettl's Video Lab 2.1* CD-ROM, you are actually engaged in nonlinear editing.

Efficiency　Unfortunately, nonlinear editing also has some drawbacks, one of which is learning the editing software program. Some programs are quite complex and require considerable effort and practice before you feel comfortable using them. Another drawback is expediency. You may think that the random access to video and audio makes nonlinear editing much faster than linear editing; but although the selection and sequencing of shots is much faster, digitizing and transferring the source tapes to hard drives is very time-consuming, unless the source tapes were shot with a digital camera and you can transfer the information directly to the nonlinear system. Even then, backing up compressed video files (strongly recommended) is another agonizingly slow process. Even skilled editors will tell you that, overall, nonlinear editing is not necessarily faster than linear editing— but it is definitely more flexible.

Editing Preparations

As with all other production activities, editing requires diligent preparation. The only editing for which preparations are kept to a minimum is in news. There is no way to predict the number and nature of stories you may have to edit every day, and you always have precious little time to make deliberate editing decisions. All you can do is try to select the most telling shots and sequence them into a credible story.

　　Although all other productions allow more time for postproduction, you will always wish you had more editing time. To make the best use of the time available, you need to pay attention to these editing preparations: (1) shooting with continuity in mind, (2) making protection copies, (3) adding time code to the source tapes, (4) making a window dub, (5) reviewing and logging source tapes, (6) transcribing audio text, and (7) laying a control track on the edit master tape, (8) digitizing source tapes, and (9) backing up files.

Shooting for continuity   It may sound strange, but the postproduction process starts in the shooting phase. Good directors and camera operators not only have the ability to visualize each shot and give it composition and meaning, they also think ahead about how those shots will look in sequence and how they will cut together. In complicated productions, such as dramas or carefully constructed video essays and commercials, sequencing is determined by a storyboard. The *storyboard* shows not only key visualizations, but also the major sequencing of shots. **SEE 11.21** 🔘 *READY ZVL 3*

11.21

STORYBOARD

The storyboard shows key visualizations and the major sequencing points, with action and audio information given below. It can be hand-drawn on preprinted storyboard paper or computer-generated.

shot 1

ACTION: LONG SHOT -- DRAMATIC

The SUN rises behind a picturesque WINDMILL.

shot 2

ACTION:

The light gleams through the windmill blades.

We hear: DISTANT JINGLING.

shot 3

ACTION:

MATCH CUT TO:

shot 3 continued

ACTION: CLOSE ON A SILVER HARNESS-BELL

Slightly tarnished. It JINGLES from the motion of the horse. The sun gleams on its surface, the cross-cut of the bell's face reminiscent of the blades of the windmill.

shot 4

ACTION: WIDE -- DRAMATIC

DON QUIXOTE and SANCHO PANZA ride "screen left." the bell on Don Quixote's harness JINGLING as his makeshift armor CLATTERS.

shot 5

ACTION:

D.Q. reacts dramatically to the windmill ahead.

DON QUIXOTE
Lo! The enemy is sighted!

But even if you don't have the time or luxury to prepare a storyboard, you can still facilitate postproduction editing by using the following list of tips during production:

PRODUCTION TIPS TO MAKE POSTPRODUCTION EASIER

☑ ***Slate each take***   Identify each take with a visual or at least a verbal slate. As pointed out in chapter 10, this is usually done with the C.G., as shown in figure 10.12. In the field you should have a handheld slate that contains at least the date of the shoot, the tape number, the scene number, and the take (shot) number. If you don't have a visual slate available, slate the various takes verbally. Open the camera or the talent mic and have somebody read the information; record the audio on the videotape. After calling out the take number, count backward from five to zero. This counting helps in locating the approximate beginning of a shot after the slate. Such information greatly speeds up the editing process, especially if the slate is also recorded on a field log.

☑ ***Leave margins for editing***   When videotaping *do not* stop the tape exactly at the end of a shot—record a few more seconds before stopping. For instance, if the company president has finished describing the latest nonlinear video system, have her remain silent and in place for a few seconds before cutting the action and stopping the tape. When starting the next segment, roll the camera for a brief period before calling for action; when finished, have everybody remain in place for a few seconds before stopping the tape. Such pads give you a little more flexibility in deciding on the exact in- and out-points.

☑ ***Record background sounds***   Always record a few minutes of ambient sound (room tone, traffic sounds, the sounds of silence in the mountains) before changing locations or finishing the taping. This environmental sound will help make silent periods during the edit or within a shot less noticeable.

☑ ***Keep a field log***   Keep an accurate record of what you tape. Such a record, called a *field log*, should at least show the name of the production, the tape number, the scene number, and the number and subject of each take. Label all tapes and boxes with the tape number and production title. The field log will aid you greatly in locating the videotaped material during the first screening.

☑ ***Tape cutaway shots***   Get some cutaways for each scene. A *cutaway* is a brief shot that will help improve or establish visual continuity between two shots. The cutaway is usually related to the event, such as a bystander looking at a parade or a reporter's camera during a hearing. Make the cutaways long enough—at least fifteen to twenty seconds. Cutaways that are too short are almost as frustrating to an editor as getting no cutaways at all. When cutaways are too short, they look more like mistakes than continuity links. When shooting cutaways, always let the camera run for just a few more seconds than you think necessary—the cutaway will then be just about long enough.

Make protection copies   Your production efforts are wasted if you lose the source tapes or damage them in some way. As pointed out earlier, experienced production people always make protection copies of all source material as soon as possible after the taping. If you shoot in a videotape format that suffers from generation loss during extensive postproduction editing, such as Hi8, or S-VHS, you should "bump up" your source footage (dub it onto a higher-quality videotape format). This dubbing fulfills a dual purpose: It gives you a protection copy of your original source tapes, as well as new high-quality source tapes that will have much less generation loss during extensive postproduction editing.

 KEY CONCEPT 13   **Always make a protection copy of the original source tapes.**

Add time code   Unless you recorded the time code during the videotaping, you may need to add it to all source tapes. You do this by "laying in" the time code signals from a time code generator on the address track of the videotape or on one of the audio tracks. You can set the hour digits of the code so that they match each tape number written on the label.

Make a window dub   When dubbing, or simply making a protection copy, you should simultaneously do another dub, called the ***window dub***. This is a lower-quality, bumped-down (usually VHS) copy that has the time code "burned in"—keyed over each frame. Each frame displays a box, called a window, which shows its time code address.   **SEE 11.22** Even if you know which takes are unacceptable, it is usually easier to window-dub all video, regardless of whether the takes are OK

11.22

SMPTE TIME CODE WINDOW DUB

The time code can be keyed directly into the copy of the source tape for off-line editing. Each frame displays its own unique time code address.

or NG (no good). Every once in a while, the video from an initially NG take proves invaluable as a cutaway or substitute shot in the actual editing.

This window dub will serve you in the accurate logging of all videotaped shots, preparing an *EDL* (edit decision list), which lists the in- and out-points of each edit, and even in performing a *rough-cut* (a preliminary version of the edit master tape). *READY ZVL 4*

Review and log the source tapes   It is now time to make a list of everything recorded on the source tapes, regardless of whether the take was properly field slated and is usable or not. This log—called a *VTR log*—will help you locate specific shots without having to preview the source tapes over and over again. Although logging may initially seem like a waste of time, an accurate, carefully prepared, VTR log will save you time, money, and ultimately nerves during the actual editing. Besides the usual data, such as the production title, the name of the director, and the production number and date, the VTR log should contain the following information:

▶ Tape number

▶ Scene number

▶ Take number

▶ Beginning (in-number) and ending (out-number) of each shot

▶ Whether the shot is OK or no good (NG) (if you don't have a designated OK/NG column, you can simply circle the good takes in the third column)

▶ Prominent sounds

▶ Remarks (brief description of the scene or event)

▶ Vector type and direction

Although you may not find one in commercially available VTR log forms or computer displays, a vector column provides extremely important logging information. As discussed in chapter 5, vectors depict lines and something pointing or moving in a particular direction. (We elaborate on vectors further in chapter 12.) The advantage of this vector designation is that you can easily find a shot that has objects moving in the opposite direction from the previous shot without having to view the source tapes again. All you need to do is glance down the vector column and look for shots whose *m* symbol (indicating a motion vector) has arrows pointing in an opposing direction. As you can see, the vector notations in figure 11.23 use arrows for the main direction of *g* (graphic), *i* (index), and *m* (motion) vectors. A circled dot ⊙ indicates somebody looking at or moving toward the camera; a single dot • indicates somebody looking or moving away from the camera. Don't worry too much about the vector column right now. But after you have read chapter 12, you should revisit figure 11.23 and study the vector column once more. See whether it helps you to visualize the shot sequence listed on this VTR log. **SEE 11.23** *READY ZVL 5*

11.23

VTR LOG

The VTR log contains the necessary specifications about all video and audio information recorded on the source tapes. Notice the notations in the vectors column: *g, i,* and *m* refer to graphic, index, and motion vectors. The arrows show the principal direction of the index and motion vectors. Z-axis index and motion vectors are labeled with ⊙ (toward the camera) or • (away from the camera).

Production Title:			_Traffic_	Production No:	_114_			Off-line Date: _07/15_
Producer: _Hamid Khani_				Director:	_Elan_			On-line Date: _07/21_

Tape No.	Scene/ Shot	Take No.	In	Out	OK/ NG	Sound	Remarks	Vectors
4	2	1	01 44 21 14	01 44 23 12	NG		mic problem	m ←
		②	01 44 42 06	01 47 41 29	ok	car sound	car A moving Through stop sign	m ←
		③	01 48 01 29	01 50 49 17	OK	brakes	car B putting on brakes (Toward camera)	⊙ m
		④	01 51 02 13	01 51 42 08	ok	reacTion	pedesTrian reaction	→, i
	5	1	02 03 49 18	02 04 02 07	NG	car brakes ped. yelling	ball noT in fronT of car	⊙ m ← m ball
		2	02 05 02 29	02 06 51 11	NG	"	Again, ball problem	⊙ m ← m ball
		③	02 08 40 02	02 11 17 03	OK	car brakes ped. yelling	car swerves To avoid ball	⊙↓m ← m ball
	6	①	02 13 01 29	02 14 58 10	ok	ped. yelling	kid running inTo sTreeT	→i ← m child
		②	02 20 22 01	02 28 37 19	ok	car	cuTaways car moving	⊙•m ↘ ↙
		3	02 30 05 29	02 34 35 15	NG	sTreeT	lines of sidewalk	↔ g

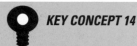

> **KEY CONCEPT 14** **The vector notations on the VTR log facilitate locating shots that show people or objects pointing or moving in a specific direction.**

A variety of computer programs are available for logging source tapes. Instead of filling out the log by hand, you enter all vital information on a computer form. Some software allows you to enter actual pictures of the first and last frames of each shot, which is a great help when locating certain shots. In this case, you can skip the vector column because you can now clearly see the main vectors of the beginning and end frames of the various shots.

The advantage of a computerized log is that you can quickly find a particular scene by entering either the name of the scene or the time code number. You can then have it automatically transferred to the final EDL, which will guide the final sequencing of the edit master tape. When doing some preliminary sequencing, you can copy the log and shift the various entries into the desired sequence. Some computer logs locate certain shots by subject rather than by time code. For example, if you typed *motorcycle*, the computer would find and display all shots containing a motorcycle.

Transcribe speech   Transcribing all speech to typed pages is another time-consuming but important preediting chore. Once accomplished, it definitely speeds up the editing. If you need to edit a long interview, for example, or cut a speech so that it fits the allotted time slot, the printed page gives you a much quicker overview than listening to the videotape again. Because it is much less linear than tape, the printed page allows you to go back and jump ahead in the text with great speed. Of course, in news coverage you do not have time for such transcriptions; all you can do is run the tape and take notes about which portions you would like to keep and where in the tape you have to make the cuts.

Lay a control track   As explained earlier in this chapter, when editing in the insert mode, *you must record a black signal on the tape that is to become the edit master tape.* By recording black you will also record a continuous control track whose sync pulses are an essential reference for precise insert editing.

Digitize the source tapes   As discussed, all source tapes shot with an analog camera must be digitized before you can begin nonlinear editing. This means that you must change the analog information of the source tapes into digital information that can be stored on the hard drive of a nonlinear editing system. Many novice editors are surprised at how long and cumbersome this preediting step really is. Even for experienced editors, the digitizing process presents a major bottleneck in editing. This bottleneck is considerably shortened if you shot the source tapes with a digital camera and if the editing system has a *FireWire* (Apple) or *i-link* (Sony) data transfer, officially called IEEE1394. This enables you to connect a digital VTR to a nonlinear editing system; the connection transfers all digital data from the source tapes to the computer hard drive without the need for digitizing.

Back up the files   This is another agonizingly slow—yet essential—preediting task. Just like making protection dubs of your source tapes, you need to back up the digitized video and audio information on your hard drive in case the computer crashes. An added hazard arises when several people use the same nonlinear editing system for different editing tasks. They might unwittingly erase your digitized information and leave you with a blank disk. This is when the backup files are invaluable, and you will realize that the time spent making them was insignificant compared with having to redigitize the source tapes.

Off-line and On-line Editing

Off-line editing is technically part of editing preparation, because it does not produce the edit master tape that represents the finished product. But in off-line editing, you are getting more serious about making actual editing choices than in the preparation phase. The edit master tape is produced in the subsequent on-line editing.

Because on-line systems usually use more-sophisticated equipment, "on-line" is often confused with the *quality* of editing equipment used. High-quality equipment is labeled "on-line," and the lower-quality systems "off-line." What really distinguishes off-line from on-line editing, however, is not so much the equipment as the editing intent. When you edit a tape for the sole purpose of having some idea of what the final product will look like (similar to a "rough-cut" in film), you are engaged in off-line editing. When the editing is intended to produce the final edit master tape from the very beginning, it is on-line.

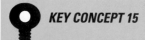

KEY CONCEPT 15   **If the intent is to produce an EDL or rough-cut, the editing is off-line. If the editing produces the edit master tape, it is on-line. On-line equipment is usually of higher quality than off-line equipment.**

Off-line editing procedures   All *off-line editing* is done to create an EDL and occasionally a preliminary videotape (called a *rough-cut*) that serves as a model for the on-line master. Although linear and nonlinear editing operate under the same aesthetics principles, the two methods differ significantly in the actual editing equipment and how it is used.

Linear off-line procedures The first step in linear off-line editing is to compile a workable edit decision list. The EDL can then be used as a guide for the on-line editing of the master tape. A simple though not always highly accurate way of doing this is by *paper-and-pencil editing*. This is how it works:

1. Think again of what it is you want to tell the viewers. This means going back to the *process message* you originally stated. The actual videotaped material may suggest a slight variation or a restatement of the original process message; but don't let spectacular shots render the original process message obsolete. After all, how can you select and assemble event essences if you don't know what the whole thing is all about?   *READY ZVL 6*

2. Watch, once again, all the window-dubbed source tapes and see which shots strike you as especially relevant and effective. This review will not only refresh your memory of what you shot, but may also suggest, however indirectly, a tentative sequence.

3. Think more seriously about sequencing the shots. While recalling the process message and the available shots, prepare a rough storyboard. Now is the time to take a good look at the VTR log and locate the various key shots. List the pulse-count or time code numbers for the beginning (in-number) and end (out-number) of each selected shot, as shown in figure 11.23

4. Decide on the various transitions between shots. If you have a single-source system, you have no choice: All transitions will be cuts. But if you have a multiple-source system, you need to determine which transitions are the most effective.

11.24

HANDWRITTEN EDIT DECISION LIST (EDL)

The EDL is the road map for on-line editing. It lists the tape number, the scene and take numbers, the in- and out-numbers for each selected shot, the transitions, and major audio information. This handwritten EDL contains the essential information for the final edit.

| Production Title: *Traffic* | Production No: *114* | Off-line Date: *07/15* |
| Producer: *Hamid Khani* | Director: *Elan* | On-line Date: *07/21* |

Tape No.	Scene/ Shot	Take No.	In	Out	Transition	Sound
1	2	2	01 46 13 14	01 46 15 02	CUT	car
		4	01 56 10 29	01 56 11 21	CUT	car
	5	3	02 05 55 17	02 05 57 20	CUT	ped. yelling—brakes
	2	4	02 22 40 02	02 24 41 07	CUT	ped. yelling—brakes
	6	1	02 26 43 17	02 28 46 01	CUT	brakes

5. Prepare an EDL. This list looks similar to your initial VTR log. It lists tape number, scene or shot number, the in- and out-numbers (pulse-count or time code), the desired transitions, and the sound. Because the in- and out-numbers designate the first and last frames of each shot, you do not need descriptions of the shot content. Also, the vector column is not needed, because you are no longer selecting shots but simply listing them for editing. You can prepare an EDL simply by watching the window dubs over and over again and listing the information on an EDL form. The EDL is your road map for actual on-line editing. **SEE 11.24** *READY ZVL 7*

There are computer programs that will ask you for key information (similar to that shown in figure 11.24). The advantage of a computer-generated EDL is that you can make changes that affect the entire editing sequence as quickly as changing a single shot. All nonlinear editing systems generate an EDL. **SEE 11.25**

KEY CONCEPT 16 **The EDL is the road map for on-line editing.**

On-line editing procedures Regardless of whether you use a linear or nonlinear editing system, ***on-line editing*** will produce the final edit master tape. In a way, on-line editing is easier than off-line editing, because the editing decisions have already been made in the off-line process and listed on the EDL. From this point on, the EDL guides most of the on-line editing procedures. In linear editing, the edit controller will read the in- and out-numbers and help you set up the source and record VTRs for the final edits. In nonlinear editing, the computer will use the

11.25

COMPUTER-GENERATED EDL

Like the handwritten EDL, the computer-generated EDL contains the event (scene) number, source reel ID (source tape) number, edit mode, transition type, and the in- and out-numbers for each shot. All nonlinear systems generate an EDL.

```
TITLE: TRAFFIC SAFETY
                            Header

001    003      V    C          00:00:03:12   00:00:05:14   01:00:20:01   01:00:22:03
001    004      V    W001 204   00:00:06:24   00:00:12:23   01:00:08:12   01:00:14:11
EFFECTS NAME IS SWING IN

002    004      V    C          01:16:22:03   01:16:29:02   01:00:06:24   01:00:13:25
002    001      V    W003 204   01:18:27:15   01:18:34:09   01:00:06:24   01:00:13:18
EFFECTS NAME IS SWING IN

003    004      V    C          01:18:33:15   01:00:25:14   01:00:13:18   01:00:20:12
003    001      V    W000 204   01:18:38:02   01:18:44:26   01:00:13:18   01:00:20:12
EFFECTS NAME IS SWING IN

004    004      V    C          01:19:10:02   01:19:15:03   01:19:20:12   01:19:25:12
004    001      V    W002 204   01:19:23:19   01:19:30:13   01:00:20:12   01:00:27:06
EFFECTS NAME IS SWING IN

005    004      V    C          01:34:12:02   01:34:16:04   01:00:22:05   01:00:26:06
005    001      V    W011 203   01:50:15:29   01:50:22:22   01:00:27:06   01:00:33:29
EFFECTS NAME IS ZOOM

006    003      V    C          01:52:14:25   01:52:16:05   01:00:33:29   01:00:35:15

007    001      V    C          01:39:08:00   01:39:14:24   01:00:58:15   01:01:05:09
```

Event number	Source reel ID	Edit mode	Transition type	Source in	Source out	Record in	Record out

so-called off-line edit decisions and eventually transfer video and audio information to the edit master tape.

But there are still two points that you will discover and need to remember: (1) Editing is always more time consuming than you initially thought and budgeted for; and (2) despite the great assistance from edit controllers and nonlinear computing power, it is still you who has to make the decisions about which shot goes where. How to make the right aesthetic decisions is the subject of chapter 12.

 ONCE AGAIN, REMEMBER...

■ Switching

Switching is a form of instantaneous editing. It means that you select and join various video sources, such as the pictures supplied by live cameras, videotape recorders, or from the electronic still store (ESS) system, with various transitions (cuts, dissolves, wipes, and fades) while the production is under way. This process is made possible by the switcher. The switcher can also be used in postproduction.

Production Switcher

The production switcher is used in production studios and large remote trucks. It has various buses (program, preview, mix/effects, key) for specific switcher functions. Some of the buses can be delegated multiple switching functions.

Linear Editing

A linear editing system uses VTRs for its source machines and the record VTR. The video signal can be analog or digital. The end product is an edited videotape—the edit master tape.

Edit Controller

The edit controller, also called the editing control unit, is used in linear editing to assist in various functions, such as marking edit points, rolling source and record VTRs in sync, and integrating effects.

Address Code

The address code, such as the SMPTE time code, marks each frame with a specific address number. The pulse-count system is not a true address code, because it counts pulses but does not give each frame a unique address.

Assemble Editing

In assemble editing, everything that is recorded on the selected portions of the source tape is transferred to the edit master tape. The advantage of assemble editing is that it is fast, because it does not require the prior recording of a continuous control track on the edit master tape. The disadvantages are that you cannot edit audio and video separately and that the edits might tear at the edit points.

Insert Editing

Insert editing requires the prior laying of a control track (by recording black) on the edit master tape. The continuous control track makes the edits highly stable and tear-free. The insert mode allows the separate editing of audio tracks and the adding or deleting of shots in the middle of an edited sequence. The disadvantage is that insert editing is slower than assemble editing.

Nonlinear Editing

A nonlinear system works exclusively with digital video and audio information and uses high-capacity hard drives for the storage and retrieval of the video and audio material. The nonlinear system permits random access to every video frame and its accompanying audio. The end product of nonlinear editing can be an EDL (edit decision list), or (with high-quality equipment) an edited video sequence that can be directly transferred to the edit master tape.

Off-line and On-line Editing

Off-line editing produces a rough-cut and an EDL (edit decision list). On-line editing produces the final edit master tape.

Z E T T L ' S   V I D E O   L A B   2 . 1

*Click on the **editing** monitor; Veronica has some useful information for you on editing systems and especially on how to prepare for postproduction editing.*

RUN ZVL 1 Load tape 3 **Tape Basics** and play module 3 **System**. As you can see, the single-source system is normally a cuts-only editor. The expanded system with the edit controller and switcher allows other transitions (dissolves, wipes, and fades) between shots.

RUN ZVL 2 Play module 2 **Time code**. Veronica demonstrates the SMPTE time code. Note especially that the time code rolls over (changes into) minutes after the twenty-ninth frame, because the thirtieth frame is read as the next second of program material. The code changes to the next minute or hour after fifty-nine elapsed seconds or minutes, respectively.

RUN ZVL 3 Load tape 5 **Location Procedures** and listen to Veronica's introduction. Note that efficient postproduction editing starts in the shooting phase. Whenever you frame a shot, think not only about its composition, but also about how it affects the entire shot sequence.

RUN ZVL 4 Go back to tape 3 **Tape Basics** and play module 2 **Time code** again. Note how a window dub actually looks after the time code has been "burned in" and how fast the frame numbers flash by when running the tape at normal speed. You need to be a pretty good speed reader to catch each frame number as it flashes by. You can locate a specific frame easily, however, with the shuttle control on the edit controller. A computer can locate the time code of a specific frame and advance the source or record tape to the exact address.

RUN ZVL 5 Now load tape 8 **Pre-edit Procedures**, listen to Veronica's introduction, and play module 2 **Logs**. Note the vector column in Veronica's log and how the various symbols look on the screen. You need to learn to translate the major shots into simple vector diagrams and then interpret the diagrams back into the actual shot sequence. Such vector diagrams on the VTR log will save you hours of searching through the source tapes for various shots.

RUN ZVL 6 Go back to Master Control, load tape 8 **Pre-edit Procedures**, and play Veronica's introduction again. She brings up the process message: The process message briefly states what the show is supposed to accomplish. It is an essential context within which to select the most effective shots and their sequence.

RUN ZVL 7 Play module 1 **Preparations**. It reminds you that you need to know exactly what you want to tell the viewers before starting with the preliminary selection and sequencing of shots. Use only shots that contribute to the process message.

Module 3 **Paper edit** shows how a good script can help you with the selection and sequencing of shots and how to prepare an EDL. A simple and efficient way of doing a preliminary EDL is to watch selections of your window dubs and write down the in- and out-numbers of each shot. This list will then be your guide for the first rough-cut in off-line editing.

K E Y   C O N C E P T S

- Switching means instantaneous editing from simultaneously available video sources.

- Switchers allow the selection of multiple video inputs and the immediate creation of various transitions and effects.

- The program bus sends the selected video inputs directly to the line-out. It is a cuts-only device.

- Mix buses (or buses in the mix mode) let you do cuts, dissolves, superimpositions, and fades.

- The effects and key buses can accomplish various wipes, keys, and special effects.

- The use of VTRs designates linear editing, whether the recording is analog or digital.

- The basic principle of linear editing is copying sections of the source tapes to the edit master tape in the desired sequence.

- Normally, single-source VTR editing systems are limited to cuts-only transitions.

- Dissolves, wipes, and other special-effects transitions are possible with multiple-source editing systems.

- The time code provides a unique address for each frame of recorded video.

- The edit master tape must be prepared for insert editing by first recording black on it.

○ **The basic nonlinear editing principle is file management.**

○ **Always make a protection copy of the original source tapes.**

○ **The vector notations on the VTR log facilitate locating shots that show people or objects pointing or moving in a specific direction.**

○ **If the intent is to produce an EDL or rough-cut, the editing is off-line. If the editing produces the edit master tape, it is on-line. On-line equipment is usually of higher quality than off-line equipment.**

○ **The EDL is the road map for on-line editing.**

complexity editing Building an intensified screen event from carefully selected and juxtaposed shots. Does not have to adhere to the continuity principles.

continuity editing Assembling shots so that vector continuity is ensured.

continuing vectors Graphic vectors that extend each other, or index and motion vectors pointing and moving in the same direction.

converging vectors Index and motion vectors that point toward each other.

cutaway A shot of an object or event that is peripherally connected with the overall event and that is neutral as to screen direction. Used to intercut between two shots in which the screen direction is reversed.

diverging vectors Index and motion vectors that point away from each other.

jogging Frame-by-frame advancement of videotape, resulting in a jerking motion.

jump cut An image that jumps slightly from one screen position to another during a cut.

mental map Tells us where things are or are supposed to be on- and off-screen.

vector line An imaginary line created by extending converging index vectors, or the direction of a motion vector.

Editing Principles

NOW that you are familiar with the basics of linear and nonlinear editing systems and their use in postproduction editing, the head of the Triple-I postproduction editing group is telling you that the real challenge of editing is not necessarily in mastering the equipment, but rather in telling a story effectively and, especially, in selecting shots that bring about an effective shot sequence. According to her, a master editor must know aesthetics, not just machines. But what does this mean? This chapter will clarify some of the basic aesthetic editing principles.

■ **EDITING PURPOSE**
Why we edit

■ **EDITING FUNCTIONS**
Combining, condensing, correcting, and building

■ **AESTHETIC PRINCIPLES OF CONTINUITY EDITING**
The mental map, vectors, and on- and off-screen positions

■ **AESTHETIC PRINCIPLES OF COMPLEXITY EDITING**
Intensifying the event and supplying meaning

EDITING PURPOSE

Editing means selecting certain portions of an event or events and putting them into a meaningful sequence. The nature of such sequencing depends on the specific editing purpose: to cut a twenty-minute videotape of an important news story to twenty seconds to make it fit the format; to join a series of close-up details so that they make sense and flow without any visual bumps; or to juxtapose certain shots so that they take on added meaning.

Basically, we edit to tell a story with clarity and impact. All editing equipment is designed to make the selection of shots, and their joining through a variety of transitions, as easy and efficient as possible. But whether you work with simple cuts-only videotape-editing equipment or a highly sophisticated nonlinear computerized editing system, the functions and basic aesthetic principles of editing remain the same. *READY ZVL 1*

KEY CONCEPT 1   **Editing means selecting significant event details and putting them into a specific sequence to tell a story with clarity and impact.**

EDITING FUNCTIONS

The specific editing functions are: (1) combine, (2) condense, (3) correct, and (4) build. Although these functions frequently overlap, there is always a predominant one that determines the editing approach and style—the selection of shots, their length and sequence, and the transitions with which they are joined.

Combine

The simplest kind of editing is *combining* program portions. For instance, you may want to combine the various segments you videotaped during your vacation so that they are in chronological sequence on a single tape. Your carefully kept field log will aid you greatly in locating the source tapes and the various shots. Because you simply hook the various videotaped pieces together, there is no need for transitions; you can use "cuts only." The more aware you are of the desired sequence during the actual shooting, the easier it will be for you to combine the various shots in this postproduction phase. *READY ZVL 2*

Condense

Often you edit simply to *condense* the material—to reduce the overall length of the program or program portion. The most drastic condensing is done in television news. As an editor of news footage, you are often called upon to cut extraordinary stories to unreasonably brief segments. It is not unusual to have to shorten a half-hour speech to ten seconds, the twenty hours of a rescue operation to a mere twenty seconds, or the fifty minutes of graphic war footage, videotaped by a daring camera crew, to a mere five seconds. The infamous "sound bites" are a direct outgrowth of such drastic editing. Statements by public officials are tailored to a series of brief and memorable catch phrases rather than sensible narrative, very much in the spirit of advertising slogans.

But even in less drastic editing, you will find that it is often hard to part with some of the footage, especially if it took extra effort to videotape. As an editor, try to detach yourself as much as possible from the preproduction and production efforts and concentrate simply on what you *need* to show and say, rather than what you have available. Don't use three shots if you can communicate the same message with one. Such editing requires that you identify the essence of an event and use only shots that best communicate that essence.   **READY ZVL 3**

KEY CONCEPT 2   **The condensing function of editing requires a recognition of the essence of an event and the selection of shots that best express that essence.**

Correct

Editing to fix production mistakes can be one of the most difficult, time-consuming, and costly postproduction activities. Even simple mistakes, such as the company president misreading a word during his monthly address, can present a problem when trying to match the body positions and voice levels of the old (before the mistake) and new (after the mistake) takes. A good director will not pick up the speech exactly where the mistake was made, but go back to where a new idea is introduced in the speech so that a change in shots is properly motivated. Starting the "pickup" (new shot) from a different point of view (tighter or looser shot, or different angle) will make the cut and a slight shift in voice level appear deliberate and ensure continuity.

More-serious production problems, such as trying to match uneven colors and sound, can become a real headache for the editor. White-balancing the camera in each new lighting environment and watching the VU meter while listening carefully to the sound pickup is certainly easier than trying to "fix them in post."

Such seemingly minor oversights as the talent wearing her coat unbuttoned while standing up, and buttoned when sitting, cannot be fixed in post even by the most experienced editor; rather, they call for costly retakes. Again, meticulous attention to all preproduction details and keeping a close watch on every aspect of production can eliminate much of the costly "fixing in post" activities.   **READY ZVL 4**

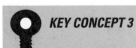

KEY CONCEPT 3   **Careful attention to preproduction and production details can obviate most corrective editing.**

Build

The most satisfying editing is done when you can *build* a show from a great many carefully taped shots. Some postproduction people think—not without cause—that the videotaping during the production provides merely the bricks and mortar and that it is up to the editor to construct the building—to give the raw material shape and meaning. Regardless of whether editing is done to show an event as clearly as possible, or to reveal its intensity and complexity—or a combination of the two— you need to apply one or both of the major aesthetic editing principles: *continuity* and *complexity*.   **READY ZVL 5**

AESTHETIC PRINCIPLES OF CONTINUITY EDITING

Continuity editing means creating seamless transitions from one event detail to the next so that the story seems to flow even though a great deal of information is purposely left out. The aesthetic principles of continuity editing are concerned not so much with the logic of the story line and narrative flow, but rather with how the pictures and sound from one shot carry over to the next. Unlike the painter or still photographer, who is concerned merely with the effective composition of a single image, as a video editor you must compare the aesthetic elements of one picture with those of another and see whether they lead smoothly from one to the other when seen in succession. Over the years of filmmaking, certain ways of achieving visual continuity became so firmly established that they matured from conventions to principles and now apply equally to video production.

The major principles of continuity editing are (1) the mental map, (2) vectors, and (3) on- and off-screen positions.

Mental Map

Every time we watch television or a film, we automatically try to make sense of where things are and in what direction they move on and off the screen. In effect, we construct a *mental map* that tells us where things are or are supposed to be. For example, if you see somebody looking screen-left in a two-shot, he should also be looking screen-left in a close-up. **SEE 12.1**

12.1

MENTAL MAP

To help establish the mental map of where things are in off-screen space, you need to be consistent with where people look.

A When someone looks screen-left in a medium shot…   **B** …he should look in approximately the same direction in a close-up.

If you see a person in a close-up looking screen-right during a two-way conversation, your mental map suggests that the other person is located somewhere in the right off-screen space. **SEE 12.2** According to the established mental map, the next shot must show a close-up of the partner looking screen-left, with the first person having moved into the left off-screen space. **SEE 12.3** To show both persons

12.2

MENTAL MAP OF RIGHT OFF-SCREEN POSITION

If you show person A looking and talking screen-right in a close-up, we assume person B to be located in the right off-screen space, looking screen-left.

A   B

12.3

MENTAL MAP OF LEFT OFF-SCREEN POSITION

When we now see person B in a close-up looking and talking screen-left, we assume person A to be in the left off-screen space.

A   B

12.4

DIFFERENT MENTAL MAP OF OFF-SCREEN POSITION

Showing persons A and B looking in the same direction in subsequent close-ups would suggest that both are talking to a third person.

Shot 1—A

Shot 2—B

looking in the same direction in subsequent shots would go against the mental map and suggest that both are talking to someone else. **SEE 12.4**

If, during a three-way conversation, you see a single person in a close-up first looking screen-right and then screen-left, you expect somebody to be sitting on both sides of him or her rather than two people on one side or the other. **SEE 12.5** But if you see in a close-up a man consistently looking screen-right during the three-way conversation, you expect the two other people to sit screen-right of him, although we cannot actually see them. **SEE 12.6** A three-shot of all the speakers shows that your mental map was accurate. **SEE 12.7**

12.5

PERSON LOOKING SCREEN-RIGHT AND SCREEN-LEFT

When a person in a close-up looks screen-right in shot 1, and then screen-left in shot 2, we expect the other people to sit on both sides of him.

Shot 1

Off-screen space

Off-screen space

Shot 2

12.6

SCREEN-RIGHT POSITION OF PARTNERS

When someone continues to look screen-right during a three-way conversation, we expect his two partners to sit in the right off-screen space.

12.7

ACTUAL SCREEN POSITIONS

When seen in a long shot, the mental map of off-screen space coincides with the actual positions of the three people.

As you can see, the mental map covers not only on-screen space but also off-screen space. Once such a mental map is established, you must adhere to it, unless you want to shake the viewers purposely out of their perceptual expectations. Applying continuity principles will keep the map intact.

 **KEY CONCEPT 4** **Continuity editing means preserving the location and motion of objects over a series of shots to help the viewer establish and maintain a mental map of where things should be or where they should move.**

Vectors

As you recall, vectors are directional forces that lead our eyes from one point to another on the screen, and even off it. They can be strong or weak, depending on how forcefully they suggest or move in a specific direction. Keeping the mental map intact requires proper vector continuity.

Continuity of graphic vectors   If you shoot a scene with a prominent graphic vector as the horizon line, such as a skyline, the ocean, the desert, or a mountain range, you need to make sure that the height of the horizon line is consistent in subsequent shots and that it does not jump up or down. **SEE 12.8** You can accomplish this vector continuity simply by marking the horizon line of the first shot with a piece of tape on the viewfinder and aligning all subsequent shots according to the tape.

12.8

GRAPHIC VECTOR CONTINUITY

To prevent the horizon line from jumping up and down during subsequent shots, you need to make sure that it forms a continuous graphic vector from shot to shot.

Shot 1

Shot 2

Shot 3

Directions of index and motion vectors   Index and motion vectors can be (1) continuing, (2) converging, or (3) diverging.

Continuing vectors follow each other or move or point in the same direction. **SEE 12.9** They must "continue"—point in the same screen direction—even if shown in separate shots. **SEE 12.10** If you show one of the people looking in the opposite direction in the close-up, you will jolt the established continuity. Instead of the two people looking in the same direction, the mental map now tells us that they must be looking at each other. **SEE 12.11**

12.9

CONTINUING VECTORS IN A SINGLE SHOT

Continuing vectors point or move in the same direction. The continuous vectors of these two people suggest that they are looking at the same target object.

A   B

12.10

CONTINUING VECTORS IN SUCCESSIVE SHOTS

Even when seen in two successive close-ups (shots 1 and 2), these continuing index vectors suggest that the two persons (A and B) are looking at a common target object.

Shot 1—A   **Shot 2—B**

12.11

VECTOR REVERSAL IN SUCCESSIVE SHOTS

By reversing one of the index vectors (shot 2), we assume that the two persons (A and B) are looking at each other instead of at a common target object.

Shot 1—A   **Shot 2—B**

Converging vectors move or point toward each other. **SEE 12.12** To maintain the mental map, you must maintain their direction in subsequent single shots. **SEE 12.13**

Diverging vectors move or point away from each other. **SEE 12.14** Again, subsequent close-ups must maintain the diverging vector direction. **SEE 12.15**

12.12

CONVERGING INDEX VECTORS IN A SINGLE SHOT

Converging vectors must point or move toward each other. The index vectors of the two people (A and B) looking at each other converge.

A   B

12.13

CONVERGING INDEX VECTORS IN SUCCESSIVE SHOTS

When seen in successive close-ups (shots 1 and 2), the index vector of A must converge with that of B.

Shot 1—A   **Shot 2—B**

Vectors, of course, can change their directions in a single shot. In that case, the follow-up shot must continue the index or motion vector as seen just before the cut. For instance, if you show somebody running screen-left who then turns in midscreen and runs screen-right, the subsequent shot must show the person continuing to run screen-right.

12.14

DIVERGING INDEX VECTORS IN A SINGLE SHOT

When two persons (A and B) look away from each other in a two-shot, their index vectors are diverging.

A   B

12.15

DIVERGING INDEX VECTORS IN SUCCESSIVE SHOTS

To show that the index vectors are diverging in successive close-ups (shots 1 and 2), the index vector of A must lead away from that of B.

Shot 1—A   **Shot 2—B**

12.16

CONVERGING Z-AXIS INDEX VECTORS

Shot 1 establishes the index vectors of A and B as converging. By establishing that the vectors converge (shot 1), we perceive the subsequent z-axis close-ups of A and B in shots 2 and 3 also as converging.

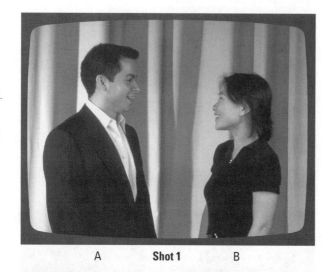

A   **Shot 1**   B

Shot 2—A

Shot 3—B

If someone looks directly into the camera or walks toward or away from it, we speak of a *z-axis* index or motion vector. As you recall, the z-axis is the depth dimension or the imaginary line that stretches from the camera to the horizon. Whether we perceive a series of z-axis shots as continuing, converging, or diverging depends on the event context. If you follow a two-shot that shows two people looking at each other with successive close-ups of each person looking into the camera, we perceive their successive z-axis vectors as converging: They are still looking at each other. **SEE 12.16**

If the context (two-shot) shows that they are looking away from each other, we perceive the identical z-axis close-ups as diverging index vectors. **SEE 12.17**

12.17

TWO-SHOT WITH
DIVERGING INDEX
VECTORS

If the context in shot 1 establishes the two people (A and B)
as looking away from each other,
the subsequent z-axis shots
(2 and 3) are also perceived
as diverging vectors.

A   Shot 1   B

Shot 2—A

Shot 3—B

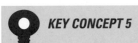 **KEY CONCEPT 5**   **Graphic, index, and motion vectors play an important part in
establishing and maintaining continuity from shot to shot.**

On- and Off-screen Positions

As shown in figures 12.1 through 12.7, we tend to create a mental map that helps us
tell where people are located even if we can't see them. Such an off-screen map
helps preserve visual continuity and ultimately stabilize the environment. In vector

12.18

PRESERVING ON-SCREEN POSITIONS

When B is first seen screen-right (shot 1), we expect her to remain there even when cutting to a different point of view in this over-the-shoulder sequence (shot 2). Our mental map would be disturbed if B would appear screen-left in the over-the-shoulder shot (shot 3).

A   **Shot 1**   B   A   **Shot 2**   B   B   **Shot 3**   A

terms, we place a person off-screen wherever the on-screen index vector points. The same is true for on-screen positions. Once we establish person A on screen-left and person B on screen-right, we expect them to remain there even if we cut to a different point of view. Such position continuity is especially important in over-the-shoulder and cross-shots. **SEE 12.18** In shots 1 and 2, person A remains screen-left and person B screen-right. Our mental map would be greatly disturbed if we saw A and B change places in subsequent shots—we would perceive them as playing musical chairs, as shown in shot 3 of figure 12.18.

A slight position change from shot to shot is called a *jump cut*, because the object or person seems to jump, or jerk, from one place to another for no apparent reason. This often happens when you try to align the camera and subject in exactly the same position when setting up subsequent shots. Unfortunately, neither the camera nor the subject will remain in exactly the same place as the previous shot, but will inevitably shift positions ever so slightly. When two such shots are cut together, the slight shift appears as a sudden and highly noticeable jump. To prevent jump cuts, you should always change the angle and/or field of view, getting a looser or tighter shot.

Although the jump cut is undesirable in continuity editing, it has become an effective device in complexity editing, which is discussed later in this chapter.

The vector line The navigation device that helps maintain on-screen positions and motion continuity (as you will see later) is called the *vector line*, the *line of conversation and action*, the *hundredeighty* (for 180 degrees), or, simply, the *line*. The vector line is an extension of converging index vectors, or the extension of a motion vector in the direction of travel. **SEE 12.19**

To maintain on-screen positions during over-the-shoulder shooting (with A screen-left and B screen-right), you must keep the cameras on the same side of the vector line. **SEE 12.20** Crossing the line would result in a musical chair–like switch of A and B. **SEE 12.21** Although you may argue that you would not confuse A and

12.19

FORMING THE VECTOR LINE

The vector line is formed by extending converging index vectors or by extending a motion vector.

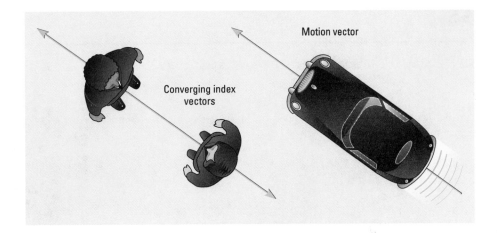

Motion vector

Converging index vectors

12.20

VECTOR LINE AND PROPER CAMERA POSITIONS

To maintain the screen positions of A and B in over-the-shoulder shooting, the cameras must be on the same side of the vector line.

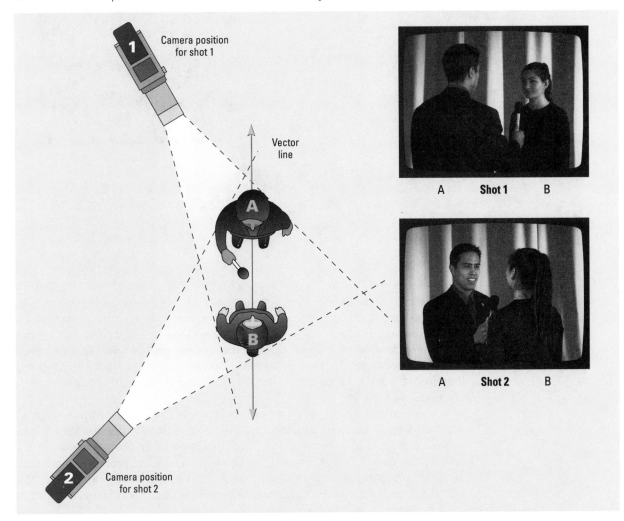

Camera position for shot 1

Vector line

A   **Shot 1**   B

A   **Shot 2**   B

Camera position for shot 2

12. 21

CROSSING THE VECTOR LINE

Crossing the line with one of the two cameras will result in a position switch of A and B. They will seem to play musical chairs.

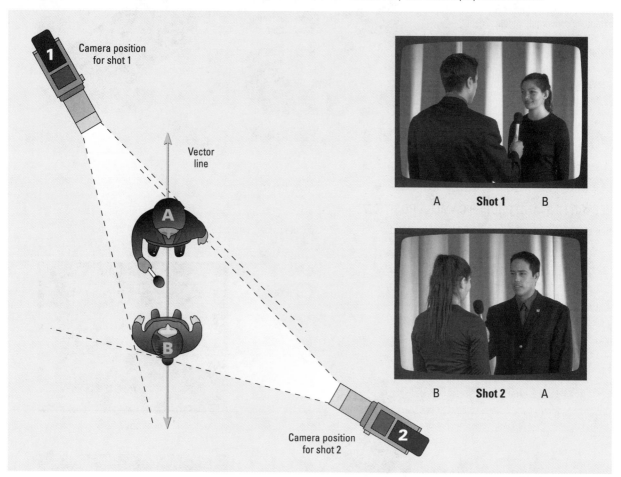

Camera position for shot 1

Vector line

A **Shot 1** B

B **Shot 2** A

Camera position for shot 2

B even if they switched screen positions, crossing the line would definitely disturb the mental map and generate a big continuity bump; it is considered a serious sequencing mistake.

A similar problem occurs if you shoot two side-by-side people from the front and the back along the z-axis. Such a sequencing problem is common when covering a wedding, when you shoot the bride and groom first from the front, and then from the back. When cutting the two shots together, the two people switch positions. **SEE 12.22**

To get around this position switch, you can move to the side with the camera when the couple walks by and see them change positions within the shot. When cutting to the shot from behind, they have already switched positions.

When *cross shooting*, crossing the line will change the properly converging index vectors to improperly continuing vectors. Instead of having two people look at and talk with each other, they seem to be talking to a third person. **SEE 12.23**

12.22

Z-AXIS POSITION SWITCH

When shooting two people side-by-side (A and B) from the front and from the back along the z-axis, they will switch positions when the shots are edited together.

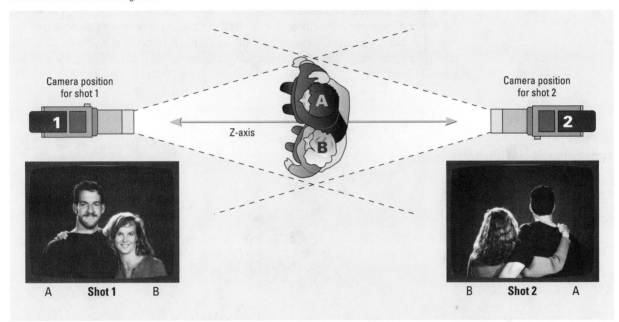

12.23

CROSSING THE LINE IN CROSS SHOOTING

When crossing the line in cross shooting, A and B seem to be looking in the same direction.
The converging index vectors have become continuing ones.

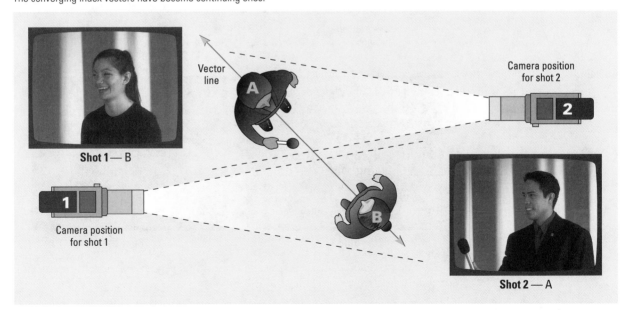

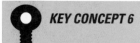

KEY CONCEPT 6 **To maintain on-screen positions and vector continuity, both cameras must be kept on the same side of the vector line.**

When placing cameras on both sides of the *motion vector line*, the object motion will be reversed with each cut. **SEE 12.24** To preserve the direction of the object motion, you need to position both cameras on one or the other side of the motion vector line. (Covering a football game from both sides of the field is not a good idea.)

12.24

CROSSING THE MOTION VECTOR LINE

When crossing the motion vector line, the object motion will be reversed with each cut.

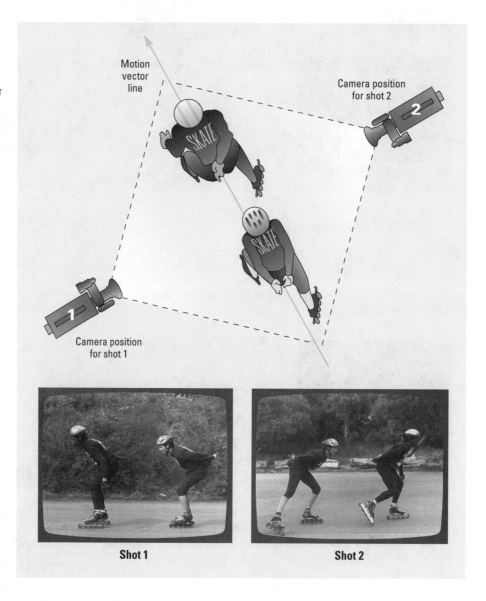

12.25

CUTAWAY

If you want to show that subjects continue to move in the same direction although the successive shots show them moving in opposite directions (shots 1 and 3), you can establish a continuing motion vector by inserting a neutral cutaway (shot 2).

Shot 1

Shot 2

Shot 3

If you need to pretend that an object moves in a single direction although two successive shots show the object moving in opposite directions, you can insert a *cutaway* shot—a thematically related, usually nonmoving, shot that separates the two opposing motion vectors. **SEE 12.25** *READY ZVL 6*

AESTHETIC PRINCIPLES OF COMPLEXITY EDITING

Complexity editing is done primarily to intensify an event and to give it meaning—to help us gain deeper insight into the event. In this sort of editing, you may not always want to follow the rules of continuity editing but instead opt to edit for heightened emotional impact, even at the risk of jarring the viewer's mental map.

Intensifying the Event

Although you were just advised not to shoot motion from both sides of the vector line, crossing the motion vector line is one of the more popular intensification devices. For example, if you want to emphasize the power of a sports car, you might shoot it first from one side of the street (which represents the motion vector line), and then from the other. The converging motion vectors of the car will clash and thus increase the aesthetic energy of the shots. Because this is the only car in the two shots, we are not likely to perceive a switch in direction or see two cars, but a single one moving in the same direction. **SEE 12.26**

Crossing the vector line Many MTV segments show rapid switching of screen directions, such as dancers or singers who flip rapidly from looking and moving in one screen direction to the opposite one. You probably noticed that this effect is accomplished by purposely crossing the vector line with the camera. When shooting from both sides of the line, you reverse the singer's index and motion vectors every time you cut. The purpose of crossing the vector line is to

12.26

INTENSIFICATION THROUGH CONVERGING MOTION VECTORS

Juxtaposing two converging motion vectors of a single prominent object, such as a powerful sports car, will intensify the object motion without destroying its vector continuity. Note that here the pictures of the car create index rather than motion vectors.

Shot 1

Shot 2

increase the energy of the shot sequence. The more rapid the switching, the more frantic the sequence appears.

Jump cut   The *jump cut* has become a common device in complexity editing. It became fashionable through newscasts, when editors did not have time to insert appropriate cutaways when editing interviews. They simply tried to find a few interesting spots on the sound track and cut these pieces together regardless of the video. Because most news interviews are shot with a single camera that is focused on the guest throughout, the final edited version of the interview shows a series of jump cuts.

Although the jump cut is traditionally considered an aesthetic offense, it was eventually accepted by viewers, because they were given some indication of where the interview had been trimmed. It is now used in commercials and even dramatic situations—not so much as an indicator of condensing time, but rather as a perceptual prodding device. Like crossing the line, the jump cut jolts us out of our perceptual complacency.

Jogging   Producing a similar jolt to visual continuity, *jogging* consists of a slowed-down frame-by-frame advance of a motion, which is normally used to locate a specific frame for editing. When shown within a high-intensity shot, it draws attention to the motion itself and can heighten the drama of the scene.

Sound track   The *sound track* is, of course, one of the most effective and widely used intensifiers. There is hardly a car chase that—besides the squealing tires—is not accompanied by high-energy, highly rhythmic music. As you have undoubtedly experienced at rock concerts or other musical performances, it is primarily the rhythm—the beat—of the music that supplies its basic energy. We transfer this basic sound energy readily to the video event.

Supplying Meaning

You can create meaning not only through the actual content of a scene, but also by a specific shot sequence. For example, if we see in the first shot a police officer struggling with a person, and then, in the second shot, the person running across the street, we presume that the culprit has escaped. If we see the person running first, however, and then the police officer struggling, we believe that the officer has caught up with the culprit.

You can supply additional meaning by juxtaposing the primary event with either related or contrasting events. For example, by showing how the homeless seek shelter in the city plaza and then switching to a scene with limousines driving up and elegant people entering the opera house across the street, you will not only intensify the plight of the homeless but also imply the idea of social injustice. Such a juxtaposition is called *collision montage*. A *montage* is a carefully calculated juxtaposition of two or more separate event images that, when shown together, combine into a larger and more intense whole.[1] You can also create audio/video montages, in which the audio event either parallels or counters the basic theme of the video event, such as a slow-motion battle scene accompanied by symphonic music, as if it were an elegantly choreographed ballet.

You need to realize that complexity editing does not imply that there are no sequencing rules. Ignoring the conventions and rules of continuity editing will not automatically lead to an event intensification, but more likely to viewer confusion. Exactly when and how to break the rules of continuity for effective complexity editing requires, first and foremost, a thorough knowledge of the rules, plus your deliberate judgment.

With a firm grasp of the vector concept, you will be ahead of many editors who do their editing more or less intuitively. There is nothing wrong with this so long as everything goes right. But when something goes wrong, intuition might not be sufficient to fix the problem. Best of all, knowledge of basic editing aesthetics will give you confidence in making optimal shot selections and sequencing choices the first time around. *READY ZVL 7*

---

1. See Herbert Zettl, *Sight Sound Motion: Applied Media Aesthetics*, 3d ed. (Belmont, Calif.: Wadsworth Publishing Co., 1999), pp. 300–304. See also Steven D. Katz, *Film Directing Shot by Shot* (Studio City, Calif.: Michael Wiese Productions, 1991).

ONCE AGAIN, REMEMBER...

■ Editing Functions

The basic editing functions are to combine various shots, condense footage, correct production mistakes, and build a show from various shots.

■ Continuity Editing

Continuity editing means to create seamless transitions from one event detail (shot) to the next.

■ Mental Map

Editing must help the viewer construct a mental map of where things are, where they should be, and where they are going, even though only certain parts of the scene are shown in successive shots.

■ Vectors

Index and motion vectors can be continuing (pointing or moving in the same direction), converging (pointing or moving toward each other), or diverging (pointing or moving away from each other).

■ Vector Line

The vector line is established by extending converging index vectors or extending a motion vector. To maintain position and directional continuity, the camera must shoot from only one side of the vector line. In multicamera use, all cameras must shoot from the same side of the vector line.

■ Complexity Editing

Complexity editing frequently violates continuity principles, such as crossing the vector line, to intensify the screen event. The jump cut and jogging are employed as energizing devices.

Z E T T L ' S   V I D E O   L A B   2 . 1

*Click on the **editing** monitor. You may want to play tape 1 **Meet Veronica** again. After having read about editing principles in this chapter, you will probably understand why she recommends that you play the tape once for content, and then several more times to observe some technical aspects of the source tapes and especially how applicable they are to the aesthetic principles of continuity editing. You may want to start by running ZVLs 6 through 9, and then go back to ZVLs 1 through 5. The reason for this switch is that you will then know the aesthetic principles necessary for making the right editing decisions in the first five ZVL segments.*

RUN ZVL 1

Load tape 2 **Functions**. In her introduction to editing functions and in module 1 **Select**, Veronica explains what editing is all about and stresses the various factors that can influence your decision making. The most important thing to remember is that the viewer should remain largely unaware that you select and combine event essences instead of show the whole event. Notice also that the juxtapositions of shots, such as the cows grazing and the woman eating a hamburger, can generate specific meanings that are not contained in either of the two shots.

RUN ZVL 2

Module 2 **Combine** shows how you can combine shots to tell a story. Veronica's friend certainly did not jump over the cliff, but her editing skills produced such an effect. What kind of shots were essential for Veronica to fake such a cliff jump in the editing room?

RUN ZVL 3

Play module 3 **Condense**. News editing consists mostly of combining only the most telling shots. Heed Veronica's advice and don't let the production effort of a particular shot influence your selection. Even if you have to cut a thirty-minute speech to ten seconds, try to pick the few sound bites that are most representative of the entire speech. In this case, content certainly overrules aesthetics.

RUN ZVL 4

Play module 4 **Correct**. Yes, you have heard it before: "Fix it in post" is not the way to go about correcting production mistakes. Fix it during the production, not after it. The two examples Veronica shows you are enough to make it nearly impossible to remedy a simple talent mistake in postproduction. The first example shows a jump cut, a common problem when you try to exactly match the shot just prior to where the mistake occurred. The second example shows trying to match the lighting and color. Matching colors in postproduction is possible, but takes a great amount of time and effort. A simple pickup of the talent's speech at a logical point before the mistake occurred would have fixed the problem in minutes.

RUN ZVL 5

Load tape 2 **Functions** and replay module 2 **Combine**. Veronica showed us her vacation picture and how she manufactured the story of her friend jumping off the cliff. This was a good example of building an event through editing.

Load tape 7 **Cutting Procedures** and play module 1 **Trim**. You learn the finer points of combining. Watch carefully just why a specific cut is not as good as the others, although they combine the proper shots. Now aesthetic principles of continuity editing come into play. Play module 7 **Quiz** to check on your precise judgment on when to cut.

RUN ZVL 6

Load tape 4 **Continuity** and play module 1 **Vectors**. Before you can make intelligent choices about establishing and maintaining the mental map, you need to know about vectors. The graphic and index vectors Veronica is showing you are similar to the ones you saw in the text, but the book of course could not show a motion vector. Here you see a real motion vector: an object or person moving. You will now more clearly understand how we form a mental map.

Now play module 2 **Mental Map**. As you can see, vectors are important in establishing or maintaining a mental map. Pay particular attention to the last part of the module and click on the cameras. Notice how the various camera positions help or hinder your maintaining a mental map on where the people are or are supposed to be on the close-ups. When you cross the line and cut from a camera at the bottom of the line to one on the top, the two people will talk away from each other instead of to each other. The mental map has definitely been upset.

Now load tape 5 **Location Procedures** and play module 2 **Cutaways**. The two important things to remember are that cutaways must be thematically related to the event (CU of the piano when the woman talks about the jazz greats) and they should be long enough. A cutaway that is too short is useless. The nodding of the interviewer is a favorite cutaway to bring variety into a long answer. In module 3 **Pickups**, Veronica gives you practical advice on how to maintain continuity during a pickup. Just for good measure, play module 4 **Vectors** again. Observing such vector continuity in the shooting phase will eliminate many continuity problems in postproduction editing.

RUN ZVL 7

Load tape 4 **Continuity** again and play module 4 **Complexity**. Note how the jazz sequence is intensified by purposely having some of the vectors clash. It also allows you more insight into the creative energy of the musicians.

Module 6 **Sound** gives excellent examples of how the sound track can influence one's perception of an event. With one type of background sound, the woman seems to be happily skipping along; with another, she seems in imminent danger. Remember the juxtaposition of the two shots—the cows grazing and the woman eating a hamburger on tape 2 **Functions** module 1 **Select**? If not, run it again and figure out the underlying meaning. By the way, this montage is called *comparison montage*, because we compare the eating habits of one with those of the other.

K E Y   C O N C E P T S

○ Editing means selecting significant event details and putting them into a specific sequence to tell a story with clarity and impact.

○ The condensing function of editing requires a recognition of the essence of an event and the selection of shots that best express that essence.

○ Careful attention to preproduction and production details can obviate most corrective editing.

○ Continuity editing means preserving the location and motion of objects over a series of shots to help the viewer establish and maintain a mental map of where things should be or where they should move.

○ Graphic, index, and motion vectors play an important part in establishing and maintaining continuity from shot to shot.

○ To maintain on-screen positions and vector continuity, both cameras must be kept on the same side of the vector line.

PART IV

CONTENTS

CHAPTER 13

Talent, Clothing, and Makeup

CHAPTER 14

Production Environment: The Studio

CHAPTER 15

Field Production and Synthetic Environments

316

Talent and the Production Environment

BEFORE moving you up to assist one of their topnotch directors, the Triple-I management would like you to learn more about the people who work in front of the camera—the talent—and what they must do to convey the desired process message.

They would also like you to learn more about the studio and its associated control areas and how to use various field environments effectively in your video productions. The final three chapters can help you meet Triple-I's requirements.

KEY TERMS

actor A person who appears on-camera in dramatic roles. The actor always portrays someone else.

blocking Carefully worked-out movement and actions by the talent and for all mobile video equipment used in a scene.

cue card A large hand-lettered card that contains copy, usually held next to the camera lens by floor personnel.

foundation A makeup base, normally done with water-soluble pancake makeup, that is applied with a sponge to the face and sometimes to all exposed skin areas. Pancake foundation reduces unwanted light reflection.

I.F.B. Stands for interruptible foldback or feedback. A prompting system that allows communication with the talent while on the air. A small earpiece worn by on-the-air talent that carries program sound (including the talent's voice) or instructions from the producer or director.

moiré effect Color vibrations that occur when narrow, contrasting stripes of a design interfere with the scanning lines of the video system.

performer A person who appears on-camera in nondramatic shows. The performer does not assume someone else's character.

talent Collective name for all performers and actors who appear regularly in video.

teleprompter A prompting device that projects moving copy over the lens so that the talent can read it without losing eye contact with the viewer.

Talent, Clothing, and Makeup

THE **incredible amount of equipment and effort** that goes into making even a relatively simple production, such as somebody announcing on-camera the latest company news, is generally lost on viewers. All they judge the show by is whether the person on the screen is likable and whether he or she is doing a credible job of delivering the news. Similarly, viewers attribute the success of a talk show primarily to the host, not on how it is lighted or how the cameras are handled.

Video *talent* refers (not always too accurately) to all people performing in front of the camera. We divide talent into two groups: performers and actors. *Performers* are primarily engaged in nondramatic activities. They play themselves and do not assume the role of other characters; they are aware of the viewers and usually communicate directly with them by addressing the camera lens. *Actors*, on the other hand, always portray someone else; they assume a character role, even if the role is close to their own personality. They normally do not acknowledge the presence of the viewers, but interact with other actors. Because performance and acting requirements differ in several major ways, they are discussed separately here. Specifically, this chapter focuses on the techniques and other aspects of appearing in front of the camera.

■ **PERFORMING TECHNIQUES**
Performer and camera, audio and lighting, and timing and prompting

■ **ACTING TECHNIQUES**
Environment and audience, small screen and close-ups, and repeating action

■ **AUDITIONS**
How to prepare

■ **CLOTHING**

Texture, detail, and color

■ **MAKEUP**

Technical requirements, close-ups, and materials

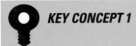

KEY CONCEPT 1　　**Talent refers to video performers and actors. Performers portray themselves; actors portray somebody else.**

PERFORMING TECHNIQUES

As a performer you are always aware of the viewers. Your goal is to establish as much rapport as possible with them and to have them share in what you do and say. Because video is normally watched by individuals or small groups of people who know one another, your performance techniques must be adjusted to this kind of communication intimacy. Always imagine that you are looking at and talking with somebody you know, seated comfortably a short distance from you. Some performers prefer to imagine that they are talking to a small group or a small family; in any case, don't ever envision that you are at a mass rally, addressing "millions of people out there in videoland." When viewers watch you at home, it is you who is "out there," and not they. They are not visiting you; you are visiting them.

To help you establish this intimate viewer contact and perform effectively in front of the camera, you need to familiarize yourself with some production aspects of (1) performer and camera, (2) audio and lighting, and (3) timing and prompting.

■ Performer and Camera

As a performer you have a communication partner: the video camera. It represents the viewer with whom you are talking. You may find it difficult at first to consider the camera your communication partner, especially when all you actually see while talking is the camera or the screen of the prompting device, a few lights shining into your eyes, and perhaps a few production people who are more interested in operating the equipment than in what you have to say.

Eye contact　To establish eye contact with the viewer, you need to look at the *lens,* not the camera operator or the floor manager. In fact, good performers keep constant eye contact with the lens and seem to look *through* it, rather than merely at it. When pretending to look through the lens, you will more readily extend your glance through the screen—toward the viewer—than if you simply stare at the camera. Also, you must maintain eye contact with the lens much more directly and constantly than when engaged in a real interpersonal conversation. Even a small glance away from the lens will be highly distracting for the viewer; it will not be seen as a polite relief from your stare, but rather as an impolite loss of concentration or interest on your part.

If two or more cameras are used while demonstrating a product, you need to find out which of the two cameras will remain on you and which will take the close-up of the product. Keep looking at the camera (or, rather, through the lens of the camera) that is focused on you, even when the director switches to the close-up camera that is focused on the product. This way you will not get caught looking at the wrong camera when your camera is switched back on the air.

If both cameras are on you and switched according to the director's cues, you must shift your view from one camera to the other to maintain eye contact. A good floor manager will greatly assist you in this task. He or she will warn you that a switch is coming up by pointing on the director's "ready" cue to the camera you are addressing and then motioning you over to the other camera on the "take" cue. On the floor manager's cue, shift your glance quickly but smoothly in the new direction. Unless told otherwise, always follow the floor manager's cues (as shown in figure 13.1) and not the tally light that indicates the hot camera.

If you discover that you are talking to the wrong camera, look down as if to collect your thoughts, and then look up into the on-the-air camera. Such a shift works especially well if you use notes or a script as part of your on-camera performance. You can simply pretend that you are consulting your notes, while changing your view from the wrong to the right camera. *READY ZVL 1*

 KEY CONCEPT 2 **Eye contact with the camera lens establishes eye contact with the viewer.**

Close-ups   On video you will be shown more often in a close-up than a medium or long shot. The camera scrutinizes and magnifies your expressions and every move. It does not look politely away when you scratch your ear or touch your nose; it reveals faithfully the nervous twitch or mild panic when you have forgotten a line. More so, the close-up does not give you much room to maneuver. A slight wiggle of the product you are holding will look in a tight close-up as though an earthquake has struck. The close-up also accelerates your actions. If you lift up a book at normal speed to show its cover, you will most certainly yank it out of the close-up camera's view. Here are a few important rules for working with close-ups:

▶ When on a close-up, do not wiggle, but remain as steady as possible.

▶ Keep your hands away from your face, even if you feel your nose itching or perspiration collecting on your forehead.

▶ Slow down all movements.

▶ When demonstrating small objects, keep them as steady as possible in one position. Better yet, put them on a display table.

▶ If they are arranged on a table, do not pick them up. You can point to them or tilt them a little to give the camera a better view.

There is nothing more frustrating for the camera operator, the director, and especially the viewer than a performer who snatches the object off the table just when the camera has a good close-up of it. A quick look at the studio monitor will tell you whether you are holding or tilting the object for maximum visibility.

Also, don't ask the camera to come a little closer to get a better look at what you are demonstrating. As you well know, the camera operator can get a close-up not just by dollying in with the camera, but much more quickly and easily by zooming in. And you will not make the director very happy by asking for specific shots when the shot is already on the air, or when there are technical problems that prevent the director from calling up the desired material. Talent—however eager they may be to look good on the air—should not try to outdirect the director.

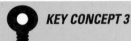 **KEY CONCEPT 3**   **When on a close-up, keep your gestures small and slow.**

Audio and Lighting

A clear, resonant voice alone will not make you a good performer. Besides having something to say and saying it clearly and convincingly, you need to be aware of the various audio requirements.

Microphone techniques   At this point you should briefly review the use of microphones in chapter 8. Here is a short recap of the main microphone techniques of concern to you as a performer:

▶ Treat all microphones gently. They are not props, but highly sensitive electronic devices that translate your voice into electrical signals.

▶ If you work with a *lavaliere microphone,* don't forget to put it on. Run the cable underneath your jacket or blouse and fasten the mic on the outside of your clothing. Unless you are wearing a wireless lavaliere, once "wired" you have a highly limited action radius. Don't forget to remove the mic and lay it gently on the chair before walking off the set.

▶ When using a *hand mic,* see how far the microphone cable will let you move. In normal situations hold the hand mic chest high and speak across it, not into it. In noisy surroundings hold it closer to your mouth. When interviewing a guest with a hand mic, hold it near you when speaking and toward the guest when he or she responds. Gently pull the microphone cable with your free hand when moving about. If you need both hands for something else, tuck the mic under your arm. A wireless hand mic will make your movements less restricted, but will add some liabilities of losing your mic signal on its way to the receiving station. Unless you are in a controlled environment, such as a television or recording studio, stay away from wireless hand mics.

▶ Once a *desk mic* has been put in place by the audio engineer, don't move it. Check with the audio engineer if you think it should be closer to you or pointing more toward you. Talk toward it, not away from it.

▶ When using a *stand mic*, adjust the height of the stand so that the mic is a little below your chin, pointing toward your mouth.

▶ When a *fishpole* or *boom mic* is used, be aware of where the mic is when you are moving, but don't look at it. Move slowly and avoid fast turns. If you see that the boom operator can't follow you with the mic, stop, and move on when the problem is fixed.

Taking a level   When asked to test the mic or to take a level, don't blow into it, but say your opening remarks at the volume you will use when on the air. Performers who rapidly count to ten or speak with a low voice off the air and then blast their opening remarks when on the air will not help the audio engineer adjust the volume to an optimal level.

Do not speak louder simply because the camera moves farther away from you. Although you correctly assume that the camera is the viewer with whom you are communicating, the camera distance has nothing to do with how close the shot actually is. More important, the distance of the camera has nothing to do with how close the mic is. If you wear a lavaliere, you are heard at the same level regardless of whether the camera is two or two hundred feet away from you.

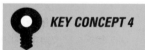

KEY CONCEPT 4   **When taking a level, speak at the volume you will actually use during the performance, and speak long enough to set the optimal level on the audio console.**

Checking lighting   Although as a performer you should not be concerned with lighting, it does not hurt to quickly check the lighting before going on the air. When outdoors, don't stand against a brightly lighted background, unless you want to be seen in silhouette. When in the studio and there is no light hitting your eyes, you are not in the lighted area. Ask the director where you should stand so that you are in a properly lighted area. In a play, when you happen to get off the rehearsed blocking into a dark area, move a little until you feel the heat of the light or see the lights hitting you. Such concern for lighting should not encourage you to take over the director's function. Always check with the director if you have any questions about the technical setup and your activities in it.

Timing and Prompting

A good performer can accurately judge a ten-second or thirty-second duration without looking at a clock or stopwatch. Such timing skills are not inborn, but acquired through practice. Even if you think that you have an unfailing sense of timing, you should always mind the floor manager's cues.

As a performer you need to be acutely aware of time, whether on the air or not. Even nonbroadcast video programs are packaged according to a rigid time frame. Because the audience has no idea about your time restrictions, you need to appear relaxed and unhurried even if you have only two seconds left or you have to fill unexpectedly for an additional fifteen seconds. Good radio personalities can teach you a lot in this respect. They seem to be totally relaxed and never hurried, even when working up to the last second of the segment. Don't put too much trust in your timing instincts; use a clock or stopwatch for precise timing. In any case, respond immediately to the floor manager's time cues.

The I.F.B. system   As a performer you must rely on—or put up with—a variety of *prompting devices*. The most direct prompting device is the *I.F.B.—interruptible foldback* or, as it is also called, *interruptible feedback*—system. You have probably seen performers or interview guests touch one of their ears as though they were adjusting a hearing aid. This is exactly what they are doing.

When using interruptible foldback, you wear a small earpiece that carries the total program sound, including your own remarks, unless the producer or director (or some other production member connected to the I.F.B. system) interrupts the program sound with specific instructions. For example, if you interview the CEO of a new Internet company, the producer may cut in and tell you what question to ask next, to slow down, to speed up, or to tell the guest that she has only fifteen seconds to respond to your request to explain the latest multiplatform software. The trick is to not let the viewer know that you are listening to somebody other than the guest.

If you conduct an interview long-distance, with the guest in a remote location, he or she may also wear an I.F.B. earpiece that transmits your questions on a separate I.F.B. channel. You may find that many guests experience some problem with the I.F.B. system, especially when the guest location is relatively noisy. Try to test the system in advance to make the guest more comfortable using I.F.B.

Floor manager's cues   Normal *time, directional,* and *audio* cues are usually given by the floor manager. As a performer you will quickly learn that the floor manager is your best friend during the production. A good floor manager will always be in your vicinity, telling you whether you are too slow or fast, whether you are holding the product correctly for the close-up camera, and whether you are doing a good job. Unlike other prompting devices, the floor manager can react immediately to your needs and to unforeseen performance problems. Normally, the floor manager cues you through a variety of hand signals. **SEE 13.1**

As a performer you must react to the floor manager's cues immediately, even if you think that the cue is inappropriate. Good performers don't think they can run the show all by themselves: They react to the floor manager's cues quickly and smoothly.

Don't look around for the floor manager when you think that you should have received a time cue; he or she will make sure that you see the signal without having to break eye contact with the lens. As you just learned, even a brief glance away from the lens will tend to interrupt the contact you have established with the viewer. Once you have seen a cue, don't acknowledge it in any way. The floor manager can tell by your subsequent actions whether or not you received the cue.

13.1

FLOOR MANAGER'S CUES

Because the microphone is live during production, the talent must rely on visual time, directional, and audio cues from the floor manager.

CUE	SIGNAL	MEANING	SIGNAL DESCRIPTION
TIME CUES			
Standby		Show about to start.	Extends hand above head.
Cue		Show goes on the air.	Points to performer or live camera.
On time		Go ahead as planned. (On the nose.)	Touches nose with forefinger.
Speed up		Accelerate what you are doing. You are going too slowly.	Rotates hand clockwise with extended forefinger. Urgency of speedup is indicated by fast or slow rotation.
Stretch		Slow down. Too much time left. Fill until emergency is over.	Stretches imaginary rubber band between hands.

13.1

FLOOR MANAGER'S CUES *(continued)*

CUE	SIGNAL	MEANING	SIGNAL DESCRIPTION
		TIME CUES	
Wind up		Finish up what you are doing. Come to an end.	Similar motion to speed up, but usually with arm extended above head. Sometimes expressed with raised fist, good-bye wave, or hands rolling over each other as if wrapping a package.
Cut		Stop speech or action immediately.	Pulls index finger in knifelike motion across throat.
5 (4, 3, 2, 1) minute(s)		5 (4, 3, 2, 1) minute(s) left until end of show.	Holds up five (four, three, two, one) finger(s) or small card with a number on it.
Half minute		30 seconds left in show.	Forms a cross with two index fingers or arms. Or holds card with number.
15 seconds		15 seconds left in show.	Shows fist (which can also mean wind up). Or holds card with number.
Roll VTR (and countdown) 2–1 Take VTR		VTR is rolling. Tape is coming up.	Holds extended left hand in front of face, moving right hand in cranking motion. Extends two, one finger(s); clenches fist or gives cut signal.

13.1

FLOOR MANAGER'S CUES *(continued)*

CUE	SIGNAL	MEANING	SIGNAL DESCRIPTION
		DIRECTIONAL CUES	
Closer		Performer must come closer or bring object closer to camera.	Moves both hands toward self, palms in.
Back		Performer must step back or move object away from camera.	Uses both hands in pushing motion, palms out.
Walk		Performer must move to next performance area.	Makes a walking motion with index and middle fingers in direction of movement.
Stop		Stop right there. Do not move any more.	Extends both hands in front of body, palms out.
OK		Very well done. Stay right there. Do what you are doing.	Forms an *O* with thumb and forefinger, other fingers extended, motioning toward talent.

13.1

FLOOR MANAGER'S CUES *(continued)*

CUE	SIGNAL	MEANING	SIGNAL DESCRIPTION
		AUDIO CUES	
Speak up		Performer is talking too softly for present conditions.	Cups both hands behind ears or moves hand upward, palm up.
Tone down		Performer is too loud or too enthusiastic for the occasion.	Moves both hands toward studio floor, palms down, or puts extended forefinger over mouth in *shhh*-like motion.
Closer to mic		Performer is too far away from mic for good audio pickup.	Moves hand toward face.
Keep talking		Keep on talking until further cues.	Extends thumb and fingers horizontally, moving them like a bird beak.

KEY CONCEPT 5   **Always respond promptly to the floor manager's cues.**

Teleprompter   The *teleprompter* makes it possible for you to read copy without taking your eyes off the lens, by projecting the copy off a small monitor onto a glass plate mounted directly in front of the lens. **SEE 13.2** While you read the copy on

13.2

TELEPROMPTER

The teleprompter consists of a small video monitor that reflects the copy onto a glass plate directly in front of the lens. The talent can see the copy clearly, while it remains invisible to the camera lens.

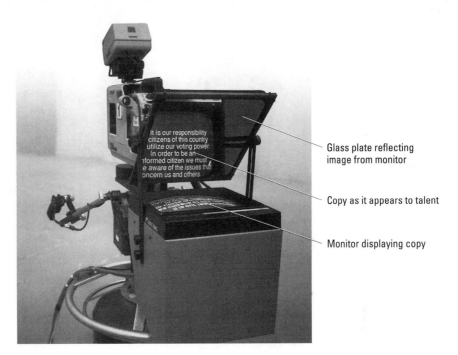

It is our responsibility citizens of this country utilize our voting power. In order to be an informed citizen we must e aware of the issues that oncern us and others.

— Glass plate reflecting image from monitor

— Copy as it appears to talent

— Monitor displaying copy

the glass plate, the lens can view the scene through the plate without seeing the lettering. All newscasters and hosts of shows with a newslike format use teleprompters, as do people who deliver on-camera speeches. The copy itself is normally generated by a word processing program and sent by a desktop computer to the teleprompter monitor on each camera that focuses on you. The computer rolls the copy from the bottom of the teleprompter screen to the top exactly at your reading speed. If you have to change your reading speed to stay within the allotted time, the copy speed can be adjusted accordingly. Some of the older systems use a *copy-bed* device, in which the typed copy is transported at variable speeds along a small table (the copy-bed) and photographed with a small black-and-white camera. The camera's video is then sent directly to the teleprompter monitors.

When you are using a teleprompter, the camera should be far enough away that the viewers don't see your eyes moving back and forth while reading, yet close enough that you can clearly see the copy. Experienced performers still manage to look *through* the lens and make eye contact with the viewer even while reading the copy in front of the lens.

For the small teleprompters that can be used in the field, the copy originates from a laptop computer that also controls the speed of the scroll. Simple prompters use a paper roll that projects hand-lettered copy over a glass plate in front of the lens. Some field prompters have the paper roll mounted below or to the side of the

13.3

HANDLING CUE CARDS

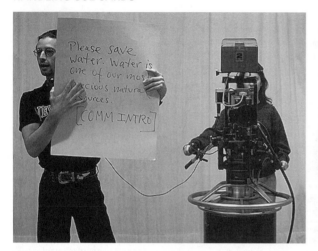

A This is the wrong way to hold cue cards. The card is too far away from the lens, and the floor manager is covering part of the copy, is not reading it with the talent, and is therefore unable to change cards when necessary.

B This is the correct way to hold cue cards. The cards are as close to the lens as possible, and the floor manager reads along with the talent to facilitate smooth card changes.

lens. The roll is battery-powered and can be adjusted to various speeds. If nothing else is available, use a clipboard for the copy and hold it low enough so that you can read it just out of camera range.

Cue cards   One of the simplest yet most highly effective cuing devices is *cue cards*—sheets of paper or posterboard on which the copy is hand-lettered with a marker. The size of the cards depends on how well you can see and how far away the camera is when you're reading the copy. A floor person must hold the cards as close to the lens as possible so that you don't have to glance too far away, thereby losing eye contact with the viewer. You must learn to read the copy out of the corner of your eye while looking at the lens. If possible, practice your peripheral reading with the floor person handling the cards. Decide on an optimal distance, then make sure that the cards are in the right order and that the floor person holds them close to the lens without covering the copy. **SEE 13.3** Practice changing the cards with the floor person; this must occur while you are reading the last few words. See to it that the floor person does not dump the used cards on the floor, but puts them quickly and quietly on a nearby chair.   *READY ZVL 2*

ACTING TECHNIQUES

To become a good video or television actor, you must first learn the art of acting. Whereas performers always portray themselves, actors always assume somebody else's character and personality. Even the best stage or film actors must adjust their acting methods and style to the specific requirements of the video medium. Some of the major requirements are (1) working in a technical environment without an audience, (2) adjusting to the small video screen and the frequent use of close-ups, and (3) repeating the action.

Environment and Audience

As a video actor, you will be surrounded by much more technical equipment than if you were on stage. Worse, you do not have an audience whose reaction you can see or feel. Unless you have a studio audience, all you see are lights, cameras, and production people who do not pay much attention to you. In fact, you will often feel that you are neglected even by the director. But you should realize that the director has to coordinate numerous pieces of production equipment and a great many personnel, and that some of the technical operations may need more of the director's attention than you do.

You may even feel more abandoned because of the lack of a live audience. Unlike the theater, where the audience remains in a fixed place and gives you direct or indirect feedback, the camera or cameras do not respond to your performance, but stare at you impassively and move quietly all around you. They may look at your eyes, your back, your feet, your hands, or whatever the director chooses for the viewer to see. It is a little like acting for theater-in-the-round, except that in video the viewers, as represented by the cameras, sit at arm's length and even join you on the stage to get a better look.

Because the viewer is in such close virtual proximity, you need not, and should not, project your actions and emotions to somebody sitting in the last row. The camera, which is doing the projecting for you, can make a small gesture into a grand act. When on a close-up, there is no need for you to act out your role; instead, you must *feel* it. Internalization of your role is a key factor in acting for video.

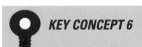

KEY CONCEPT 6   **When acting for the video medium, you must *feel* the role, rather than merely act it out.**

The intimacy of video also influences the way you speak. You must reduce the customary stage declamation and voice projection to clear but normal speech. Good writers help you in this task. Instead of having you, as Oedipus, dramatically request, "Who planned the crime, aye, and performed it, too?" on video you would simply ask, "Who did it?" Getting rid of exaggerated voice projection is one of the hardest things to learn when stage actors switch over to the video medium. Precise enunciation is often more important than speech volume and projection.

Most important, you must be able to memorize your lines quickly and accurately. Although you may have a variety of prompting devices available (mainly cue cards), you cannot and should not rely on them if you want to be convincing in your role. Because many of your lines serve as important video and audio cues and trigger all sorts of production activity, you cannot afford to ad-lib. Ad-libbing a cue line will inevitably cause chaos in the control room and prompt a retake of the scene.

Small Screen and Close-ups

The small screen and the frequent use of close-ups do not give you much room to move. Sometimes you must stand unnaturally close to other actors, or move much more slowly than normal without appearing to do so to stay within camera range. The close-up also limits your gestures. If, when seated, you lean back or move forward unexpectedly, you may fall out of focus, and weaving sideways just a little may carry you out of the frame.

The close-up shots require you to be extremely exact in following the rehearsed *blocking*—the carefully worked out movements and actions relative to other actors and the camera. If you stray even a few inches from the rehearsed blocking, you may be out of camera range or obstructed by another actor. To help you remember the major blocking positions, the floor manager will usually mark the floor with chalk or masking tape.

In an over-the-shoulder shot, if you or the other actor is off the mark, you may be obstructed from camera view by the other actor. You can tell whether the camera sees you simply by looking for the camera lens. If you see the lens, the camera can see you; if you don't see the lens, you aren't being seen. If you can't see the lens, inch to one side or the other without obviously searching for it. Although the camera can be adjusted to get the proper over-the-shoulder shot, it is usually easier for you to move than the camera.

To remember blocking, you may want to establish a mental road map that has prominent landmarks, for example: "First stop, the left corner of the table. Second landmark, couch. Move to the couch and sit on the right. Third landmark, telephone. Get up and move behind the telephone table facing the center camera. Pick up the phone with the left hand."

Although good directors will block you as much as possible so that your movements are natural, you will occasionally be in a position that seems entirely wrong to you. Do not try to correct this position until you have consulted the director. A special shot or effect may very well warrant such blocking.

KEY CONCEPT 7   **Meticulously follow the rehearsed blocking during each take.**
If you can't see the camera lens, you won't be in the shot.

Repeating Action

Unlike the theater, where your performance is continuous and according to plot progression, video acting—like acting for film—is usually done piecemeal. You may have to switch from the happy opening scene to the intensely sad closing scene, merely because they both play in the same location. By remembering the exact blocking, you can also help preserve continuity. For instance, if you held the telephone receiver in your right hand during the medium shots, don't switch it to your left hand during the close-ups.

In single-camera productions, it is normal to repeat the same scene over and over again. Such repetitions are done to get a variety of camera angles or close-ups or to correct major or minor technical problems. In repeats you must not only duplicate exactly the lines and blocking for each take; *you must also maintain the same energy level throughout.* You cannot be "on" during the first takes and "off" later during the close-ups.

AUDITIONS

Auditions are a test of your ability as a performer or actor—and of your self-confidence. Not getting the part does not mean that you gave an inferior performance, but that somebody else was more suitable for the part. What you must do is take all auditions equally seriously, whether you are trying out for a starring role in a big television drama or for a one-line off-camera utterance for a product demonstration.

Although you may not know beforehand what will be asked of you in the audition, you can still prepare for it. Wear something that's appropriate and looks good on-camera. Be properly groomed. Get to the place on time and don't be intimidated by either the number or the caliber of people auditioning with you. You all have an equal chance; otherwise you would not have been called to try out for the part. Have a brief monologue ready that shows the range of your ability. Keep your energy up even if you have to wait half a day before being asked to perform.

If you get a script beforehand, study it carefully. If the script calls for you to talk about or demonstrate a specific product, such as a new computer, familiarize yourself with the product ahead of time. The more you know about the product, the more confidence shows in your delivery. Ask the person conducting the audition what shots the camera will take. If close-ups predominate, slow down your actions and avoid excessive movements. Remember that you are not addressing a large audience, but an individual or a small family seated not too far away from you.

As an actor be sure that you understand the character you are to portray. If you are not sure what the segment you are to read or the character you are to portray is all about, ask the person conducting the audition (casting director or producer)—but don't ask for the proper motivation. As a professional actor, you are expected to know how to motivate yourself. Be inventive, but don't overdo it. When working in video, little mannerisms, such as a specific way of keeping your eyeglasses from slipping down your nose, playing with keys, or using a slightly rusty fingernail clipper while engaged in a serious conversation, tend to sharpen your character more readily than simply working up to a high emotional pitch.

CLOTHING

What you wear is dependent not only on your preference and taste, but also on how the camera sees what you wear. Because the camera can look at you from extremely close range or from a distance, you need to consider the overall line of your clothing as well as the texture and details.

The video camera has the tendency to add a few extra pounds. Clothing that is cut to a slim silhouette usually looks more favorable than something loose and baggy. Avoid horizontal stripes; they emphasize width instead of length and make you look wider around the middle.

Texture and Detail

Because of the frequent close-ups in video, you need to pay special attention to texture and detail. Textured material and ties look better than plain, so long as the texture is not too busy or contrasting. Even the best video cameras have a difficult time handling closely spaced and highly contrasting patterns, such as black-and-white herringbone weaves or checks. The electronic scanning of the video image "beats together" with the frequency of the high-contrast pattern of the clothing. In its frustration, the camera creates a new, highly distracting frequency that shows up on the screen as vibrating rainbow colors and patterns, called a *moiré effect*.

Prominent, high-contrast horizontal stripes may also extend beyond the clothing fabric and bleed through surrounding sets and objects as though you were superimposing Venetian blinds. On the other hand, extremely fine detail in a pattern will either look busy or, more likely, show up on the screen as smudges.

You can always provide the necessary texture by adding such details as jewelry or a prominent tie or scarf. Although you will undoubtedly prefer wearing jewelry you like, refrain from wearing overly large or too many pieces. Too much jewelry tends to look gaudy on a close-up, even if the jewelry is of high quality.

Color

Again, the colors you select are not entirely up to you, but must fulfill certain technical requirements. If the set you work in is primarily beige, a beige dress or suit will certainly get lost in it. Avoid wearing saturated, chroma-key-like blue if you are part of a chroma-key effect (such as a weathercaster in front of a chroma-keyed weather map). As you recall, the chroma-key process renders transparent everything blue and lets the background show through. If you wear a blue tie or suit, you will see the keyed background image in place of the blue clothing.

Although you may like red, the video camera doesn't. Except for top-of-the-line cameras, most video cameras show highly saturated reds as vibrating and bleeding into other areas. Such video problems, called *artifacts,* are especially noticeable in low-light conditions.

You should also avoid wearing colors of highly contrasting brightness, such as dark blue and white, or black and white. If you wear a black jacket over a reflecting white shirt, the camera, or the video operator, does not know whether to adjust for the high brightness values of the white or the low values of the black. If the VO (video operator) tries to lighten the black areas to see some shadow detail, the white areas become overexposed and begin to "bloom." If the VO tries to control the overly bright areas by "clipping the whites," the shadow areas collapse into a uniformly dark area and your skin tones get a few shades darker. Obviously, if you are a dark-skinned performer, you should not wear a starched white shirt or blouse. If you wear a dark suit, reduce the brightness contrast by wearing a pastel shirt rather than a white one.

This contrast problem is especially noticeable when the camcorder is on automatic iris. The automatic iris will seek out the brightest spot in the picture and close down the aperture to bring this excess light under control. As a consequence all other picture areas darken accordingly. If, for example, you wear a brilliantly white blouse while standing in front of a relatively dark restaurant set, the automatic iris will close to darken the brightness of your blouse, but, unfortunately, the already dark set as well. What you will get is a properly exposed blouse in front of an underlighted set.

All makeup is used for three reasons: (1) to enhance appearance, (2) to correct appearance, and (3) to change appearance.

Most video productions require makeup that accentuates the features rather than changes them. For female performers, normal makeup does just fine on camera; male performers may need some makeup primarily to reduce the light reflections off the forehead and perhaps to cover up some wrinkles and skin blemishes. In both cases, makeup must be adjusted to the technical requirements of the camera and the tight scrutiny of the close-up.

KEY CONCEPT 8 　 **Makeup is used to enhance, correct, or change appearance.**

Technical Requirements

The video camera likes warmer (more reddish) makeup colors better than cooler (more bluish) ones. Especially under high-color-temperature lighting (outdoor or fluorescent lighting, which is bluish), bluish red lipsticks and eye shadow look unnaturally blue. Warm makeup colors, with their reddish tint, look more natural and provide sparkle, especially when used on a dark-skinned face.

Regardless of whether you are a dark-skinned or light-skinned performer, you should use *foundation* makeup that matches your natural skin color. This foundation is available in various types of *pancake* makeup. If you perspire readily, you should use a generous amount of foundation makeup. The foundation makeup will not prevent your perspiration, but will make it less visible to the camera.

Close-ups

Because the camera usually takes a close look at you, your makeup must be smooth and subtle. This requirement is the reverse of theatrical makeup, which you need to exaggerate as much as possible for good effect for the spectators sitting some distance from the stage. Good video makeup should accentuate your features but remain invisible, even on a close-up.

If possible, check your makeup by having the camera take a close-up of you in the performance area. You may consider this method a frivolously expensive mirror, but it will benefit you during the performance.

Always apply makeup in the lighting conditions in which the production is done. If you apply your makeup in a room that has bluish fluorescent (high 5,600°K color temperature) lights, and then perform under normal studio lights (with a lower color temperature of 3,200°K), your makeup will be excessively reddish and your face will look pink. The opposite is true if you apply your makeup in especially low-color-temperature reddish lights (below 3,200°K). When moving into the performance area with the normal indoor illumination (3,200°K), and especially when moving outdoors (5,600°K), your makeup will look unnaturally bluish.

If you need to use makeup to change your appearance, you should have a professional makeup artist do it for you.

KEY CONCEPT 9   Apply makeup under lights that have the same color temperature as those in the performance area.

Materials

You can easily find a great variety of excellent makeup materials for video. Most large drugstores carry the basic materials for improving a performer's appearance. Women performers are generally experienced in using cosmetic materials and techniques; men may, at least initially, need some advice.

The most basic makeup item is a *foundation* that covers minor skin blemishes and cuts down light reflections from oily skin. Water-based pancake makeup foundations are preferred over the more cumbersome grease-based foundations. The Krylon CTV-1W through CTV-12W pancake series is probably all you need for most makeup jobs. The colors range from a warm light ivory color for light-skinned performers to a very dark tone for dark-skinned performers.

Women can use their own lipsticks or rouge, so long as the reds do not contain too much blue. Other materials, such as eyebrow pencils, mascara, and eye shadow, are generally part of every performer's makeup kit. Additional materials, such as hairpieces or even latex masks, are part of the professional makeup artist's inventory. They are of little use in most nondramatic productions.

A solid knowledge of basic video production techniques will aid you greatly not only when working behind the camera but also when working in front of it. In fact, talent who know basic production techniques seem to be more relaxed in front of the camera and more prepared to cope gracefully with unexpected problems while on the air than performers who know little or nothing about video production.

Even if you don't aspire to become a video performer or actor, the Triple-I people will be especially happy to see that you understand and successfully deal with video talent and are able to give expert advice to those who are standing in front of the camera for the first time.

ONCE AGAIN, REMEMBER...

■ Talent

Talent are people who work in front of the camera. Talent includes performers, who are primarily engaged in nondramatic activities, and actors, who portray someone else.

■ Performance Techniques

The performer must imagine the video camera as his or her communication partner, keep eye contact with the lens when addressing the viewers directly, handle the various microphones for optimal sound pickup, and use prompting devices without making the viewer aware of it.

■ Acting Techniques

Good video actors learn how to work well within a highly technical environment, adjust to the small video screen and the frequent use of close-ups, and repeat certain actions the same way and at the same intensity level.

■ Prompting Devices

In addition to the floor manager's cues, the major prompting devices are the I.F.B. (interruptible foldback) system, the studio or field teleprompter, and cue cards.

■ Clothing

On-camera clothing should have a slim silhouette, and textures and colors that are not too busy or contrasting. The camera does not like closely spaced, high-contrast herringbone weaves or checks and highly saturated reds.

■ Makeup

Makeup is used to enhance, correct, and change appearance.

Z E T T L ' S   V I D E O   L A B   2 . 1

Although there are no tapes that deal specifically with talent, you have ample opportunity to observe the performers in the various tapes. Pick the ones you consider to be especially effective and try to identify the performance features that contribute to their effectiveness.

RUN ZVL 1   Watch the various performers' eye contact with the lens and see whether you feel that they are, indeed, talking to you. Also, observe their actions in close-ups.

RUN ZVL 2   All "mentors"—Sonny, Mary, Phil, Veronica, and Herb—and most of the other performers appearing on this CD-ROM use field teleprompters. Do you feel that they are "reading" their copy? If not, what makes them seem to be talking to you?

K E Y C O N C E P T S

- **Talent refers to video performers and actors. Performers portray themselves; actors portray somebody else.**

- **Eye contact with the camera lens establishes eye contact with the viewer.**

- **When on a close-up, keep your gestures small and slow.**

- **When taking a level, speak at the volume you will actually use during the performance, and speak long enough to set the volume on the audio console.**

- **Always respond promptly to the floor manager's cues.**

- **When acting for the video medium, you must *feel* the role, rather than merely act it out.**

- **Meticulously follow the rehearsed blocking during each take. If you can't see the camera lens, you won't be in the shot.**

- **Makeup is used to enhance, correct, or change appearance.**

- **Apply makeup under lights that have the same color temperature as those in the performance area.**

cyclorama A U-shaped continuous piece of canvas or muslin for backing of scenery and action. Hardwall cycs are permanently installed in front of one or two of the studio walls. Also called *cyc*.

flat A piece of standing scenery used as background or to simulate the walls of a room. There are hardwall and softwall flats.

intercom Short for *intercommunication system*. Used for all production and engineering personnel involved in the production of a show. The most widely used system has telephone headsets to facilitate voice communication on several wired or wireless channels. Includes other systems, such as I.F.B. and cellular telephones.

master control Controls the program input, storage, and retrieval for on-the-air telecasts. Also oversees technical quality of all program material.

monitor High-quality video receiver used in the video studio and control rooms. Cannot receive broadcast signals.

P.L. Stands for private line or phone line. Major intercommunication device in video studios.

props Short for *properties*. Furniture and other objects used by talent and for set decoration.

S.A. Stands for studio address system. A public address loudspeaker system from the control room to the studio. Also called *studio talkback* or *P.A.* (public address) *system*.

studio control room A room adjacent to the studio in which the director, producer, various production assistants, TD (technical director), audio engineer, and sometimes the LD (lighting director) perform their various production functions.

Production Environment: The Studio

T'S time for a studio visit. Although the Triple-I people have their own small studio, they usually rent local video production studio facilities for their bigger jobs.

Why use a studio? After all, the highly portable camcorders and lights make it possible to originate a video program anywhere, indoors or out. In tandem with portable transmission equipment and satellite uplinks, you have the whole earth as a stage. The reason video production studios are still used extensively is that they are independent of the weather and they offer maximum production control and optimal use of the production equipment. They provide for the proper environment and coordination of all major production elements—cameras, lighting, sound, scenery, and the action of production personnel and performers. Studios make video production highly efficient.

THE VIDEO PRODUCTION STUDIO
Physical layout and major installations

THE STUDIO CONTROL ROOM
Image control and sound control

MASTER CONTROL
Functions

STUDIO SUPPORT AREAS
Scenery and property storage, and makeup

SCENERY, PROPERTIES, AND SET DRESSINGS
Softwall and hardwall flats, set and hand props, and set dressings

SET DESIGN
Process message, floor plan, prop list, setup, and evaluating the floor plan

THE VIDEO PRODUCTION STUDIO

Video production studios are designed not only for multicamera productions and teamwork, but also to provide an optimal environment for single-camera video productions. Most studios are fairly large rectangular rooms with smooth floors and high ceilings from which the lighting instruments are suspended. They have a number of other technical installations that facilitate a great variety of productions and help make them highly efficient. **SEE 14.1**

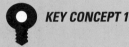

KEY CONCEPT 1   **The studio provides maximum production control.**

14.1

VIDEO PRODUCTION STUDIO

A well-designed studio provides optimal control for multicamera and single-camera video productions. It facilitates teamwork and the coordination of all major production elements.

Physical Layout

When evaluating a production studio, you should look not only at the electronic equipment it houses, but also at its physical layout—its size, floor and ceiling, and doors, walls, and air-conditioning.

Size   If you just do an interview, or have a single performer talk to the audience on a close-up, you can get by with amazingly little studio space. But if you plan a more ambitious project, such as a large panel discussion or the videotaping of a music show or drama, you need a larger studio. In general, it is easier to place a small show into a large studio than a large show into a small one. But you will quickly learn that large studios are usually harder to manage than small ones. Somehow, large studios require more energy to get a production started than do smaller ones; they necessitate longer camera and audio cables, more lighting instruments, and usually more crew.

If you have a choice, use a studio that fits your production needs. You don't need a Hollywood sound stage for a two-person interview. In fact, some news sets are placed right in the middle of an actual newsroom. On the other hand, don't try to squeeze a large dance troupe into a small studio just because you feel the small studio is more manageable.

Because studios are often used to store scenery or large set properties, the actual usable floor space of a studio is considerably smaller than the floor plan might indicate. Note that *all scenic design must be based on usable floor space.*

Floor and ceiling   A good studio must have a hard, level, and even floor so that cameras can travel freely and smoothly. Most studios have a concrete floor that is polished or covered with hard plastic or seamless linoleum. Wood floors are simply too soft to withstand the constant moving of scenery, heavy set properties and platforms, and camera dollies.

One of the most important design features of a good studio is adequate ceiling height. The ceiling must be high enough to accommodate normal 10-foot scenery and to provide enough space for the lighting grid or battens. Although you may get by with a minimum ceiling height of 14 feet for very small studios, most professional studios have ceilings that are 30 or more feet above the studio floor. Such a high ceiling makes it possible to suspend the lighting instruments above even tall scenery, and leaves enough space above them to dissipate the heat.

Doors, walls, and air-conditioning   Studio doors seem rather unimportant until you have to move scenery, furniture, and large equipment in and out. Undersized studio doors can cause a great deal of frustration for the production crew and frequently damage to equipment and scenery. Good studio doors must also be soundproof enough to keep all but the loudest noises from leaking into the studio.

The studio walls and ceiling are normally treated with sound-absorbing material to "deaden" the studio. A fairly "dead" studio minimizes reverberation, which means that it keeps the sounds from bouncing indiscriminately off the walls.

At least two or three sides of the studio are normally covered with a *cyclorama*, or *cyc*—a continuous piece of muslin or canvas suspended from a pipe or heavy curtain track. The light-gray or light-blue colored cyc serves as a convenient neutral background for a variety of setups, as shown in figure 14.1. A *ground row*, which is a curved piece of scenery placed on the studio floor in front of the cyc, helps to blend the vertical cyc into the studio floor to form a seamless background. **SEE 14.2**

Some cycloramas are suspended from a double track, with the front track holding a variety of additional curtains, called *drops*. The most frequently used drops are the chroma-key drop, which consists of a large piece of chroma-key blue cloth, and a black one, used for special lighting effects.

Some studios have *hardwall cycs* built into them. These are erected directly in front of one of the studio walls. The ground row is part of the hard-wall cyc. **SEE 14.3**

The advantages of a hardwall cyc are that it does not wrinkle or tear even after longtime use and it can be easily repainted when soiled. The disadvantages of a hardwall cyc are that it has a high degree of sound reflectance, often causing unwanted echoes, and it takes up considerable studio space.

14.2

GROUND ROW

The ground row is a curved piece of scenery that is placed on the studio floor in front of the cyclorama to blend the two into a seamless background.

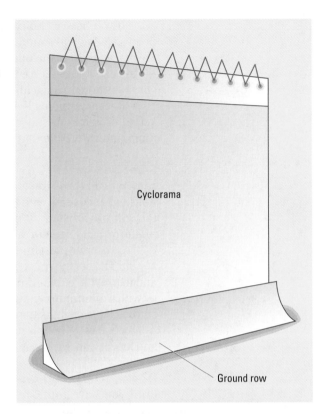

14.3

HARDWALL CYC

The hardwall cyc is constructed of fiberboard and placed in front of one of the studio walls. The ground row is built in.

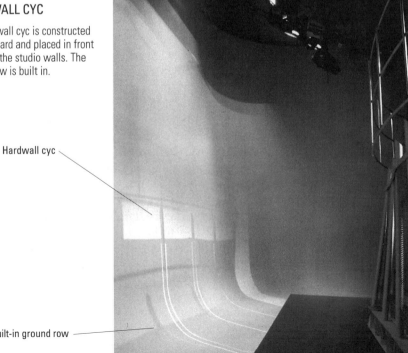

Many studios suffer from air-conditioning problems. Because the lighting instruments generate so much heat, the air-conditioning system must work overtime. When going full-blast, all but the most expensive systems create air noise, which is inevitably picked up by the sensitive studio mics and duly amplified in the audio console. You must then decide to keep the air-conditioning going despite the noise it makes, or turn it off, exposing talent, crew, and equipment to uncomfortably high studio temperatures. *READY ZVL 1*

Major Installations

Regardless of size, all studios have similar basic technical installations, which include lights, wall outlets, intercom systems, monitors, and studio speakers.

Lights   As you remember from chapter 7, most of the lighting instruments used in a video production studio are suspended from a lighting grid or movable battens, as shown in figure 14.3. Hanging the lighting instruments above the scenery and action keeps the lights out of camera range, allows the cameras and people to move freely about, and minimizes the time needed for lighting a scene. Many studios have the lighting patchboard (which routes various lights to a specific dimmer), and even the actual dimmer controls, in the studio itself. When using computerized light control units, you may find the major control unit in the control room, but an identical control unit in the studio. The one in the studio is used for setup and rehearsals; the one in the control room for the actual studio production.

Outlets   You may not consider wall outlets an important factor in studio design, unless you discover that there are not enough of them or that they are in the wrong places. There should be several groups of outlets for cameras, microphones, monitor lines, intercommunication headsets, and regular AC power distributed along all four walls. If all the outlets are concentrated on only one wall, you will have to string long power cables and extension cords throughout the studio to get the equipment into the desired positions around the scenery.

All outlets must be clearly marked so that you will not plug a certain piece of equipment into a wrong outlet. For example, if you plug your headset XLR connector into a mic outlet instead of the intercom outlet, the director's cues will not reach you, regardless of the director's voice level. Plugging the XLR mic cable into the intercom outlet will similarly interrupt the expected signal flow. This marking is especially important when the outlets are behind the cyc, where it is usually dark and there is little space to maneuver.

Intercommunication system   Reliable *intercom* systems are one of the most important technical installations. Normal studio intercoms use *P.L.* and *I.F.B.* systems. The **P.L.** *(private line* or *phone line)* system allows all production and engineering personnel to be in constant voice contact with one another. Each member of the production team and technical crew wears a headset with a small microphone for talkback. Such systems can be wired (through the camera cables or separate intercom cables) or, in larger studios, wireless. Most P.L. systems operate on at least two channels, so that different groups can be addressed simultaneously yet separately.

As you already know, the I.F.B. (interruptible foldback or feedback) system allows the director or producer to communicate directly with the talent, who wear tiny earpieces instead of telephone headsets while on the air.

Monitors   You need at least one fairly large monitor in the studio that shows the line-out pictures to everyone on the floor. By viewing the line-out picture, the production crew can anticipate a number of production tasks. For example, the camera that is not on the air can vary its shot so that it does not duplicate that of the on-the-air camera, and the floor manager can see how close he or she can be to the talent for the necessary signals without getting into camera range. The microphone boom operator can test how far the mic can be lowered before it gets into the camera shot.

News- and weathercasters often work with several studio monitors that carry not only the line-out pictures, but also the remote feeds and videotape playbacks. Because the weathercaster actually stands in front of a plain chroma-key backdrop when pointing to the various areas on the (nonexistent) weather map, the monitor, which shows the complete key including the map, is essential for guiding the talent's gestures. For audience participation shows, you need several monitors to show how the event looks on the screen.

Studio speakers   The studio speakers do for the program sound what video monitors do for the video portion. The studio speakers can feed the program sound or any other sounds—music, telephone rings, crashing noises—into the studio to be synchronized with the action. They can also be used for the *S.A.* (studio address) system (also called *P.A.,* for public address system), which allows the control room personnel (usually the director) to talk to the studio personnel who are not on headsets. The S.A. system is obviously not used on the air, but it is helpful for calling the crew back to rehearsal, reminding them of the time remaining for the rehearsal, or advising them to put on their P.L. headsets.

THE STUDIO CONTROL ROOM

The *studio control room,* housed in a separate area adjacent to the studio, is designed to accommodate the people who make the decisions while production is under way as well as the equipment necessary to control the video and audio portions of the production.

The people normally working in the control room are the director and producer and their associates, the technical director (TD), the C.G. operator, the audio engineer, and sometimes the lighting director (LD).

The control room equipment is designed and arranged to coordinate the total production process. Specifically, it facilitates the selection and sequencing of available video images, the selection and mixing of various sound inputs, and the lighting control. Some control rooms have windows that let the control room personnel see what is going on in the studio. More often, however, you will find that the only way you can see what is going on in the studio is by watching the monitors that show the various camera points of view. *READY ZVL 2*

KEY CONCEPT 2 The control room is designed to coordinate the studio production process.

Image Control

The image control section contains the equipment necessary to select and sequence the various video inputs, to coordinate the video with the audio, and to communicate with the production people, technical crew, and talent.

Monitors   When you walk into a control room, you will probably be amazed at the great number of video *monitors* arranged in stacks. **SEE 14.4** It is not uncommon to find thirty or more monitors in the control room of a medium-sized studio. Each of the monitors displays a separate video input.

14.4

CONTROL ROOM MONITOR STACK

The control room monitors show all available video sources, such as the studio cameras, remote video, VTRs, C.G., ESS, and special effects. The large color monitors show the preview video (the upcoming shots) and the line-out (what is being sent to the videotape machine and/or the transmitter).

14.5

SIMPLE MONITOR STACK

Even this simple control room display requires fourteen monitors: three camera previews; three VTRs; two remote feeds; one each for C.G., ESS, and special effects; and one large color monitor each for preview, line, and air.

Even a small control room requires a surprising number of monitors. Let's count them and identify their functions. **SEE 14.5**

Camera preview	3	(one for each camera)
VTRs	3	(one for each playback VTR)
Remote	2	(remote feeds; can also be used for additional cameras)
C.G.	1	
Still store	1	
Special effects	1	
Preview	1	
Line	1	
Air	1	(if an on-the-air or cable station studio, this monitor will show what the home viewer sees)
Total	14	monitors

These monitors are stacked in a variety of configurations in front of the director and TD. The preview (or preset) and line monitors are usually relatively large color monitors, placed side by side. The air monitor is also a large color monitor. All other preview monitors are smaller and black-and-white. The C.G.

operator has a separate color monitor for composing the text. The text or title is then sent to the preview monitor or a separate color C.G. monitor.

You may ask how anybody can ever watch all of these monitors at the same time. Actually, you don't pay full attention to all of them all the time, but focus your attention on the monitors that carry the video most important to you. Nevertheless, you must always be aware of what the rest of the monitors are showing. Such an overview takes practice, similar to a maestro reading a complex score while conducting an orchestra.

Intercom   The director also has easy access to a variety of intercom switches that control the P.L., S.A., and I.F.B. systems. The associate director, who sits next to the director, uses the same switches. The producer, who sits next to the director or, more common, behind him or her, will normally have a duplicate set of intercom switches. This extra set enables the producer to communicate with various production people and talent without interfering with the director.

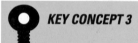

KEY CONCEPT 3   **A reliable and flexible intercom system is essential for effective teamwork in multicamera studio productions.**

Program sound   In addition to watching the preview monitors, giving instructions to various production people, and listening to the P.L., the director must also listen to the line-out audio to coordinate the video portion with the sound. A separate volume control enables the director to adjust the control room speakers, called *audio monitors,* without affecting the volume of the line-out audio. You will find that listening to the program sound is one of the hardest things to learn as a beginning director.

Switcher   The video switcher is located right next to the director's position. This proximity enables the TD (who is normally doing the switching) to use the same monitor stack as the director and be in close physical proximity with him or her. This way the director can communicate with the TD not only through the P.L. system, but also through hand gestures. For instance, by moving his or her arm at a certain speed, the director can indicate to the TD how fast a dissolve should be.

When fast cutting is required, some directors prefer to do their own switching (labor unions permitting), or snap their fingers, rather than call for a take once a shot has been readied. Such physical cues are faster and more precise than verbal ones.   **SEE 14.6** In smaller productions, directors often do the switching, a practice not recommended for complex shows.

KEY CONCEPT 4   **The director and TD must sit next to each other in the control room.**

14.6

PRODUCTION SWITCHER IN CONTROL ROOM

The production switcher is located right next to the director's position.

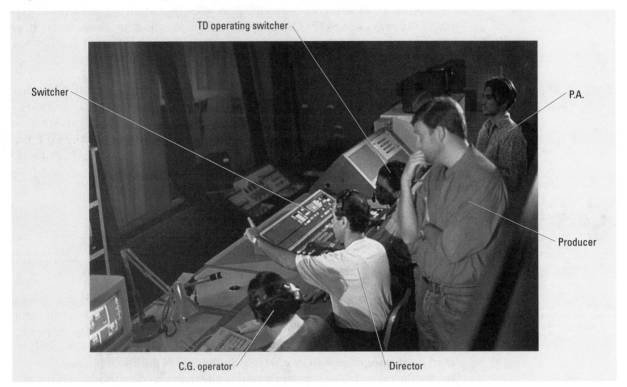

Switcher

TD operating switcher

P.A.

Producer

C.G. operator

Director

Character generator The C.G. and the C.G. operator are also located in the control room. Although most of the titles are usually prepared ahead of production, there are always some changes that need to be made. Especially during live or live-on-tape productions, the producer or director may call for titles that have not been preprogrammed. By having the C.G. operator in the control room, such changes are easily communicated and quickly done.

Clocks and stopwatches These timing tools are essential in broadcast operations where the programs are aired according to a second-by-second schedule. But even if your productions are videotaped for postproduction, the clock will tell you whether the taping session is on schedule, and the stopwatch will guide you when inserting other recorded material. Digital stopwatches—actually little clocks—give you a choice of running forward from the start of the program, or backward from the end-time. When running backward, the stopwatch will display the time actually left in the program. Some directors prefer analog clocks and stopwatches, because they can "look ahead" by watching the hands of the clock moving and thus pace the remaining program more accurately.

Lighting control and CCUs   Some control rooms house the lighting dimmer controls and/or the CCUs (camera control units) for each camera. The advantage of having this additional equipment in the control room is that all image control is in a single location, facilitating communication among the various parties. The disadvantage is that the control room gets quite crowded with additional equipment and people.

Sound Control

The audio booth is a little audio studio attached to the control room. It is usually isolated from the video control room so that the audio engineer is not disturbed by all the talk. Most audio booths have a window that allows the audio engineer to see the activities in the control room and perhaps even the director's preview monitors. Although well-equipped audio booths have both a preview and a line monitor, the additional preview monitors aid the audio engineer in anticipating and executing tight audio cues.

The audio booth normally contains an audio console, a patch bay, various DAT machines, digital carts, and CD players. The audio engineer can listen to the director via P.L. headsets or a small cue speaker and can talk to the control room and studio through the P.L. and S.A. systems. The program sound is monitored by high-quality program speakers. **SEE 14.7**

14.7

AUDIO CONTROL BOOTH

The television audio control booth contains a variety of audio control equipment, such as the control console, patchbay, CD player, DAT machines, loud-speakers, intercom systems, and a video line monitor.

Window to video control room   Computer display of console functions

Audio console   Studio talkback

MASTER CONTROL

If you use the studio strictly for producing videotaped programs, you don't need a master control room, assuming that the CCUs are located somewhere in the studio control room. But most larger nonbroadcast production houses have an equipment and communication center, called master control. If you are in the business of telecasting programs over the air or cable, master control becomes an essential electronic nerve center.

Master control normally houses the studio CCUs, various on-line VTRs and computer-controlled video cart machines, video servers, electronic still store (ESS) systems, and various installations that monitor the technical quality of every second of programming that is sent to the transmitter or cable. In nonbroadcast operations master control may contain CCUs, VTRs and other video- and audio-recording machines, C.G.s, and various monitors and intercom systems.

The basic functions of master control in broadcast operations are overseeing the technical quality of all program material and controlling program input, storage, and retrieval. *Program input* means that master control keeps track of all incoming programs, regardless of whether they come via satellite, cable, or mail. All videotaped material is stored either in bins in the master control area or in designated storage rooms. To aid retrieval each program, however long or short, is given an identification code, often called the "house number." *Program retrieval* means the selection, ordering, and distribution (on-the-air, cable, or satellite transmission) of the program material.

The *program log* is a document that dictates program retrieval and determines which program goes on the air at what time. It lists every second of programming aired on a particular day, and other important information, such as the title and type of each program and its origin (local live, videotape, or network feed). The log is distributed throughout the station by computer display and also as hard copy. **SEE 14.8**

14.8

PROGRAM LOG

The program log is a second-by-second list of all programs telecast during a broadcast day. It shows the scheduled (start) times, program title and type, video and audio origin (tape, live, or feed), the house number, and other pertinent broadcast information.

HSE NUMBER	SCH TIME	PGM	LENGTH	ORIGIN VID	AUD
N 3349	10 59 40	NEWS CLOSE	015	VT4	VT4
S11	10 59 55	STATION BR	005	ESS	CART20
E 1009	11 00 00	GOING PLACES 1	030	VT5	VT5
C5590	11 00 30	FED EX	010	VT2	VT2
C 9930-0	11 00 40	HAYDEN PUBLISHING	010	VT18	VT18
C 10004	11 00 50	SPORTS HILIGHTS	005	ESS	CART21
PP 99	11 00 55	STATION PROMO SPORTS	005	VT22	VT22
E 1009	11 01 00	GOING PLACES CONT 2	1100	VT5	VT5
C 9990-34	11 12 00	HYDE PRODUCTS	030	VT34	VT34
C 774-55	11 12 30	COMPESI FISHING	010	VT35	VT35
C 993-48	11 12 40	KIPPER COMPUTERS	010	VT78	VT78
PS	11 12 50	RED CROSS	005	ESS	CART22
PP 1003	11 12 55	STATION PROMO GOOD MRNG	005	VT23	VT23
E 1009	11 13 00	GOING PLACES CONT 3	1025	VT5	VT5
C 222-99	11 23 25	WHITNEY MOTORCYCLE	020	VT33	VT33
C 00995-45	11 23 45	IDEAS TO IMAGES	010	VT91	VT91
PS	11 23 55	AIDS AWARENESS	005	ESS	CART02
E 1009	11 24 00	GOING PLACES CONT 4	100	VT5	VT5
N 01125	11 25 00	NEWSBREAK ***LIVE	010	ST1LV	ST1
C 00944-11	11 25 10	ALL SEASONS GNRL FOODS	030	VT27	VT27
N 01125	11 25 40	NEWS CONT***LIVE	200	ST1LV	ST1
C 995-89	11 27 40	BLOSSER FOR PRESIDENT	020	VT24	VT24
PP 77	11 28 00	NEXT DAY	010	VT19	VT19

14.9

MASTER CONTROL SWITCHING AREA

Master control serves as the final video and audio control for all program material before it is broadcast or distributed by other means (satellite or cable). Computers run all master control functions, with the master control technician overseeing the automated functions and, if necessary, taking over control manually in case of emergency.

Manual master control switcher   Computer log display

The actual switching from program to program is mostly done by computer. In case the computer system goes down, however, an operator monitors the automatic switching and is ready to press the manual master control switcher into service. **SEE 14.9**

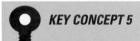 **KEY CONCEPT 5**   **Master control checks the technical quality of all programs and facilitates program input, storage, and retrieval.**

STUDIO SUPPORT AREAS

No studio can function properly without support areas that house scenery and properties, and makeup and dressing rooms. Unfortunately, even large and relatively new studios are usually lacking in such support areas. As a consequence the studios themselves become partial storage areas for scenery and even serve as makeup and dressing rooms.

Scenery and Property Storage

One of the most important features of scenery and property storage is ease of retrieval. The floor crew must be able to find and pull each piece of scenery without having to dig it out from under all others. The prop areas and boxes must be clearly labeled, especially if you store small hand props in various boxes.

Makeup

Wherever you apply makeup, it must be done in lighting conditions that are identical to those in the studio. Most makeup rooms have two types of illumination: standard indoor color temperature of 3,200°K and standard outdoor color temperature of 5,600°K. Always check your makeup on-camera in the actual performance area before the dress rehearsal and again before the performance.

SCENERY, PROPERTIES, AND SET DRESSINGS

Scenery and properties are used to create a specific environment in which the action takes place. When dealing with scenery and properties in video production, you must always keep in mind that it is the *camera* that looks at the scenic environment, not the crew or casual studio visitor. The set must be detailed enough to withstand the close-up scrutiny of the camera, yet plain enough to avoid cluttered pictures and drawing attention away from the performers or actors. Careful attention to set detail is especially important when using high-definition television cameras. The high resolution of HDTV increases the illusion of depth and makes even background detail more visible. The set must also allow for optimal camera movement and angles, microphone placement and mobility, appropriate lighting, and maximum action by the talent. It is a major factor in setting style.

KEY CONCEPT 6   **Scenery must create a certain environment and must allow for optimal lighting, audio pickup, and camera movement.**

Scenery

Although the design and construction of scenery requires special training and skills, you should know what standard set units are and how to use them for creating simple environments. Here we discuss (1) softwall flats, (2) hardwall flats, (3) set modules, (4) seamless paper and drops, and (5) special set pieces, platforms, and wagons.

Softwall flats   A *flat* is a freestanding piece of scenery used as background or to simulate the walls of a room. *Softwall flats* are background units constructed of a lightweight wood frame and covered with muslin. The wood frame consists of 1×3 lumber that is glued together and then reinforced at the corners by ¼-inch plywood pieces. To keep the frame from twisting, it is further strengthened by two diagonal braces and a toggle rail. If the studio floor is hard, you can put metal gliders on the bottom rail of the flat so you can push it around without damaging the flat or the floor. **SEE 14.10**

The traditional, and still most practical, way to tie softwall flats together is by using lashlines. When joining flats, you actually lash two pieces of scenery together with a clothesline that is attached to the right top rail of each flat and pulled through the various cleats, similar to lacing the hooks of a boot. **SEE 14.11** Flats are

14.10

SOFTWALL FLATS

Softwall flats are made of 1 × 3 lumber and covered with muslin. The hardware is needed to connect the flats for background scenery.

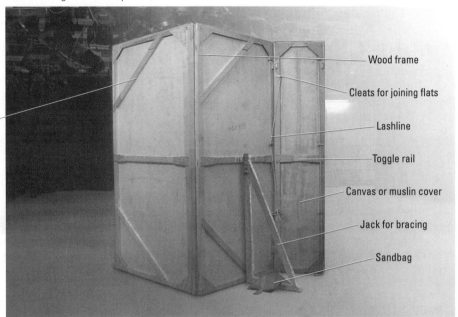

Diagonal, or corner, brace

Wood frame

Cleats for joining flats

Lashline

Toggle rail

Canvas or muslin cover

Jack for bracing

Sandbag

14.11

FLATS JOINED BY LASHLINE

Softwall flats are connected by lashing them together with a clothesline, called a lashline, and supported by a wood brace, called a jack. Jacks are weighted down with sandbags or metal weights.

supported by *jacks*—wood braces that are hinged, tied, or fastened with C-clamps to the flats and are weighted down and held in place by sandbags or metal weights.

Standard softwall flats have a uniform height but various widths. The height is usually 10 feet, or 8 feet for small sets or studios with low ceilings; width ranges from 1 to 5 feet. When two flats are hinged together, they are called

14.12

HARDWALL SCENERY

Hardwall scenery is built with a sturdy wood or metal frame and is covered with plywood or fiberboard material. Most hardwall scenery has built-in casters or is placed on small wagons for mobility.

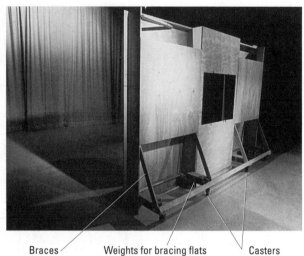

Braces with casters   Covered with hardwall material (thin plywood facing)   Braces   Weights for bracing flats   Casters

twofolds or *books* (because they open like a book); three flats hinged together constitute a *threefold.*

Softwall flats are easy to move about, assemble, and store, but their simple construction is also a disadvantage. They tend to shake when you close a door or window on the set, or if someone or something brushes against them. They are ideal for rehearsal and for less demanding productions.

Hardwall flats Most professional video production sets are constructed with *hardwall flats.* They are usually built for a specific set and do not always conform to the standard dimensions of softwall scenery. Although there is no standard way to build hardwall scenery, most flats are constructed with a sturdy wood frame or slotted steel frame (which looks like a big erector set) and covered with plywood or pressed fiberboard. Most hardwall scenery is moved with the help of built-in casters and joined with bolts or C-clamps. **SEE 14.12**

The advantage of hardwall scenery is that it is extremely sturdy; if a scene calls for slamming the door, you can do so without fear of shaking the whole set. You can also attach pictures or posters the way you would on a real wall. The disadvantages of hardwall flats are that they are expensive to build, difficult to move and set up, and even harder to store. Hardwall scenery is also apt to reflect sound and cause unwanted reverberations.

Set modules Smaller video production companies, whose scenery demands are usually limited to news, interviews, office sets, or environments in which various products are displayed and demonstrated, often use set modules. A *set module* is a series of hardwall flats and three-dimensional set pieces whose dimensions match whether they are used vertically (right-side up) or horizontally (on their sides). They can be assembled in different combinations, similar to building blocks. For example, you might use a modular hardwall set piece as a hardwall flat in one production, and as a platform in the next. Or you might dismantle a modular desk and use the boxes (representing the drawers) and the top as display units. A variety of set modules are commercially available.

Seamless paper and painted drops   As you recall, the cyclorama is a large, plain, seamless drop that serves as a neutral background, as shown in figure 14.1. In the absence of a cyc, you can construct a limited neutral area with a roll of seamless paper (usually 9 feet wide by 36 feet long) simply by unrolling it and stapling it horizontally on softwall flats. Seamless paper rolls come in a variety of colors and are relatively inexpensive.

Painted drops, on the other hand, usually refer to rolls of paper or canvas with realistic or, more often, stylized background scenes painted on them.

You can also create believable backgrounds electronically. Such synthetic environments are discussed in chapter 15.

Special set pieces, platforms, and wagons   Set pieces consist of freestanding three-dimensional objects, such as pillars, pylons (which look like three-sided pillars), sweeps (large, curved pieces of scenery), folding screens, steps, and periaktoi (plural of *periaktos*). A periaktos is a three-sided standing unit that looks like a large pylon; it moves and swivels on casters. **SEE 14.13**

14.13

SET PIECES

Set pieces are freestanding three-dimensional scenic objects used as background or foreground pieces.

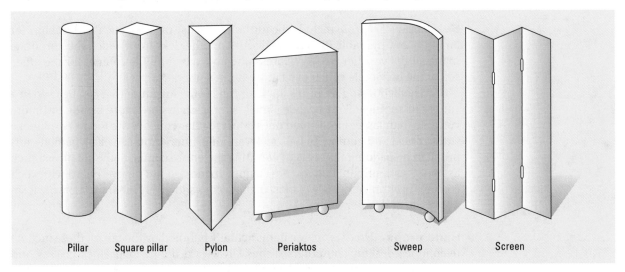

| Pillar | Square pillar | Pylon | Periaktos | Sweep | Screen |

You may want to paint a periaktos differently on at least one of the three sides to make it more versatile. For example, if one of the sides is painted a chroma-key blue, with the remaining two sides colored a warm yellow, you can quickly provide a chroma-key background simply by swiveling the periaktos (or series of periaktoi) to the blue side.

Set pieces are often constructed in modular dimensions so that they can be fitted together in various combinations. Some set pieces, such as pillars and pylons, are somewhat unstable and must be secured so that they do not tip over when bumped by a crew member, talent, or a piece of equipment. It is always better to overbrace than underbrace the set.

Platforms are elevation devices. Normal platforms are 6 inches, 8 inches, or 12 inches high and can be stacked. Sometimes the whole platform is called a *riser*, although technically a riser is only the elevation part of the platform without its top. Platforms are often used for interview and panel discussion sets so that the cameras see the participants straight-on rather than look down on them. When used for interviews, the entire platform should be covered with a piece of carpet. As well as make the set attractive, the carpet will also absorb the hollow sounds when people are moving on the platform. You can further deaden these sounds by filling the interior of the platform with foam rubber or foam spray.

Some 6-inch platforms have four heavy casters, converting the platforms into *wagons*, which can support scenery and set pieces. When mounted on a series of wagons, a heavy set becomes quite mobile and can be repositioned with relative ease. Once in place, wagons should be secured with wood wedges and/or sandbags so that they do not move unexpectedly. **READY ZVL 3**

Properties

In video production, *properties—props* for short—and *set dressings* are often more important to signify a particular environment than the background scenery. You will work with two kinds of properties: set props and hand props.

Set props *Set props* include the furniture you use on a set, such as the chairs for an interview, the table for a panel discussion, the desk from which the corporate manager delivers her weekly address, the bookcase and file cabinet for the office set, or the inevitable couch used in situation comedies.

When choosing set props, look for functional furniture that can be used in a variety of settings. For instance, small, simple chairs are more useful and more versatile than large upholstered ones. Most regular couches are too low and make sitting down and getting up look awkward on camera. You can easily remedy this problem by padding the seats or elevating the entire couch. Some set props, such as news desks or panel tables, are custom-made. Do not go overboard with such custom furniture, especially if most of the scenes show only medium shots or close-ups of the performers.

Hand props *Hand props* are items actually handled by the talent; these include telephones, desktop computers, dishes, silverware, books, magazines, glasses, and flowers. Hand props must work and they must be real. A bottle that doesn't open on cue can cause costly production delays. Because hand props are the extension of the talent's gestures and actions, and because of the close scrutiny by the video camera, you cannot get by with fake props. A papier-mâché chalice that looks regal on stage looks ridiculous on the video screen. Equally ridiculous is trying to toil under the weight of an empty suitcase. Whereas the theater audience may have some sympathy for your toil, the television viewer will more likely consider it a comic routine or an unfortunate production mistake.

If you have to use food, make certain that it is fresh and that the dishes and silverware are meticulously clean. Liquor is generally replaced with water (for clear spirits), tea (for whiskey), or soft drinks (for white and red wine). With all due respect for realism, such substitutions are perfectly appropriate.

Set Dressings

Set dressings include things that you would place in your own living quarters to make them look attractive and to express your taste and style of living. Although the flats may remain the same from one type of show to another, the dressing gives each set its distinguishing characteristic and helps establish the style of the environment. Set dressings include such items as curtains, pictures, sculptures, posters, lamps, indoor plants, decorative items for a desk and bookshelves, or a favorite toy that survived childhood. Secondhand stores or flea markets provide an unlimited source for such things. In case of emergency, you can always raid your own living quarters or office. As with props, set dressings must be realistic so that they can withstand even the probing eye of an HDTV camera.

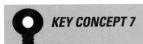

KEY CONCEPT 7 **Properties and set dressings determine the character and style of the environment.**

SET DESIGN

Although you may never be called upon to design a set, you will certainly have to tell the set designer what environment you envision and why. You will also have to know how to interpret a set design so that you can evaluate the set relative to the process message and technical requirements (such as lighting, camera and talent movement, and audio pickup).

Process Message

Once again, a clear statement of the process message will guide you in designing the appropriate environment. For example, if the process message of an interview is to have the viewer get to know the guest as intimately as possible and probe her feelings and attitudes, what kind of set do you need? Because you should show the guest in intimate close-ups throughout most of the show, you don't need an elaborate interview set. Two simple chairs in front of an uncluttered background will do just fine.

On the other hand, if the process message is to have the viewer see how the guest uses the physical environment of her office to reflect her power, you had better have the host conduct the interview on-location from the guest's actual office, or in a studio set that is a close copy of it.

As with all other medium requirements, in designing or evaluating a set you need to have a pretty good idea of what it is you want the viewer to see, hear, and feel. Once you have interpreted the process message as to scenic requirements, you must then learn to evaluate and translate the scene design—the floor plan— into an actual studio set.

Floor Plan

The floor plan is a diagram of scenery and set properties drawn onto a grid that resembles the usable floor area in the studio. To help you locate a certain spot on the studio floor, the lighting grid is normally superimposed over the floor plan, or a grid is drawn over the floor area similar to the orientation squares of a map. By using the lighting grid, the floor plan can also be used for drawing a light plot.

Elaborate set designs are always drawn to scale, such as the common ¼ inch = 1 foot. There are templates that have in-scale cutouts for typical set pieces, such as tables, sofas, chairs, beds, or chests of drawers. You can also use one of the many computer programs on the market for architectural layouts or interior design.

If the setup is relatively simple, the art director may make only a rough sketch that shows the background scenery and set props and the approximate location of the set, leaving it up to the floor manager to place the set in the most advantageous spot in the studio. **SEE 14.14** You may recall that it is much easier to place a set according to existing lighting—key, fill, back, and background lights—than rehang lighting instruments to suit an arbitrary set location. The floor plan should indicate all scenery, including doors and windows, as well as the type and location of set props and major hand props. **SEE 14.15**

14.14

SIMPLE FLOOR PLAN

The floor plan grid (often the lighting grid) helps locate the position of scenery and set props.

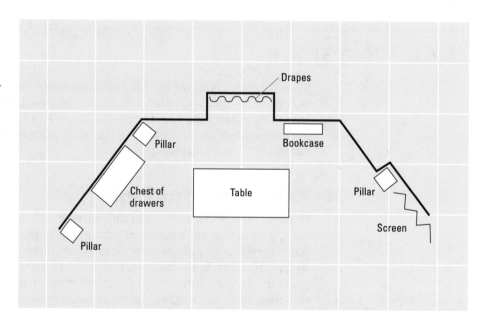

FLOOR PLAN WITH SET AND HAND PROPS

More-elaborate floor plans indicate the type and position of the set props (furniture, lamp, sculpture, paintings) and major hand props (newspaper, tea set, magazines).

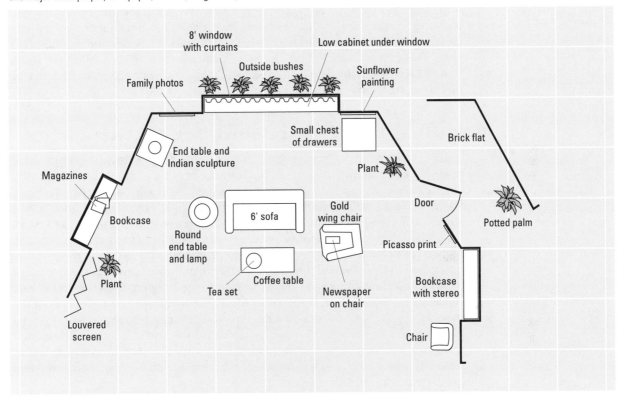

When drawing a floor plan, keep in mind that the set must be workable for the cameras: It must provide adequate backing for a variety of camera angles. A common mistake of inexperienced set designers is to show inadequate backing for the set props and talent action. Somehow the furniture in the set always seems to take up more room than anticipated. This problem is especially apparent when the floor plan is not drawn to scale.

Another frequent mistake is that the set design exceeds the available floor space. As mentioned earlier, the cyc and the items stored in the studio can radically reduce the usable floor space. The floor plan must show the space that is actually available. To help the lighting people direct the back lights at the performance areas at not too steep an angle and avoid unwanted shadows on the background flats, all active furniture (furniture actually used by the talent) must be placed at least 6 to 8 feet from the background flats, as shown in figure 14.15.

▌ Prop List

Even if the floor plan shows some of the major set and hand props, all props must be itemized on a *prop list*. Some prop lists itemize set props, set dressings, and hand props separately; but you can combine them on a single list, provided you don't forget anything. Confirm with the property manager that the props you requested are actually available on the day or days you need them, and inspect each one to see whether it fits the intended scene design. For example, a Victorian chair would certainly look out of character in an otherwise modern office set. Verify that all listed props are delivered to you and that they are not damaged in any way before taking them into the studio.

▌ Using the Floor Plan for Setup

A floor plan is useless if you can't translate it into an actual set and performance environment. You must acquire some of the skills of an architect or builder, who can look at a blueprint of a building and visualize what it will look like when erected and how people will move through and function in it. Figure 14.16 shows how a simple floor plan (floor plan 1) translates into the corresponding setup. **SEE 14.16**

The ability to read a floor plan is a necessary skill for all production personnel. A good floor plan helps the floor manager and crew put up and dress the set fairly accurately, independent of the designer. The director can map out the major talent positions and blocking and also design the principal camera shots, positions, and movements before setting foot in the studio. The lighting director can lay out the basic light plot, and the audio engineer can determine mic placement. Also, by knowing how to read the floor plan, you can catch and often solve production problems before they occur. Because the floor plan is such a critical factor in production efficiency, you should insist on having one drawn even if the setup and production are relatively simple.

14.16

FLOOR PLAN 1 AND SETUP

Simple set

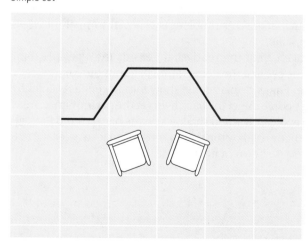
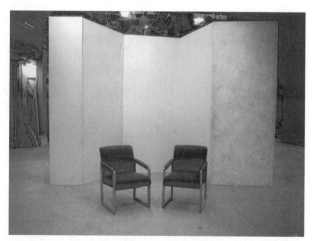

14.17

FLOOR PLAN 2

Interview set.

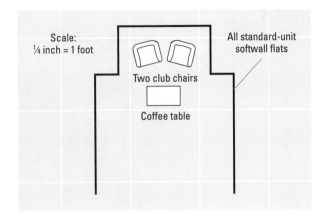

Scale:
¼ inch = 1 foot

All standard-unit
softwall flats

Two club chairs

Coffee table

Evaluating the Floor Plan

Floor plan 2 shows a set for a two-camera live interview. Take a close look at it and list all the potential production problems you can find. **SEE 14.17**

Now let's compare our lists:

▶ Assuming that the flats are drawn to the customary scale (¼ inch = 1 foot), the back wall is a 4-foot flat—hardly enough backing for two chairs and a table. The chairs and coffee table are obviously drawn to another, smaller scale.

▶ The chairs are too close to the back and side walls for good lighting. The back lights would have to come in at an extremely steep angle, and the key lights would have to strike the subjects directly from the front—not exactly what you would call good lighting.

▶ There is no way you can use two cameras. The set opening is too narrow to have the cameras stand side by side and engage in any kind of cross shooting. The only way you can use this set is to have a single camera shoot straight into the box at the chairs.

▶ The box set is bound to cause audio problems. The parallel walls are apt to reflect the sound back and forth, creating the infamous "inside a barrel" sound.

Let's do the same with floor plan 3. This one shows an office interior in which two actors demonstrate the do's and don'ts of a job interview. The script for the two-camera live-on-tape production calls for frequent over-the-shoulder and cross-shots. List the potential production problems before reading on. **SEE 14.18**

Now let's compare notes:

▶ The interviewer's chair is much too close to the background for good back lighting.

▶ The file cabinet and bookcase are useless; they are out of camera range unless one of the cameras takes an extreme straight-on long shot, in which case the camera would overshoot the back wall.

14.18

FLOOR PLAN 3

Office set.

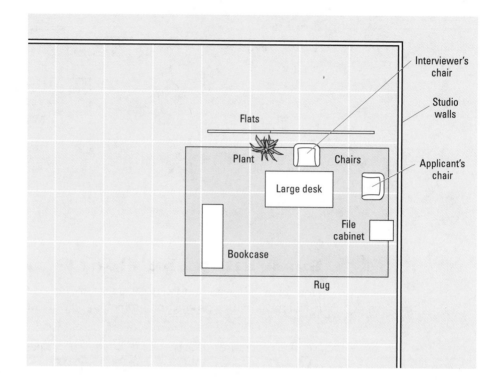

Interviewer's
chair

Studio
walls

Applicant's
chair

Flats

Plant

Chairs

Large desk

File
cabinet

Bookcase

Rug

▶ The applicant is sitting much too close to—*oops*—the studio wall. There is no backing indicated, and that means that we would see the blank studio wall. Also, there is no way to hang a back light that close to the wall.

▶ The way the people are positioned makes over-the-shoulder or cross shooting impossible. There is no room behind the interviewer for a camera, and the file cabinet will prevent the other camera from squeezing behind the applicant.

▶ Even if there were enough room for the cameras for proper over-the-shoulder shooting, the rug would make it very difficult, if not impossible, for the studio cameras to move into the set.

▶ If you removed the file cabinet and managed to have the camera look over the applicant's left shoulder, the rubber plant would be directly in back of the interviewer. Such an arrangement is bound to cause composition problems by showing the plant as though it were growing out of the interviewer's head.

How does your list compare? Did you foresee most of the production problems? What changes would you recommend to make the set more workable? A revised floor plan 3 shows one possible solution. **SEE 14.19**

14.19

REVISED FLOOR PLAN 3

Office set.

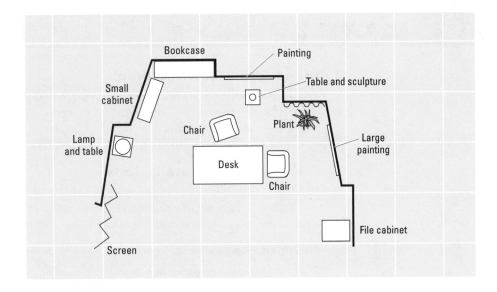

The rug is gone, and there is enough room for the cameras to maneuver for the over-the-shoulder shots. The background for each shot is interesting without competing for attention. The screen on the left side of the set and the file cabinet are a helpful way of showing the camera operators the outer limits of the set and thus preventing overshooting.

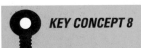 **KEY CONCEPT 8**   **The floor plan—a diagram of scenery and set props—shows the setup requirements and facilitates preproduction planning.**

You probably have a better idea now about how a studio provides an optimal production environment. First and foremost, it is independent of the weather and time of day. Rain or shine, morning or midnight make no difference when doing studio productions. The physical layout and major installations, the control room equipment, the makeup, scenery, and property areas—all are designed to facilitate a great variety of video productions. Although studio operations require a relatively large and highly coordinated production team, the studio makes video production extremely efficient. This studio visit certainly answered your question to the Triple-I people as to why all productions are not done in the field. As though the Triple-I field producer had read your mind, he suggests as your final experience that you participate in several field productions.

ONCE AGAIN, REMEMBER...

■ Video Production Studio

Video production studios are designed for multicamera productions and team-work. Important features are sufficient floor space, smooth floor for camera travel, adequate ceiling height so that the lights can be suspended, large doors, acoustically treated walls, and relatively quiet air-conditioning.

■ Major Studio Installations

The major studio installations include a lighting grid or movable battens, various wall outlets, intercommunication system between the studio and control room, studio video monitors, and studio speakers.

■ Control Room

The control room is designed and arranged to coordinate the total production process. It is usually divided into: the image control, with the switcher, C.G. monitor banks, various intercom lines, and sometimes the lighting control board; and the sound control, which resembles a small audio studio containing an audio console and various recording and playback equipment.

■ Master Control

Master control is important for television stations. Its basic functions are quality check, program input, program storage, and program retrieval. Most master control rooms house the CCUs (camera control units), various on-line VTRs (videotape recorders), video servers and other automated video playback equipment, and a link to the transmitter. Sometimes nonbroadcast production houses have a master control that contains camera control equipment, VTRs, and a variety of communication systems.

■ Studio Support Areas

Studio support areas include the scenery and property storage and the makeup and dressing rooms.

■ Scenery and Properties

The major video scenery consists of softwall and hardwall flats, a cyclorama and various drops, set pieces, platforms, and wagons. Properties include set props (such as furniture), hand props (items actually used by talent), and set dressings (artwork, lamps, and decorative plants).

ZETTL'S VIDEO LAB 2.1

*Click on the **process** monitor and load tape 6 **Methods**. It explores how the location in which you are shooting has a decisive influence on your preproduction, production, and postproduction activities.*

RUN ZVL 1 Play module 2 **Studio**. The important point made is that you don't always need a large studio to shoot effective scenes. If the script calls simply for someone to sit on a stool and talk to the audience, a small studio is all you need. Realize that large studios are harder to manage and require more personnel than small ones, but they afford more working space for multicamera shoots.

RUN ZVL 2 Play module 2 **Studio** again. This time watch the layout of the control room. Try to identify the various control room installations. Note the close proximity of the director to the TD.

RUN ZVL 3 Did you notice the large set piece being set up in the studio? You have seen it as an effective background in several of the tapes and modules of this CD-ROM. If you don't know which set piece it is, run module 2 **Studio** a third time.

KEY CONCEPTS

- The studio provides maximum production control.

- The control room is designed to coordinate the studio production process.

- A reliable and flexible intercom system is essential for effective teamwork in multicamera studio productions.

- The director and TD must sit next to each other in the control room.

- Master control checks the technical quality of all programs and facilitates program input, storage, and retrieval.

- Scenery must create a certain environment and must allow for optimal lighting, audio pickup, and camera movement.

- Properties and set dressings determine the character and style of the environment.

- The floor plan—a diagram of scenery and set props—shows the setup requirements and facilitates preproduction planning.

CHAPTER 15

KEY TERMS

contact person A person who is familiar with, and who can facilitate access to, the remote location and key people. Also called *contact*.

EFP Stands for electronic field production. Video production done outside the studio that is usually shot for postproduction (not live).

ENG Stands for electronic news gathering. The use of portable camcorders, lights, and sound equipment for the unplanned production of daily news stories. ENG is usually done for live transmission or immediate postproduction.

field production Any video production that happens outside the studio.

remote A production of a large, scheduled event done for live transmission or live-on-tape recording.

remote survey An inspection of the remote location by key production and engineering persons so that they can plan for the setup and use of production equipment. Also called *site survey*.

remote truck The vehicle that carries the control room, audio control, VTR section, video control section, and transmission equipment.

synthetic environment Electronically generated settings, either through chroma key or computer.

uplink truck Small truck that sends video and audio signals to a satellite.

virtual reality Computer-simulated environment with which the user can interact and that can change according to the user's commands.

Field Production and Synthetic Environments

FIELD *production* does not mean that you have to move your production to an actual field; rather, it refers to any video production that happens outside the studio. The MTV shoot you watched the Triple-I crew videotape in the street was an example of a field production. Field production also includes documentaries that are shot on location, or the elaborate remotes for sporting events or the Thanksgiving Day parade.

When moving your equipment outside the studio, you have the whole world as your stage. The trade-off for moving outside the studio into the field is control. In field productions you simply cannot create and control a specific production environment, but must *adapt* to one. If a shoot takes place outdoors, the weather is always a potential hazard; if you are indoors, the room may not be to your liking or conducive to effective video and audio pickup. Still, you can make the environment work for you instead of against you. This chapter gives you some hints about how to work effectively in the field, including ENG (electronic news gathering), EFP (electronic field production), and big remotes. From the field, we finally move into *synthetic environments* that are partially or entirely created by computer.

◾ **ELECTRONIC NEWS GATHERING**
News gathering and transmission

◾ **ELECTRONIC FIELD PRODUCTION**
Preproduction, including the remote survey, survey team, and location sketch; production, including the equipment checklist and shooting outdoors and indoors; and the postproduction wrap-up

◾ **BIG REMOTES**
The remote truck and remote transmission

◾ **SYNTHETIC ENVIRONMENTS**
Computer-generated settings, virtual reality, and interactive video

KEY CONCEPT 1   In field production you must adapt to the environment.

ELECTRONIC NEWS GATHERING

By its very nature, the time, specific nature, and location of news events cannot be planned. Neither can the coverage of such events, called *ENG*, or *electronic news gathering*. All you can do is run after the breaking news story and do your best to cover it. This does not mean that you give up all control over production procedures. Preproduction in ENG means that you have your equipment ready to go anywhere at any time and that your equipment will be functioning properly regardless of where you are and under what conditions you need to shoot.

News Gathering

As a news videographer, also called a "shooter," you are responsible not only for videotaping the story, but also for making the decisions on just how to tell it. In a breaking story, you must be able to assess the situation, have the equipment functioning, and capture the essence of the event—all in a matter of minutes. You rarely have time to consult your news producer or anyone else about what is going on or how to shoot it. But even in intense situations, good videographers are able to deliver well-composed shots that can be edited into a smooth sequence.

If you are sent out to cover a story with a reporter, the news-gathering process is slightly less hectic. You usually have some flexibility about where to place the field reporter for his or her "standup" report and in selecting the most effective shots for the story. You can choose as a background for the reporter a location that underlines the principal story (such as the city hall, college campus, county hospital, or airport).

Whenever possible have the reporter stand in a shaded area rather than in bright sunlight or, worse, in front of a brightly lit building. Bright sunlight will cause unflattering fast falloff and dense shadows, and the bright background will cause the reporter to be seen in silhouette. Even if you have a reflector handy to slow down the falloff, it is usually easier to place the reporter in a shaded area than to fight excessive sunlight. Do not forget to white-balance the camera for every new lighting situation. Watch what is behind the reporter so that you do not have street signs, trees, or telephone poles appear to be growing out of the reporter's head.

KEY CONCEPT 2   Whenever possible, have the reporter stand in a shaded area rather than in bright sunlight.

Be mindful of all audio requirements. Don't have the reporter deliver his or her report on the windiest corner of the street; instead, find a spot that is relatively protected. Small rooms or corridors with bare walls have a tendency to produce unwanted echoes or make reporters sound as though they are speaking inside a barrel. Take an audio level before each videotaping. Always have the camera mic open at the same time to record ambient sound on a second sound track of the videotape. At the end of the report, record at least one minute of ambient sound to help the editor bridge the sound changes at the edit points.

Transmission

When a live transmission of the news story is required, you need a production van that has the proper transmission equipment to relay the video and audio signals back to the station and ultimately to the station transmitter or satellite. **SEE 15.1**

15.1

ENG VAN

For ENG and routine productions, a large car or station wagon can serve as a production van. If the signal must be relayed to the station for live transmission or videotaping, a van that contains VTRs, generators, and microwave transmission equipment is used.

15.2

SATELLITE UPLINK TRUCK

The satellite uplink truck is a portable station that sends the video and audio signals to a specific satellite.

The signal can be sent from the camera to the van by ordinary camera cable or by a small tripod-mounted microwave transmitter connected to the camera. From the van the signal can be further relayed by microwave to the transmitter. If the signal must be directly "uplinked" to a communications satellite (positioned 23,300 miles above the earth), a truck that contains the satellite transmitting equipment, called the *uplink,* is used. **SEE 15.2** Trucks that are designed specifically to uplink news are called *SNVs (satellite news vehicles).* The satellite then amplifies the signal and sends it back to the receiving earth station or stations, called *downlinking.*

Although the signal transmission is always done by qualified engineers, you should at least know what is needed to get the live signal from the camera to the station transmitter. As you see, the casual chitchat among the host in the studio and the various guests located in different corners of the world requires a great amount of technical equipment and know-how.

ELECTRONIC FIELD PRODUCTION

Electronic field production, or *EFP,* includes all out-of-studio productions except news and the big remotes that more resemble multicamera studio productions than single-camera field productions. Documentaries, magazine news stories, investigative reports, travel shows, and exercise programs that are shot outdoors are all electronic field productions. Because all field productions are planned, you can prepare for them in the preproduction phase. The more preproduction that goes into an EFP, the more likely it is to succeed. In fact, EFP needs the most careful preparation. Unlike in the studio, where most of the equipment you need is already installed, you must take every single piece of equipment to the shoot. A wrong or missing cable can delay the production for hours or even cause its cancellation.

EFP Preproduction: Remote Survey

Except for ENG, all field productions require careful preproduction. Because you need to adapt to a specific environment, it makes sense to look at it before going there with talent, crew, and production gear.

A field inspection is called a ***remote survey,*** or *site survey.* You should do a remote survey even if the field production is relatively simple, such as interviewing someone in a hotel room. Looking at the hotel room beforehand will help you decide where to put the guest and interviewer and where to place the camera. It will also give you important technical information, such as specific lighting and sound requirements.

For example, the small table and the two chairs may be adequate for getting optimal shots of the interviewer and guest, but the large picture window behind the table will certainly cause lighting problems. If you shoot against the window, the guest and interviewer will appear as silhouettes. Drawing the curtains would require lighting the interview area with portable instruments.

Are there enough and convenient outlets for the lighting instruments? Perhaps you can put the table and chairs away from the window. Will the new setup still be workable for the interviewer and guest and, most important, the camera? Will the background be reasonably interesting, or will it interfere with the shots? Now listen to the room. Is it relatively quiet, or do you hear noises coming through the door or window or from the air-conditioning? Can you disconnect the telephone so that it won't ring during the interview? Even this relatively simple field production will benefit a great deal from such a preproduction survey.

Survey team   For more-complex productions, careful remote surveys are an essential preproduction activity. You need to find out what the event is all about, where it is to take place, how to adapt the environment to the medium requirements, and the technical facilities necessary for videotaping or telecasting the event. For a relatively simple field production, the director and/or producer usually make up the survey team. For complex productions, you need to add a technical expert— the TD or engineering supervisor. If possible, have a contact person accompany you on the initial survey.

Contact person   The *contact person,* or *contact,* is someone who is familiar with the remote location and who can help you adapt the environment to the various production requirements. For the hotel room interview, for example, the contact person should not be the guest you are about to interview, but someone who has the knowledge and authority to get certain things done in the hotel. If you overload a circuit with the lighting instruments, the contact person should be able to call the hotel engineering or maintenance department immediately and have the circuit breaker reactivated. To prevent the telephone from ringing during the interview, the contact person should be able to have the hotel operator hold all calls or the maintenance people disconnect the phone line temporarily. The contact person might even find you an empty hotel room that is better suited for videotaping the interview than the one the guest actually occupies.

If the field production involves the coverage of a scheduled event over which you have no real control, such as a parade or sporting event, the contact person must be thoroughly familiar with the event and supply you with vital information, such as names and the order of the parade entries. Most important, the contact should help you gain access to restricted areas or to facilities at times when they are ordinarily locked up. Always get the contact's full name, title, postal and e-mail addresses, and pager, cell, fax, business, and home phone numbers. Also establish an alternate contact and have one or the other accompany you on the initial remote survey.

Conducting the survey   Whenever possible, try to conduct the survey at the same time of day as the scheduled field production so that you can see just where the sun will be. The position of the sun will ultimately determine camera placement when shooting outdoors—as well as indoors when large windows are in camera view.

Be sure to prepare a *location sketch,* which is similar to a studio floor plan. The location sketch should show the major streets and structures of the outdoor production environment as well as the main features of the indoor production space, such as hallways, doors, windows, and principal furnishings. Even if the field production happens in an actual field, make a sketch that indicates the approximate size of the production area, the major crossroads, and the location of the sun. Include such items as parking areas, location of the EFP vehicle or remote truck, and the closest toilet facilities. **SEE 15.3 AND 15.4** The remote survey table lists the major survey items and the key questions you should ask. **SEE 15.5**

If you have scheduled a field production outdoors, what will you do if it rains or snows? Obviously, it is a good idea to have alternate dates for a field production, unless the event is going on regardless of weather conditions, such as a football game or the Thanksgiving Day parade.

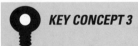

KEY CONCEPT 3   **The remote survey is an important preproduction activity for all field productions except ENG.**

15.3

OUTDOOR LOCATION SKETCH

An outdoor location sketch should show the main streets, buildings, and facilities of the immediate production area. It should also indicate the location of the EFP vehicle and the nearest toilet facilities. Also note the position of the sun during the scheduled production period.

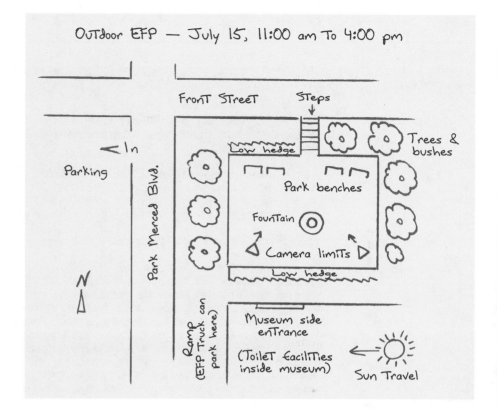

15.4

INDOOR LOCATION SKETCH

The indoor location sketch should show the principal production areas (room, hallway), windows and doors, and major furnishings, such as desks, chairs, plants, or file cabinets.

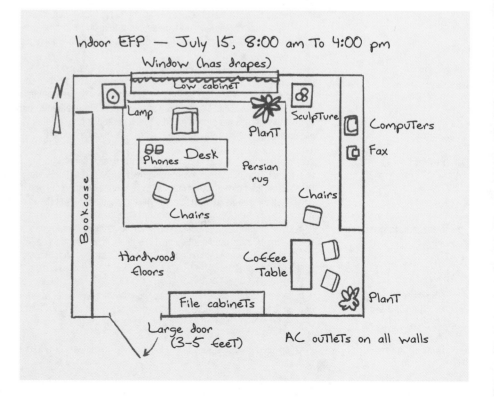

REMOTE SURVEY

SURVEY ITEM	KEY QUESTIONS
Contact	Who is the principal contact? Title; postal and e-mail addresses; and business cell, home, pager, and fax numbers. Who is the alternate contact? Title; postal and e-mail addresses; business, cell, home, pager, and fax numbers.
Place	What is the exact location of the telecast? Street address, telephone number. Where can cast and crew park and eat? Where are the closest toilet facilities?
Time	When is the remote telecast? Where is the sun at the beginning and end of the telecast?
Event	What type of action can you expect? Where does the action take place?
Cameras (Stationary)	Where are the major positions of the camcorder? When doing a multicamera remote, how many cameras do you need to cover the event? Try to use as few as possible. What are the locations of the cameras? Do not shoot from, or place the cameras on, opposite sides of the action. In general, the closer together the cameras are, the easier and less confusing the cutting will be. Shoot with the sun, not against it. Try to keep the sun behind or to the side of the cameras for the entire telecast. Are there any large objects blocking the camera view, such as trees, telephone poles, or billboards? Will you have the same field of view during the actual time of the telecast? Spectators may block a camera's field of view, although at the time of the survey the view was unobstructed. Do you need camera platforms? How high? Where? Can the platforms be erected at this particular point? If a camera is connected to a power outlet or CCU, what is its action radius? How long a cable run do you need?
Lighting	If you need additional lighting, what kind, and where? Can you use reflectors? Can the lighting instruments be conveniently placed? Can you place back lights so that they are out of camera range? Are there windows that let in a large amount of daylight? Can they be covered or filtered so that they do not cause silhouette or color temperature problems? How many watts can each circuit handle?
Audio	What type of audio pickup do you need? Where do you need to place the microphones? Which mics are appropriate? What is the exact action radius so far as audio is concerned? Which are stationary mics and which are handled by the talent? Do you need wireless microphones? Otherwise, how long must the mic cables be? Do you need special audio arrangements, such as audio foldback or a speaker system that carries the program audio to the location? Do you need long-distance mics for sound pickup over a great distance? Where should the mics be located?
Power	What is the power source? Even if you run the camcorders by battery, what about the lights? Does the contact person have access to the power outlets? If not, who does? Make sure that the contact is available at the times of the remote setup and the actual production. Do you need extension cords or power cables? Do the extension cords fit the power outlets at the remote location?
Intercommunications	What type of intercom system do you need? In a multicamera production, you need to set up a system that is similar to the studio intercom. How many I.F.B. channels and/or stations do you need, and where should they go? Do you need walkie-talkies to coordinate the crew efforts? Do you need a cellular phone hookup?
Location of Production Vehicle	If you need a large production vehicle, such as a remote truck, where can you park it? Is it close enough to the event location? Does the production vehicle block traffic? Make sure that parking is reserved for the production vehicle and the cars of talent and crew.
Miscellaneous	Will you need the assistance of the local police or other security service to control vehicle and pedestrian traffic or to secure parking?

Production

Each field production has its own requirements and difficulties. Although your careful preproduction survey should have eliminated most of the potential problems, here are a few considerations that are not part of the remote survey: (1) equipment checklist, (2) shooting outdoors, (2) shooting indoors, and (3) general production reminders.

Equipment checklist   The success of the production depends a great deal on thorough preproduction and on how well you have prepared the production schedule. Contrary to the studio, where all major installations and equipment are readily available, you need to transport every single piece of equipment to the field production site.

Prepare a checklist for all equipment and verify every item that is loaded onto the EFP vehicle. Use the same list when reloading the equipment for the return trip. The type and amount of equipment you need depends on the production requirements and, specifically, on the preproduction survey. Check the following list of equipment items you need to consider for EFP.

CHECKLIST: FIELD PRODUCTION EQUIPMENT

☑ *Camcorders*   How many do you need? If a spare camera is available, take it along, even if it is of lower quality. In case of emergency, a properly lighted interview shot with a digital consumer camcorder will certainly be better than no camcorder at all.

☑ *Camera mounts*   Always take along a tripod, even if you intend to work the camera from your shoulder. Do you need special camera mounts, such as tripod dollies, jib arms, or beanbags?

☑ *Videotape*   Do you have the proper cassettes for the camcorders and VTRs? Not all ½-inch cassettes fit all ½-inch VTRs; nor do all digital ¼-inch cassettes fit all digital camcorders. Always take along plenty of cassettes. Running out of tape is excusable when you are a tourist, but not when doing a field production. Check whether the actual length of the tape matches the label on the box. If the cassette has large reels and little tape on it, you can be sure that it will not give you ninety minutes worth of recording time, even if the label says so.

☑ *Power supply*   How are you going to power the camcorder? Are the batteries fully charged? Take several along. If you use an AC/DC power supply, do you have enough AC extension cords to reach the AC outlet? You also need extension cords for portable lighting instruments and for a field monitor. If the monitor is battery-powered, do you have the right battery? Is it fully charged? Do you have a spare battery for the monitor? Do you need a power generator?

☑ **Audio**   In addition to lavaliere microphones, take along at least one shotgun and one hand mic. For a more ambitious EFP, you need to match the mics to the acoustics of the location. Are the mic cables long enough to reach the camcorders or audio mixer? All remote mics need windscreens. Shotgun mics need additional windsocks. Do you need mounting equipment, such as clamps, stands, or fishpoles? Do you need a mixer or an additional ATR (audiotape recorder)? Take along plenty of audiocassettes or audiotape. Test the ATR or DAT (digital audiotape) recorder before taking it on location. Don't forget headsets for the mic operator and the audio-recording technician.

☑ **Cables and connectors**   Do you have the appropriate cables and connectors? Most professional equipment operates with BNC connectors for the video coax cables and XLR connectors for audio cables, as shown in figure 8.25. Consumer-type equipment usually comes with RCA phono and mini jacks and plugs, also shown in figure 8.25. Bring along some adapters for video and audio cables. Double-check all connectors and adapters. If you need to connect the camera to an RCU (remote control unit), do you have enough camera cable?

☑ **Monitor and test equipment**   Be sure to take a monitor along for playback. If you do a multicamera EFP with a switcher, each camera input needs a separate preview monitor. If you have a narrator describing the action, you need a separate monitor for him or her. In field productions that require high-quality pictures, you need an RCU for each camera, and special test equipment (waveform monitor and vectorscope). Ordinarily, the TD is responsible for such items, but you still should see to it that they are part of the equipment package.

☑ **Lighting**   More often than not, you will need at least one or two portable lighting kits, each containing several lighting instruments, barn doors, diffusers, light stands, and spare bulbs. Use floodlights (softlights) or diffusion umbrellas for large-area lighting. Do the spare bulbs actually fit the lighting instruments? Do they burn with the desired color temperature (3,200°K or 5,600°K)? Use light-blue and pale-orange gels on the lighting instruments if you need to raise or lower the color temperature, unless the lights come with color temperature filters. White diffusion material is always needed to soften shadows. You may also need sheets of pale-orange (warm) color media for windows to change the high outdoor color temperature to the lower indoor one, or sheets of ND (neutral density) filters that lower the light intensity without changing the color temperature. Reflectors (white cards, foam core, aluminum foil, or collapsible reflectors) are essential for outdoor productions. Even when shooting indoors, reflectors are often much easier to handle than additional lights.

The lighting package should also include: a piece of muslin to cover an off-camera window; a piece of black cloth to cut down on unwanted reflections; diffusion umbrellas; a light meter; extra light stands; and clamps and sandbags for securing the light stands. Unless you have access to sophisticated expandable battens, take some pieces of 1 × 3 lumber along; they will come in handy for constructing supports for small lighting instruments. Pack a roll of aluminum foil for making reflectors, heat shields, or makeshift barn doors. Take enough AC extension cords and adapters that fit the various household outlets.

☑ *Intercom*   In small field productions, you do not need elaborate intercom setups, but you should always leave a telephone number at home base where you can be reached in case of an emergency. A cellular phone is a must if you primarily do EFP. For larger field productions, you need a small power megaphone or walkie-talkies to reach a spread-out crew. If you use a multicamera and switcher system, you need to set up a regular P.L. intercom system.

☑ *Miscellaneous*   Here is what you should take along on every EFP: extra scripts and production schedules; field log forms; a slate and water-based marker; several large rain umbrellas and "raincoats" (plastic covers) to protect equipment and crew in case of rain; a white card for white-balancing; a large newsprint pad and marker for writing cue cards or other information for the talent while on the air or recording; if necessary, a remote teleprompter with batteries and all necessary cables; several rolls of gaffer's tape and masking tape; white chalk; several clothespins to hold things in place; a makeup kit; a large bottle of water; a small plastic bowl; paper towels; a broom and trash bag; and lots of sandbags.

Test all equipment before loading it into an EFP vehicle. At the very least, you should do a brief recording with the camcorder to see whether video and audio portions can be properly recorded. If you don't have a battery tester, attach the batteries one by one to the camera to see that they are properly charged. Test each mic and each lighting instrument before loading it. All this checking may seem like a waste of time—until you get stuck far away from your production facility with a malfunctioning camcorder, mic, or light that you neglected to test.

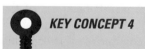

KEY CONCEPT 4   **Prepare a checklist of all equipment needed, and test all equipment before taking it to the remote location.**

Shooting outdoors   When shooting outdoors, the production environment is determined by the specific EFP location. All you can do is decide which portions of the environment you want to show.

Weather   When outdoors you are at the mercy of the elements—always be prepared for bad weather. As mentioned previously, take raincoats along for the cameras (a plastic tarp will do in an emergency) and rain gear for the crew. As old-fashioned as it may seem, a large umbrella is still one of the most effective means of keeping rain off of people and equipment.

If you move from a chilly outside location to indoors, let the camcorder or VTR warm up a bit. The extreme temperature change could cause condensation in the videotape recorder, shutting down its operation automatically. Such a shutdown will certainly put a crimp in the production schedule. In extremely cold weather, zoom lenses and even the videotape transport in camcorders have a tendency to stick. Keep the camera in a vehicle and run the camcorder for a while when it is exposed to the cold temperature to prevent the lens and VTR from sticking. Some mics will refuse to work properly in extremely low temperatures unless protected by a windscreen. Always have an alternate production plan in case it rains or snows.

Most important, watch the weather for shot continuity. If videotaping a brief scene of two people talking to each other requires several takes that stretch over an hour or so, you may have a cloudless sky as the background for the first few takes and a cloudy one for the last takes. The sudden appearance of clouds or rain between question and answer does not exactly contribute to continuity. So long as you are aware of the problem, you can try to choose a background that does not show the time progression, or arrange the shooting schedule so that the time change does not jeopardize postproduction editing.

Foreground With a prominent foreground piece in the shot—a tree, fence post, mailbox, or traffic sign—you can dramatically improve the scene, make the composition more dynamic, and give it depth. If there is no natural foreground piece, you can often plant one. Instead of looking for a convenient foreground tree, you might simply handhold and dip a small tree branch into the shot. The viewer's mind will fill in the rest and "see" the whole tree.

Background Always look beyond the main action to the background to avoid odd juxtapositions between foreground and background. You must also be careful to maintain background continuity in postproduction editing. For instance, if you show a prominent tree in the background of shot 1 but not in the following shot with the same background, the tree will seem to have mysteriously disappeared when the two shots are edited together. An alert editor will probably rule against such an edit.

Jump cuts can be caused not only by slight position changes of the foreground pieces but also by a background shift. To avoid background jump cuts, try to keep a prominent horizon line or an especially conspicuous background object, such as the single tree on a distant hill, in the same screen portion in subsequent shots. 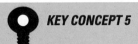 *READY ZVL 1*

KEY CONCEPT 5 **Watch the weather and background for shot continuity when shooting outdoors.**

Shooting indoors When shooting indoors you may have to rearrange the furnishings and (more often) the pictures on the wall to get optimal shots. Always make a record of what the room looks like (by drawing a small sketch, taking Polaroid shots, or videotaping the room with a camcorder) before you start moving things around. Such a record will greatly assist you in putting things back where they belong.

Lighting Be especially aware of the specific lighting requirements. Again, check the available outlets. Be extremely careful when placing lights inside a room. Do not overload the circuits. Turn off the lights whenever you don't need them. Sandbag all light stands and make a heat shield out of aluminum foil, especially when the lighting instrument is close to curtains, sofas, books, or other combustible material.

Even on a cloudy or foggy day, the color temperature of the light coming through an outside window is considerably higher than that of indoor light. In this case, you must make a decision to boost the color temperature of the indoor light, or lower the daylight color temperature coming through the window. *READY ZVL 2*

Audio Except for simple interviews, good audio always seems to be a bigger problem than good video. This is because the microphones are often placed at the last moment without adequate consideration of the acoustics of the room or specific sound pickup requirements. You should include a brief audio rehearsal in the EFP production schedule so that you can listen to the sound pickup before videotaping. If you have brought along several types of mics, you can choose the one that sounds best in that environment.

As you recall, it is better to record the principal sounds and ambient sounds on separate videotape tracks rather than mix them in the field. If careful mixing between foreground and background sounds is required, you can do it much better in the postproduction studio. If you mix the sounds in the field, you pretty much eliminate any further adjustment of the mix in postproduction.

General production reminders Very much like certain routines developed for striking the studio sets, rolling up the cables, putting the cameras back in their regular "parking place," and sweeping the studio floor, there are some general guidelines for EFP.

Respecting property Whenever you are on someone else's property, be mindful that you are a guest and are actually intruding with your video gear and production people. Working in video does not give you a special license to invade people's homes, upset their routines, or make unreasonable demands on them. When you shoot a documentary in somebody's well-kept garden, don't trample on carefully tended flowers or other plants just to get a good camera position. Dragging equipment dollies or camera cases along polished floors or valuable rugs is not appreciated by the owner. Even if pressed for time, do not get caught up so much in the production activities that you lose common sense.

Safety As in studio productions, you need to be constantly aware of proper safety precautions. Don't be careless with extension cords, especially if you string them outside in damp weather. Tape all connections so that they become waterproof. If you have to lay cables across busy corridors or doorways, tape them down with gaffer's tape and put a rubber mat over them. Better yet, try to string them above so that people can walk below them unhindered. When shooting in rain, protect all cameras with raincoats. If possible, have someone hold an umbrella over the camera and operator. Ask the police to assist you when shooting along a freeway or in downtown traffic.

Logging During the shoot keep an accurate field log of all takes, good or bad. Label all tapes and boxes and put them in a container used solely for transporting the videotaped material. Activate the tape cassette protection devices so that the source tapes cannot be accidentally erased.

Putting things back and cleaning up If you need to rearrange furniture or pictures when shooting indoors, first ask whether it is all right to do so, and tell the person in charge why you need to do it. Before you start moving things around, make a rough sketch of where the items are located or take several Polaroid pictures of the interior.

When you are finished, verify that all things are put back where you found them. Remove all gaffer's tape that you may have used to tape down cables, pick up all extension cords, sandbags, and especially empty soft drink cans and other lunch remnants. An EFP team, who had finally gained access to an old and venerable family ranch only after weeks of pleading by the show's producer, was invited back with a smile for the follow-up show because the production team had brought a broom along and swept the area clean.

Loading the equipment When loading the equipment into the remote vehicle after the shoot, pull out the checklist again. Check off every item that is loaded up for the return trip. Look for missing items right away; it is usually easier to find them right after the production than days or weeks later. Check that all source tapes are properly labeled and that the field logs match the labels. Keep them close to you until you return to home base. **READY ZVL 3**

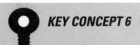

KEY CONCEPT 6 **After the production make sure that you leave the location the way you found it and that you brought back everything you took to the field.**

Postproduction: Wrap-up

The first order of business is to make protection copies of all source tapes. If necessary, you can combine this dubbing with simultaneously bumping up the source tapes to a higher-quality format with time code for on-line editing and making VHS copies with time code windows for off-line editing. If you have used a high-quality camcorder (such as a BetacamSP) and generated the time code in the field while shooting, make VHS copies for off-line editing and save the original source tapes for the on-line editing process.

As with all other postproduction activities, you now need to review the tapes and prepare an accurate VTR log that lists all shots by in- and out-numbers, identifies good and bad takes, indicates predominant vectors, and lists the principal audio for each shot. Then it is up to the postproduction people to put it all together into a comprehensive message that, hopefully, will convey the intended process message.

BIG REMOTES

While learning basic video production, you will probably not be called upon to participate in a "big remote." But you should have at least some idea of what a remote is all about and what major equipment it uses for its field production. A *remote* is the field production of a large, scheduled event done for live transmission or live-on-tape recording.

Big remotes are devoted to the coverage of major events, such as parades, sports, significant international events, and political gatherings. Big remotes resemble multicamera studio productions in every respect, except that the "studio" is now a remote location: the plaza in front of city hall, the major sports stadium, or the Senate chambers. Also, the event is not staged specifically for video (at least not obviously).

All big remotes use high-quality field cameras (studio cameras with lenses that can zoom from an extreme long shot to a tight close-up) and high-quality EFP cameras. All cameras are normally connected to the remote truck by cable.

The *remote truck* represents a compact studio control room and equipment room. It contains the following: an *image control center* with preview and line monitors; a switcher with special effects; a character generator (C.G.); various intercom systems (P.L., P.A., and elaborate I.F.B. systems); an *audio control center* with a fairly large audio console, ATRs, monitor speakers and intercom systems; a *VTR center* with several high-quality VTRs that can handle regular recordings, do instant replays, and play in slow-motion and freeze-frame modes; and a *technical center* with CCUs (camera control units), technical setup equipment, and patchbays for camera, audio, intercom, and light cables. **SEE 15.6**

Although remote trucks can draw power from available high-capacity electrical sources, most engineers prefer to use portable power generators. Because big remotes are often done live, remote trucks have various microwave transmission facilities that range from small links from camera to truck, to larger ones that transmit the signal from truck to transmitter. Some large trucks have their own satellite uplink; others connect to an *uplink truck* if a direct satellite feed is necessary. In very big remotes, one or more additional trailers may be used for supplemental production and control equipment.

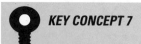

KEY CONCEPT 7   **Big remotes resemble multicamera studio shows, except that the event takes place outside the studio, and the control room is located in a truck.**

15.6

REMOTE TRUCK

The remote truck is studio control center on wheels. It contains the program, audio, and video control centers, a number of VTRs, and transmission equipment.

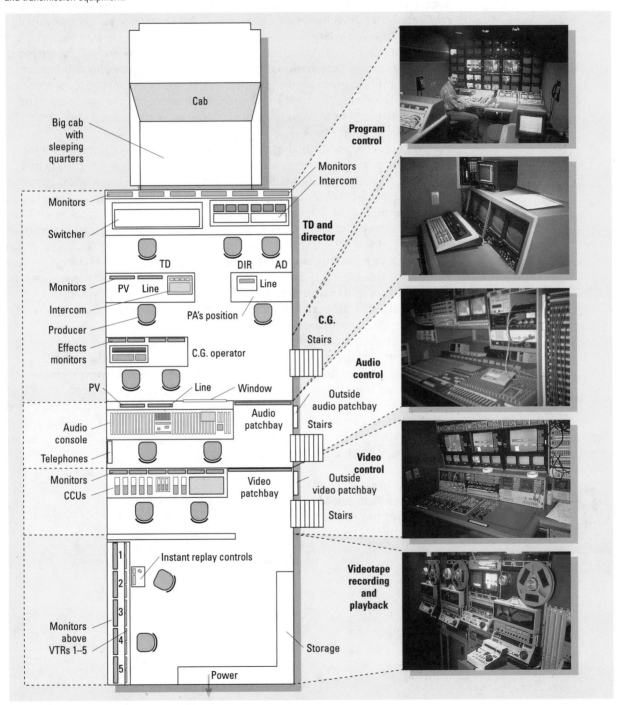

Cab

Big cab
with
sleeping
quarters

Monitors
Intercom

**Program
control**

Monitors

Switcher

**TD and
director**

TD

DIR   AD

Monitors   PV   Line   Line

Intercom

Producer   PA's position

Effects
monitors   C.G. operator

C.G.

Stairs

PV   Line   Window

Audio
console   Audio
patchbay

Telephones

**Audio
control**

Outside
audio patchbay

Stairs

Monitors
CCUs   Video
patchbay

**Video
control**

Outside
video patchbay

Stairs

1

2

Instant replay controls

3

4

Monitors
above
VTRs 1–5

5

Storage

Power

**Videotape
recording
and
playback**

SYNTHETIC ENVIRONMENTS

Not all environments are lens-generated (photographed by the video camera); they can be synthetic as well. *Synthetic environments* are generated electronically.

You can create a great variety of backgrounds through the chroma-key process. Recall that the chroma-key process uses a specific color, usually blue, for the background into which various still or moving images can be keyed. The actual foreground action then appears to be playing in the keyed environment. Because you can use any photograph, videotape, or computer-generated effect as a chroma-key source, your choices of background are unlimited. **SEE COLOR PLATE 6**

■ Computer-Generated Settings

Despite all the skills you might have acquired to adapt the real environment to your video needs, the computer offers new alternatives. Indoor sets, or at least parts of sets, can be partially matted in through various blue-screen techniques similar to the chroma-key process or they can be computer-generated in postproduction. As you can see in figure 15.7, the two chairs that were photographed in front of some softwall flats in a television studio have now been transported by the magic of a computer and the skills of a computer artist into a luxurious interior setting. You can, of course, use the same technique and put a real desk and chair into a computer-generated office. A favorite use of computer-generated sets is to "lay in" the ceilings and floor coverings of studio sets in postproduction. That way the camera travel and lighting remain unrestricted during the production. **SEE 15.7** There are *fractal* computer programs available

15.7

COMPUTER-
GENERATED SET

This set background is computer-generated. The set props are actual pieces of furniture.

that can generate a variety of realistic or fantasy landscapes—anything from a realistic western street to a moonscape. **SEE COLOR PLATE 8**

Virtual Reality

Virtual reality consists of computer-generated environments and events that are animated. You could, for example, change the peaceful scene of vacationers traveling happily along a sun-drenched country road into a frightening event by replacing the harmless background clouds with a huge computer-generated twister. Depending on the program, you can also generate objects, animals, or even people, and place them in, or have them move through, this virtual environment. There are synthetic environments that appear to be three-dimensional, provided you wear 3D glasses when viewing the video screen.

Whether you combine the blue-screen or virtual reality environment with real actors or performers moving about, you must pay particular attention to the lighting so that the shadows of the synthetic environment fit the ones displayed in the actual scene. The size relationships between foreground and background also become a major concern. Unless you want to achieve a special effect, the synthetic environment should fit the dimensions of the people keyed into it and change according to camera angles.

Interactive Video

As discussed in a previous chapter, *interactive video* refers to the viewer's having some control over the choice of programs and over the video display itself. For example, there are programs that produce from a floor plan an actual scenic environment. Once the virtual scenery is set up, you can try out a number of color schemes and textures for the walls, doors, windows, and floor. For example, you may try out a blue rug, change it to red or beige, and take it out again if you don't like it—all by simply clicking the mouse. You can also put virtual furniture into the set and dress it with various properties. You use the mouse to select the various items from a menu and drag them into the desired positions. If you don't like what you selected, simply delete the images and try new ones.

Other such programs let you light the set, with a menu offering various lighting instruments that you can drag into the set and aim at the elements of the virtual production environment. You can test different lighting setups until you are satisfied. *READY ZVL 4*   Finally, you can have a virtual camera move through this virtual space to show you what shots you can get from various angles and lens settings. Some sophisticated programs let you generate virtual performers and move them through the synthetic space.

Even if you do not use the virtual display as the "actual" environment for your production, such interactive displays of various setups, colors, and camera and talent positions are an invaluable preproduction aid.

When combined with live action, such virtual environments can create startling effects. The availability of high-speed desktop computers and high-capacity hard drives brings virtual reality environments into your nonlinear editing bay. The marriage of television and computers opens up an additional wealth of picture and sound information that you can use in your productions. All you need now is a thorough knowledge of video basics and plenty of imagination.

KEY CONCEPT 8 Synthetic environments can be built partially or entirely by computer.

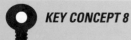 *O N C E   A G A I N ,   R E M E M B E R . . .*

■ Field Production

All productions that happen outside the studio are called field productions, including ENG (electronic news gathering), EFP (electronic field production), and large remote telecasts.

■ Electronic News Gathering (ENG)

This process involves newspeople and equipment for reacting quickly to a developing news event. The event is either videotaped and edited for a regularly scheduled broadcast or, if important enough, transmitted live. Normally, the preproduction activities concern being ready to go anywhere rather than conducting a field survey.

■ Electronic Field Production (EFP)

These productions, which occur away from the studio, are thoroughly planned in preproduction. Electronic field productions include documentaries, magazine news stories, investigative reports, on-site interviews, and so on. One of the most important steps is the remote, or site, survey.

■ Preproduction

Remote surveys are necessary for all field productions except ENG. They supply important information about such technical aspects as power availability, lighting, and sound requirements and they give the director an idea of where to place the camera or cameras. Establishing a reliable contact person is an important aspect of preproduction.

■ Production

Use a checklist for taking the equipment into the field and bringing it back. When shooting outdoors, changing weather conditions and random sounds are a constant hazard and must be carefully monitored. Be aware of changing lighting conditions, which may seriously influence your editing continuity. Respect people's property and mind safety precautions at all times. When shooting indoors, be careful where and how you place lighting instruments. Carefully monitor the audio pickup.

■ Big Remotes

Big remotes are devoted to live or live-on-tape coverage of large scheduled events, such as parades, sports, and significant international events. Big remotes are coordinated from the remote truck, which houses a complete program control room, audio control, elaborate intercom facilities, videotape and video control sections, various other technical facilities, and transmission equipment.

■ Synthetic Environments

Environments can be electronically generated through the chroma-key process and computer-generated backgrounds. Interactive virtual reality programs can create an entirely synthetic, computer-generated environment. These programs can also simulate certain production situations (camera positions, scenery colors, or lighting), which can be changed by the user to find the most effective one. Such a simulation is a valuable preproduction aid. Interactive video, which combines television and computer communication, provides access to a great amount of video and audio information and allows you to make program choices.

 Z E T T L ' S   V I D E O   L A B   2 . 1

RUN ZVL 1 Click on the **editing** monitor and review tape 5 **Location Procedures**. Although you know all about vectors by now, watch module 4 **Vectors** again, keeping an eye on the horizon line in subsequent shots. If you have a prominent horizon in a series of shots, mark the viewfinder with a piece of tape and line up the horizon to the tape to ensure smooth vector continuity.

RUN ZVL 2 Click on the **lights** monitor and review some of the major points of field lighting. Load tape 9 **Field** and play module 3 **Mixed**. In module 1 **Outdoor**, Mary praises the soft shadows when shooting on an overcast day. You can achieve the same effect by moving out of the sun and into a shadow. Watch how much a reflector can lighten up dense shadows. In module 2 **Indoor**, heed Mary's advice to not get too fancy with lighting, but to get as much baselight as possible. Module 3 **Mixed** illustrates a common but serious lighting problem. Go back to tape 5 **Color Temperature** to review how to adjust the color temperatures to a single one.

RUN ZVL 3 Click on the **editing** monitor, load tape 5 **Location Procedures**, and play module 1 **Basics** again. Yes, you have heard it before, but it is important enough to hear Veronica tell us again to label all tapes and keep an accurate field log before returninfrom the EFP shoot.

RUN ZVL 4 Click on the **lights** monitor. The lighting exercises on tape 7 **Triangle Lighting** are an example of this type of interactive virtual reality.

RUN ZVL 5 Upon the successful completion of all ZVL 2.1 quizzes, the computer and Triple-I will award you a *Certificate of Completion.* Congratulations!

KEY CONCEPTS

- In field production you must adapt to the environment.

- Whenever possible, have the reporter stand in a shaded area rather than in bright sunlight.

- The remote survey is an important preproduction activity for all field productions except ENG.

- Prepare a checklist of all equipment needed, and test all equipment before taking it to the remote location.

- Watch the weather and background for shot continuity when shooting outdoors.

- After the production make sure that you leave the location the way you found it and that you brought back everything you took to the field.

- Big remotes resemble multicamera studio shows, except that the event takes place outside the studio, and the control room is located in a truck.

- Synthetic environments can be built partially or entirely by computer.

Epilogue

CONGRATULATIONS! You have successfully completed the tough Triple-I internship. The senior director calls you back for a last "once again, remember" bit of advice:

You are now in command of a powerful means of communication and persuasion. Use it wisely and responsibly. Treat your viewers with respect and compassion, regardless of whether they are third-graders, the local university alumni association, bank employees, or a worldwide audience. Whatever role you play in the production process—pulling cables or directing a complex show—do the very best you can muster. Ultimately, your video accomplishments, however modest they may seem, will make a difference and help us all see the world with heightened awareness and joy.

Selected Readings

Adams, James L. *Conceptual Blockbusting*. 3d ed. Reading, Mass.: Addison-Wesley, 1990.

> An insightful treatment of how we habitually block creativity as well as many practical examples of how to overcome these blocks. Somewhat dated but still extremely helpful for understanding the creative process.

Alten, Stanley R. *Audio in Media*. 5th ed. Belmont, Calif.: Wadsworth Publishing Co., 1999.

> An excellent, comprehensive, and practical introduction to audio principles and techniques, including audio for video production. Gives specific information on sound pickup, mixing, postproduction, and the latest digital sound techniques.

Armer, Alan A. *Writing the Screenplay*. 2d ed. Belmont, Calif.: Wadsworth Publishing Co., 1993.

> A thorough and easy-to-read discussion of the writing processes for video and film, as well as such aspects as format, style, conflict, dialogue, and the elements of entertainment. There are numerous helpful script samples.

Barr, Tony. *Acting for the Camera*. Revised ed. New York: HarperCollins, 1997.

> A thoughtful and practical treatment of how to perform in front of the camera and how to visualize dialogue in various contexts. It is a must-read for talent and the video director.

Browne, Steven E. *Nonlinear Editing Basics*. Boston: Focal Press, 1998.

> A useful guide to nonlinear editing in the preproduction, production, and postproduction phases. Useful illustrations.

Burrows, Thomas D., Lynne S. Gross, and Donald N. Wood. *Television Production: Disciplines and Techniques*. 7th ed. New York: McGraw-Hill, 1998.

> Moves from job opportunities and the production team to the tools of production.

Byrne, Terry. *Production Design by Television*. Newton, Mass.: Focal Press, 1993.

> Shows how the principles of color and composition are used for storyboards and floor plans and how sets, props, lighting, and graphics interact in various production designs.

Clark, Barbara, and Susan J. Spohr. *Guide to Postproduction for TV and Film: Managing the Process.* Boston: Focal Press, 1998.

> Explains the basic organizational steps of postproduction editing.

Compesi, Ronald J. *Video Field Production and Editing.* 5th ed. Boston: Allyn & Bacon, 2000.

> Well-organized, illustrated text on all major aspects of field production. Explains video field production tools and their optimal use.

Gross, Lynne S., and Larry W. Ward. *Electronic Moviemaking.* 4th ed. Belmont, Calif.: Wadsworth Publishing Co., 2000.

> Discusses in detail the common elements of film and single-camera video production. Written from a film production perspective, it shows how to transfer traditional film techniques to video production.

Hausman, Carl, Lewis B. O'Donnell, and Philip Benoit. *Announcing: Broadcast Communicating Today.* 4th ed. Belmont, Calif.: Wadsworth Publishing Co., 2000.

> Covers the principles and practices of on-air announcing and performing; stresses the announcer-performer as a communicator. Includes a wealth of practice material.

Hyde, Stuart. *Television and Radio Announcing.* 8th ed. Boston: Houghton Mifflin Co., 1998.

> Presents up-to-date information on performance techniques, voice and diction, and the proper use of American English on the air. Contains tips on effective announcing in specific programs, such as interviews, news, music, and sports.

Jarvis, Peter. *The Essential TV Director's Handbook.* Woburn, Mass.: Focal Press, 1999.

> The television director's role and activities explained in terms of various types of production grammar.

Kaufmann, Sam. *Avid Editing.* Boston: Focal Press, 2000.

> Although specifically written for the Avid editing system, many of the principles apply to other nonlinear editing systems as well. Includes a useful CD-ROM.

Katz, Steven D. *Film Directing Shot by Shot.* Studio City, Calif.: Michael Wiese Productions, 1991.

> A richly illustrated treatment of how to visualize shots and shot sequences for a variety of screen events. Although primarily aimed at film production, most principles apply equally to video. A good primer for framing shots for HDTV.

Kenney, Ritch, and Kevin Groome. *Television Camera Operation According to Ritch.* 2d ed. Burbank, Calif.: Tellem Publications, 2000.

> A valuable how-to guide for basic camera handling.

Mager, Robert. *Preparing Instructional Objectives.* 2d rev. ed. Belmont, Calif.: Wadsworth Publishing Co., 1984.

> A classic book on knowing and defining precise learning tasks before you expect others to perform them. It can be directly applied to defining objectives in video production.

Millerson, Gerald. *The Technique of Lighting for Film and Television.* 3d ed. Boston: Focal Press, 1991.

> Covers the technical aspects of lighting for television and film. Emphasis is on major studio productions.

Millerson, Gerald. *Television Production.* 13th ed. Woburn, Mass.: Focal Press, 1999.

> A thorough treatment of the major production tools and their application. Richly illustrated. Excellent reference source for equipment and techniques.

Morley, John. *Scriptwriting for High-Impact Videos: Imaginative Approaches to Delivering Factual Information.* Belmont, Calif.: Wadsworth Publishing Co., 1992.

> A practical guide to strategies and techniques for writing informative videos with flair.

Moshkovitz, Moshe. *The Virtual Studio: Technology and Techniques.* Boston: Focal Press, 2000.

> Provides a good overview of the various blue-screen matting techniques. Text is reinforced by color plates and a CD-ROM.

Murch, Walter. *In the Blink of an Eye: A Perspective on Film Editing.* Los Angeles: Silman-James Press, 1995.

> A series of interesting and rich lectures that range from why cuts work and the six rules of editing to the theory that whenever we blink we change our train of thought.

Ohanian, Thomas D. *Digital Nonlinear Editing.* 2d ed. Woburn, Mass.: Focal Press, 1999.

> A good treatment of technical and creative processes of nonlinear editing, from logging shots to digital compression. Can be used by editors using desktops or high-end digital editing equipment.

Rico, Gabriele Lusser. *Writing the Natural Way.* Los Angeles: J. P. Tarcher, 1983.

> A pioneering book that describes "clustering"—a visual way of brainstorming. Especially helpful to writers and producers who are handed a specific program topic.

Rubin, Michael. *Nonlinear: A Guide to Digital Film and Video Editing.* 3d ed. Gainesville, Fla.: Triad Publication Co., 1995.

> Discusses the major equipment and techniques of nonlinear editing.

Schihl, Robert. *Studio Drama: Processes and Procedures.* Woburn, Mass.: Focal Press, 1992.

> Practical guide of how to move from script analysis to multicamera blocking.

Tomlinson, Holman. *5.1 Surround Sound: Up and Running.* Boston: Focal Press, 2000.

> A thorough discussion of what surround sound is, how to capture it, and how to reproduce it. Includes good diagrams.

Utz, Peter. *Camcorder and Studio Television Production.* Englewood Cliffs, N.J., 1999.

> An up-to-date discussion of studio and location production equipment and processes.

Viera, Dave. *Lighting for Film and Electronic Cinematography.* Belmont, Calif.: Wadsworth Publishing Co., 1993.

> Covers basic principles for planning lighting setups for film and video, and offers lighting analyses for more than sixty photos. Includes a section on electronic cinematography that applies film lighting concepts to video.

Ward, Peter. *Basic Betacam and DVCPRO Camera Work.* 2d ed. Boston: Focal Press, 1998.

> Valuable practical hints about how to operate the camera and compose optimal shots.

Ward, Peter. *Picture Composition for Film and Television.* Woburn, Mass.: Focal Press, 1996.

> Basic material on picture composition for television and movie aspect ratios, light, color, movement, staging, and the importance of context.

Whittaker, Ron. *Video Field Production.* 3d ed. Mountain View, Calif.: Mayfield Publishing Co., 1996.

> A detailed treatment of production approaches to shooting on-location, and ENG/EFP equipment and techniques.

Zettl, Herbert. *Television Production Handbook.* 7th ed. Belmont, Calif.: Wadsworth Publishing Co., 2000.

> A comprehensive treatment of television and video tools and production processes. Includes detailed chapters on digital processes, production, and directing.

Zettl, Herbert. *Sight Sound Motion: Applied Media Aesthetics.* 3d ed. Belmont, Calif.: Wadsworth Publishing Co., 1999.

> Detailed analyses of the major aesthetic image elements—light, space, time-motion, and sound—and how they are used in video and film.

Glossary

720p The scanning system of DTV (digital television). The *p* stands for *progressive,* which means that each complete television frame consists of 720 lines that are scanned one after the other. See *progressive.*

1080i The scanning system of HDTV (high-definition television). The *i* stands for *interlaced,* which means that a complete frame is formed from two interlaced scanning fields. Each field consists of 539½ lines. As with the traditional NTSC analog television system, the 1080i produces 60 fields, or 30 complete frames, per second.

above-the-line Category for nontechnical personnel, such as producers, directors, and talent. Also used as a budget category.

AB-roll editing Creating an edit master tape from two source VTRs, one containing the A-roll, and the other the B-roll. Transitions other than cuts, such as dissolves and wipes, are possible.

AC Stands for *alternating current;* electric energy as supplied by normal household outlets.

actor A person who appears on-camera in dramatic roles. The actor always portrays someone else.

actual process message The real effect of the program on the viewer.

AD Stands for *associate* or *assistant director.* Assists the director in all production phases.

additive primary colors Red, green, and blue. Ordinary white light (sunlight) can be separated into the three primary light colors. When these three colored lights are combined in various proportions, all other colors can be reproduced.

address code An electronic signal that marks each frame with a specific address. See *SMPTE time code.*

ad-lib Speech or action that has not been scripted or specially rehearsed.

AGC Stands for *automatic gain control.* Regulates the volume of the audio or video levels automatically, without using pots.

ambience Background sounds.

analog A signal that fluctuates exactly like the original stimulus.

analog sound recording Audio recording system in which the electrical sound signal fluctuates exactly like the original sound stimulus over its entire range.

aperture Iris opening of a lens; usually measured in *f*-stops.

arc To move the camera in a slightly curved dolly or truck.

aspect ratio The ratio of the width of a television screen to its height. In STV (standard television), it is 4×3 (four units wide by three units high); for HDTV (high-definition television) it is 16×9 (sixteen units wide by nine units high).

assemble editing Adding shots on videotape in a consecutive order without first recording a control track on the edit master tape.

ATR Stands for *audiotape recorder.*

attached shadow Shadow that is on the object itself. It cannot be seen independent of (detached from) the object.

audio The sound portion of video and its production. Technically, the electronic reproduction of audible sound.

audio track The area of the videotape used for recording the audio information.

auto focus Automatic focusing system on most consumer camcorders and some ENG/EFP cameras.

auto iris Automatic control of the aperture (lens opening).

background light Illumination of the set pieces and backdrop. Also called *set light*.

back light Illumination from behind the subject and opposite the camera. Usually a spotlight.

barn doors Metal flaps in front of a lighting instrument that control the spread of the light beam.

baselight Even, nondirectional (diffused) light necessary for the camera to operate optimally. Refers to the overall light intensity.

beam See *electron beam*.

beam splitter Optical device within the camera that splits the white light into the three primary colors: red, green, and blue.

below-the-line Category for technical personnel, including camera operators, floor persons, and audio engineers. Also used as a budget category.

BetacamSP A high-quality ½-inch VTR format. Cannot be interfaced with other ½-inch VTR formats, such as VHS or S-VHS.

bidirectional The microphone can hear best from two opposite sides.

big remote A production outside the studio to televise live and/or record live-on-tape a large scheduled event that has not been staged specifically for television. Examples include sporting events, parades, political gatherings, or government hearings.

binary digit (bit) The smallest amount of information a computer can hold and process. A charge is either present, represented by a 1, or absent, represented by a 0. One bit can describe two levels, such as on/off or black/white. Two bits can describe four levels (2^2 bits), three bits eight levels (2^3 bits), four bits sixteen (2^4 bits), and so on. A group of eight bits (2^8) is called a *byte*.

blocking Carefully worked-out movement and actions by the talent and for all mobile video equipment used in a scene.

boom (1) Audio: microphone support. (2) Video: part of a camera crane. (3) To move the boom of the camera crane up or down; also called *crane*.

bump-down Copying a videotape to a lower-quality tape format. Also called *dub-down*.

bump-up Copying a videotape to a higher-quality tape format. Also called *dub-up*.

byte A group of eight bits. It describes 256 (2^8) levels.

calibrate the zoom lens To preset a zoom lens to keep in focus throughout the zoom.

camcorder A portable camera with the VTR built into it.

camera chain The camera and associated electronic equipment, consisting of the power supply, the sync generator, and the CCU (camera control unit).

camera control unit (CCU) Equipment, separate from the actual camera, that allows the VO (video operator) to adjust the color and brightness balance before and during the production.

cam head A camera mounting head that permits extremely smooth tilts and pans.

cant Tilting the camera sideways.

cap (1) Lens cap: a rubber or metal cap placed in front of the lens to protect it from light, dust, or physical damage. (2) Electronic device that eliminates the picture from the camera CCD.

cardioid A unidirectional microphone pickup pattern.

cart See *cartridge*.

cartridge An audiotape recording or playback device that uses tape cartridges. A cartridge is a plastic case containing an endless tape loop. Also called *tape cartridge*, or *cart* for short.

cassette A plastic case containing tape that runs on two reels: a supply reel and a takeup reel. Used for audio and video recording and playback.

cast shadow Shadow that is produced by an object and thrown (cast) onto another surface. It can be seen independent of the object.

CCD Stands for *charge-coupled device*. An image-sensing element that translates the optical image into a video signal.

C-clamp A metal clamp with which lighting instruments are attached to the lighting batten.

CCU See *camera control unit*.

CD Stands for *compact disc*. A small, shiny disc that contains audio and/or video information in digital form.

C.G. (character generator) A small computer dedicated to the creation of letters and numbers in various fonts. Its output can be directly integrated into video images.

chroma key Special key effect that uses color (usually blue) for the key source background. All blue areas are replaced by the base picture during the keying.

close-up (CU) Object or any part of it seen at close range and framed tightly. The close-up can be extreme (extreme or big close-up) or rather loose (medium close-up).

closure Short for *psychological closure*.

coding To change the quantized values into a binary code, represented by 0's and 1's. Also called *encoding*.

color bars A color standard used in video production for the alignment of cameras and videotape recordings. Color bars can be generated by most professional portable cameras.

color temperature Relative reddishness or bluishness of light, as measured in Kelvin degrees. The norm for indoor video lighting is 3,200°K, for outdoors, 5,600°K.

complexity editing Building an intensified screen event from carefully selected and juxtaposed shots. Does not have to adhere to the continuity principles.

component system See *Y/C component video, RGB component video*, and *Y/color difference component video*.

composite video A system that combines the Y (black-and-white) and C (red, green, and blue) video information into a single signal. Also called *NTSC*.

compression The temporary rearrangement or elimination of redundant picture information for easier storage and signal transport.

condenser microphone High-quality, sensitive microphone for critical sound pickup. Used mostly indoors.

contact person A person who is familiar with, and who can facilitate access to, the remote location and key people. Also called *contact*.

continuing vectors Graphic vectors that extend each other, or index and motion vectors pointing and moving in the same direction.

continuity editing Assembling shots so that vector continuity is ensured.

contrast The difference between the brightest and the darkest spots in a video picture.

control track The area of the videotape used for recording synchronizing information.

control track system See *pulse-count system*.

converging vectors Index and motion vectors that point toward each other.

crane To move the boom of the camera crane up or down. Also called *boom*.

cross-shot (X/S) Similar to over-the-shoulder shot, except that the camera-near person is completely out of the shot.

CU See *close-up*.

cue card A large hand-lettered card that contains copy, usually held next to the camera lens by floor personnel.

cut (1) The instantaneous change from one shot (image) to another. (2) Director's signal to interrupt action (used during rehearsal).

cutaway A shot of an object or event that is peripherally connected with the overall event and that is neutral as to screen direction. Used to intercut between two shots in which the screen direction is reversed.

cyc See *cyclorama*.

cyclorama A U-shaped continuous piece of canvas or muslin for backing of scenery and action. Hardwall cycs are permanently installed in front of one or two of the studio walls. Also called *cyc*.

DAT Stands for *digital audiotape*.

DC Direct current.

defined process message The desired effect of the program on the viewer.

delegation controls Controls that assign a specific function to a bus.

depth of field The area in which all objects, located at different distances from the camera, appear in focus. Depends primarily on the focal length of the lens, its *f*-stop, and the distance from the camera to the object.

desktop video The use of a desktop computer, such as a PC (DOS or Windows platform), Mac (Macintosh platform), or some other type, for a variety of preproduction and postproduction jobs.

diffused light Light that illuminates a relatively large area with an indistinct light beam. Diffused light, created by floodlights, produces soft shadows.

digital Pertaining to data in the form of digits (on/off pulses).

digital recording Audio or video recording systems that translate original analog information (sound and picture signals) into digital information.

digital video effects (DVE) Video effects generated by a computer with high-capacity hard drives and special graphics software. The computer system dedicated to DVE is called a *graphics generator*.

dimmer A device that controls the intensity of light by throttling the electric current flowing to the lamp.

directional light Light that illuminates a relatively small area with a distinct light beam. Directional light, produced by spotlights, creates harsh, clearly defined shadows.

diverging vectors Index and motion vectors that point away from each other.

documentary script format Indicates major video cues in the left column and partial or fully scripted dialogue and major audio cues in the right column. Also called *two-column script*.

dolly To move the camera toward (dolly in) or away from (dolly out) the object.

downstream keyer (DSK) A control that allows the title to be keyed (cut in) over the picture (line-out signal) as it leaves the switcher.

drama script format A script that contains complete dialogue or narration and major action cues. Also called *single-column script*.

dress (1) What people wear on-camera. (2) Dress rehearsal: final rehearsal with all facilities operating. The dress rehearsal is often videotaped. (3) Set dressing: set properties.

drop Heavy curtain suspended from a track (usually in front of the cyc). A painted drop is a large piece of canvas with a background scene painted on it.

DTV Stands for *digital television*. Sometimes called *ATV (advanced television)*.

dub The duplication of an electronic recording. The dub is always one generation away from the recording used for dubbing. In analog systems, each dub shows increased deterioration.

dub-down See *bump-down*.

dub-up See *bump-up*.

DVD Stands for *digital versatile disc*. It can store 4.7 gigabytes of video and/or audio information. It can store 133 minutes of full-motion video. Also called *digital videodisc*.

dynamic microphone A relatively rugged microphone. Good for outdoor use.

edit controller A machine that assists in various editing functions, such as marking edit-in and edit-out points, rolling source and record VTRs, and integrating effects. This is often a desktop computer with a specific software program. Also called *editing control unit*.

editing control unit See *edit controller*.

EDL Stands for *edit decision list*. It consists of edit-in and edit-out points, expressed in time code numbers, and the nature and transitions between shots.

effects bus Rows of buttons that select the video sources for a specific effect. Usually the same as a mix bus that has been switched to an effects function.

effect-to-cause model Moving from idea to desired effect on the viewer, and then backing up to the specific medium requirements to produce such an effect.

EFP Stands for *electronic field production*. Video production done outside the studio that is usually shot for postproduction (not live).

electron beam A thin stream of electrons, generated by the electron gun in back of the video tube, which strikes the photosensitive color dots at the face of the tube.

encoding See *coding*.

ENG Stands for *electronic news gathering*. The use of portable camcorders, lights, and sound equipment for the unplanned production of daily news stories. ENG is usually done for live transmission or immediate postproduction.

ENG/EFP camera Highly portable, self-contained camera for electronic news gathering (ENG) or electronic field production (EFP).

ESS system Stands for *electronic still store system*. Stores many still video frames in digital form for easy access.

establishing shot See *long shot.*

facilities request Written communication that lists all facilities needed for a specific production.

fade The gradual appearance of a picture from black (fade-in) or disappearance to black (fade-out).

fader A volume control that works by sliding a button horizontally along a specific scale. Identical in function to a pot. Also called *slide fader.* See *pot.*

fader bar A lever on the switcher that activates buses and can produce superimpositions, dissolves, fades, keys, and wipes of different speeds.

falloff The speed (degree) with which a light picture portion turns into shadow areas. Fast falloff means that the light areas turn abruptly into shadow areas and there is a great difference in brightness between light and shadow areas. Slow falloff indicates a very gradual change from light to dark, and a minimal brightness difference between light and shadow areas.

fast lens A lens that permits a relatively great amount of light to pass through at its largest aperture (lowest *f*-stop number). Can be used in low-light conditions.

field One-half of a complete scanning cycle, with two fields necessary for one television picture frame. There are 60 fields per second, and 30 frames per second.

field dolly A plywood platform supported by four wheels with pneumatic tires. Used for moving a tripod-mounted camera on a rough surface.

field log A record of each take during the videotaping.

field of view The portion of a scene visible through a particular lens; its vista. Expressed in symbols, such as *CU* for close-up.

field production Any video production that happens outside the studio.

fill light Additional light on the opposite side of the camera from the key light to illuminate shadow areas and thereby reduce falloff. Usually done with floodlights.

fishpole A suspension device for a microphone; the mic is attached to a pole and held over the scene for brief periods.

flat A piece of standing scenery used as background or to simulate the walls of a room. There are hardwall and softwall flats.

floodlight A lighting instrument that produces diffused light.

floor manager In charge of all activities on the studio floor, such as setting up scenery, getting talent into place, and relaying the director's cues to the talent. In the field, basically responsible for preparing the location for the shoot and for cuing all talent. Also called *floor director* or *stage manager.*

floor plan A diagram of scenery, properties, and set dressings drawn on a grid.

focal length With the lens set at infinity, the distance from the iris to the plane where the picture is in focus. Normally measured in millimeters (mm) or inches.

foldback The return of the total or partial audio mix to the talent through headsets or I.F.B. channels.

foot-candle (ft-c) The unit of measurement of illumination, or the amount of light that falls on an object. One foot-candle is the amount of light from a single candle that falls on a 1-square-foot area located 1 foot away from the light source. See *lux.*

formative evaluation Assessment of each step during the entire production process.

foundation A makeup base, normally done with water-soluble pancake makeup, that is applied with a sponge to the face and sometimes to all exposed skin areas. Pancake foundation reduces unwanted light reflection.

frame A complete scanning cycle of the electron beam (two fields), which occurs every $\frac{1}{30}$ second. It represents the smallest complete television picture unit.

framestore synchronizer Image stabilization and synchronization system that has a memory large enough to store and read out one complete video frame. Used to synchronize signals from a variety of video sources that are not locked to a common sync signal. Can also produce a limited number of digital effects.

Fresnel spotlight One of the most common spotlights, named after the inventor of its lens, which has steplike concentric rings.

ƒ-stop The scale on the lens indicating the aperture. The larger the ƒ-stop number, the smaller the aperture; the smaller the ƒ-stop number, the larger the aperture.

gel Generic name for color filter put in front of spotlights or floodlights to give the light beam a specific hue. *Gel* comes from *gelatin,* the filter material used before the invention of much more heat- and moisture-resistant plastic material. Also called *color media.*

generation The number of dubs away from the original recording. A first-generation dub is struck directly from the source tape. A second-generation tape is a dub of the first generation dub (two steps away from the original tape), and so forth. The greater the number of nondigital generations, the greater the loss of quality.

graphics generator A computer specially designed for creating a variety of images and colors. Also called *paint box.*

hand props Objects, called *properties,* that are handled by the performer or actor.

HDTV Stands for *high-definition television.* The 1080i standard uses 60 fields per second, each field consisting of 539½ lines. A complete frame consists of two interlaced scanning fields of 539½ lines. There are 30 complete 1,080-line frames each second. Includes also the 720p system.

HDTV (high-definition television) camera A camera system that produces high-quality, high-resolution pictures.

headroom The space left between the top of the head and the upper screen edge.

hypercardioid A microphone with a very narrow pickup pattern that has a long reach. It can also hear sounds coming directly from the back.

I.F.B. Stands for *interruptible foldback* or *feedback.* A prompting system that allows communication with the talent while on the air. A small earpiece worn by on-the-air talent that carries program sound (including the talent's voice) or instructions from the producer or director.

incident light Light that strikes the object directly from its source. To measure incident light, the light meter is pointed at the camera lens or into the lighting instruments.

insert editing Produces highly stable edit. Requires the prior laying of a continuous control track by recording black on the edit master tape.

instantaneous editing Same as *switching.*

interactive video A computer-driven program that gives the viewer some control over what to see and how to see it. It is often used as a training device.

intercom Short for *intercommunication system.* Used for all production and engineering personnel involved in the production of a show. The most widely used system has telephone headsets to facilitate voice communication on several wired or wireless channels. Includes other systems, such as I.F.B. and cellular telephones.

interlaced scanning The scanning of all odd-numbered lines (first field) and subsequent scanning of all even-numbered lines (second field). The two fields make up a complete frame.

iris Adjustable lens-opening mechanism. Also called *lens diaphragm.*

jack A socket or receptacle for a connector.

jib arm A small camera crane that can usually be operated by the cameraperson.

jogging Frame-by-frame advancement of videotape, resulting in a jerking motion.

jump cut An image that jumps slightly from one screen position to another during a cut.

Kelvin degrees (°K) The standard scale for measuring color temperature, or the relative reddishness or bluishness of white light.

key An electronic effect in which the keyed image (figure—usually letters) blocks out portions of the base picture (background) and, therefore, appears to be layered on top of it.

key bus A bus (row of buttons) used to select the video source to be inserted into the background image.

key light Principal source of illumination. Usually a spotlight.

lavaliere A small microphone that is clipped onto clothing.

leadroom The space left in front of a laterally moving object or person.

lens Optical lens, essential for projecting an optical image of the scene onto the front surface of the camera imaging device. Lenses come in various fixed focal lengths or in a variable focal length (zoom lenses), and with various maximum apertures (lens openings).

lens diaphragm   See *iris*.

level   (1) Audio: sound volume. (2) Video: video signal strength.

lighting triangle   Same as *photographic principle*. The triangular arrangement of key, back, and fill lights. Also called *triangle lighting*.

light intensity   The amount of light falling on an object that is seen by the lens. Measured in lux or foot-candles. Also called *light level*.

light level   Light intensity measured in lux or foot-candles. See *foot-candle* and *lux*.

light plot   A plan, similar to a floor plan, that shows the type, size (wattage), and location of the lighting instruments relative to the scene to be illuminated and the general direction of the light beams.

linear editing system   Uses videotape as the editing medium. It does not allow random access of shots.

line monitor   The monitor that shows only the line-out pictures that go on the air or on videotape.

line-level input   Input channel on mixer or audio console for relatively high-level audio sources. See *mic-level input*.

line-out   The line that carries the final video or audio output.

live-on-tape   The uninterrupted videotape recording of a live show for later unedited playback.

location sketch   A rough, hand-drawn map of the locale for a remote telecast. For an indoor remote, the sketch shows the dimensions of the room and the locations of furniture and windows. For an outdoor remote, the sketch indicates the buildings and the location of the remote truck, power source, and the sun during the time of the telecast.

location survey   Written assessment, usually in the form of a checklist, of the production requirements for a remote.

long shot (LS)   Object seen from far away or framed very loosely. The extreme long shot shows the object from a great distance. Also called *establishing shot*.

lossless compression   Rearranging but not eliminating pixels during digital storage and transport.

lossy compression   Throwing away redundant pixels during digital compression. Most compression is the lossy kind.

lumen   The light intensity power of one candle (light source radiating in all directions).

luminance   The brightness (black-and-white) information of a video signal.

luminance channel   A separate channel within color cameras that deals with brightness variations and allows color cameras to produce a signal receivable on a black-and-white television.

lux   European standard unit for measuring light intensity. One lux is the amount of 1 lumen (one candle-power of light) that falls on a surface of 1 square meter located 1 meter away from the light source. 10.75 lux = 1 foot-candle. Most lighting people figure roughly 10 lux = 1 foot-candle.

makeup   Cosmetics used to enhance, correct, or change facial features.

master control   Controls the program input, storage, and retrieval for on-the-air telecasts. Also oversees technical quality of all program material.

matte key   The key (usually letters) is filled with gray or a specific color.

M/E bus   A single bus that can serve mix or effects functions.

medium requirements   All personnel, equipment, and facilities needed for a production, as well as budgets, schedules, and the various production phases.

medium shot (MS)   Object seen from a medium distance. Covers any framing between a long shot and a close-up.

mental map   Tells us where things are or are supposed to be on- and off-screen.

mic   See *microphone*.

mic-level input   Input channel on mixer or audio console for relatively low-level audio sources, such as microphones. See *line-level input*.

mini disc   A small optical disc that can store one hour of CD-quality audio.

mini plug   Tiny connector used for some consumer audio equipment.

mix bus   Rows of buttons that permit the mixing of video sources, as in a dissolve or super. Major buses for on-the-air switching.

mixing   (1) Audio: combining two or more sounds in specific proportions (volume variations) as determined by the event (show) context. (2) Video: combining two shots as a dissolve or superimposition via the switcher.

moiré effect   Color vibrations that occur when narrow, contrasting stripes of a design interfere with the scanning lines of the video system.

monitor   (1) Audio: speaker that carries the program sound independent of the line-out. (2) Video: high-quality video receiver used in the video studio and control rooms. Cannot receive broadcast signals.

monochrome   One color. In video it refers to a camera or monitor that produces a black-and-white picture.

morphing   Short for *metamorphosis*. Using a computer to animate the gradual transformation of one image into another (boy into old man, cat into lion).

mounting head   A device that connects the camera to its support. Also called *pan-and-tilt head*.

MPEG   A digital compression technique developed by the Moving Picture Experts Group for moving pictures.

MPEG-2   A digital compression standard for motion video.

multimedia   Computer display of text, still and moving images, and sound. Usually recorded on CD-ROM or DVD (digital versatile disc).

narrow-angle lens   Same as long-focal-length lens. Gives a narrow vista of a scene.

noise   (1) Audio: unwanted sounds that interfere with the intentional sounds, or unwanted hisses or hums inevitably generated by the electronics of the audio equipment. (2) Video: electronic interference that shows up as snow.

nonlinear editing system   Allows random access of shots. The video and audio information is stored in digital form on computer disks.

nonlinear storage system   Storage of video and audio material in digital form on a hard drive or read/write optical disc. Each single frame can be directly accessed by the computer.

noseroom   The space left in front of a person looking or pointing toward the edge of the screen.

NTSC   Stands for *National Television System Committee*. Normally designates the composite video signal, consisting of combined chroma information (red, green, and blue signals) and luminance information (black-and-white signal).

off-line editing   Refers to an editing process that will not produce an edit master tape. Equipment is used to produce a rough-cut or an edit decision list.

omnidirectional   Pickup pattern with which the microphone can hear equally well from all directions.

on-line editing   Produces the final high-quality edit master tape. High-quality VTRs are used for on-line editing.

over-the-shoulder shot (O/S)   Camera looks over the camera-near person's shoulder (shoulder and back of head included in shot) at the other person.

PA   Production assistant.

pan   Horizontal turning of the camera.

pan-and-tilt head   See *mounting head*.

pancake   A makeup base, or foundation makeup, usually water-soluble and applied with a small sponge.

patchbay   A device that connects various inputs with specific outputs. Also called *patchboard*.

pedestal   To move the camera up or down via a studio pedestal.

performer   A person who appears on-camera in nondramatic shows. The performer does not assume someone else's character.

photographic principle   The triangular arrangement of key, back, and fill lights, with the backlight opposite the camera and directly behind the object, and the key and fill lights on opposite sides of the camera and to the front and side of the object. Also called *triangle lighting*.

pickup device   In a video camera, converts the optical image into electric energy—the video signal. Also called *imaging device*.

pickup pattern   The territory around the microphone within which the mic can hear well.

P.L.   Stands for *private line* or *phone line*. Major intercommunication device in video studios.

polar pattern   The two-dimensional representation of the pickup pattern.

pop filter A bulblike attachment (either permanent or detachable) on the front of the microphone, which filters out sudden air blasts.

postproduction Any production activity that occurs after the production. Usually refers to either videotape editing or audio sweetening.

postproduction editing The assembly of recorded material after the actual production, in contrast to instantaneous editing with the switcher.

postproduction team Normally consists of the director, a video editor, and, for complex productions, a sound designer who remixes the sound track.

pot Short for *potentiometer*, a sound-volume control. See *fader*.

preproduction Preparation of all production details.

preproduction team Consists of people who plan the production. Normally includes the producer, writer, director, art director, and technical supervisor, or TD. Large productions may include a composer and a choreographer. In charge: producer.

preroll To start a videotape and let it roll for a few seconds before it is put in the playback or record mode in order to give the electronic system time to stabilize.

presetting the zoom lens To adjust a zoom lens to keep in focus throughout the zoom. Same as *calibrating a zoom*.

preview bus Rows of buttons that can direct an input to the preview monitor at the same time another video source is on the air.

preview monitor Any monitor that shows a video source, except for the line and off-the-air monitors.

process message The message actually received by the viewer in the process of watching a video program.

producer Creator and organizer of video programs.

production The actual activities in which an event is videotaped and/or televised.

production schedule A time line that lists the start times of major production events. Also called *time line*.

production switcher Switcher designed for instantaneous editing, located in the studio control room or remote truck.

production team Consists of a variety of nontechnical and technical people, such as producer and various assistants (associate producer and PA), the director and assistant (AD), and the talent and production crew. In charge: director.

program bus The bus (row of buttons) on the switcher, with inputs that are directly switched to the line-out.

progressive scanning The consecutive scanning of lines from top to bottom.

properties See *props*.

props Short for *properties*. Furniture and other objects used by talent and for set decoration.

psychological closure Mentally filling in missing visual information that will lead to a complete and stable configuration. Also called *closure*.

pulse-count system An address code that counts the control track pulses and translates this count into elapsed time and frame numbers. Also called *control track system*.

quantizing A step in the digitizing of an analog signal. It changes the sampling points into discrete values. Also called *quantization*.

quick-release plate A mechanism on a tripod that makes it easy to mount and position the camera so that it is perfectly balanced each time.

RCA phono plug Small connector used for most consumer video and audio equipment.

reflected light Light that is bounced off the illuminated object. To measure reflected light, the light meter is pointed close to the object from the direction of the camera.

refresh rate The number of complete scanning cycles per second. See *frame*.

remote A production of a large, scheduled event done for live transmission or live-on-tape recording.

remote survey An inspection of the remote location by key production and engineering persons so that they can plan for the setup and use of production equipment. Also called *site survey*.

remote truck The vehicle that carries the control room, audio control, VTR section, video control section, and transmission equipment.

RGB　Stands for *red, green,* and *blue*—the basic colors of television.

RGB component video　A system in which all three color signals are kept separate. The three signals are recorded separately on videotape. Often called *RGB system.*

ribbon microphone　High-quality, highly sensitive microphone for critical sound pickup. Produces warm sound.

S.A.　Stands for *studio address system.* A public address loudspeaker system from the control room to the studio. Also called *studio talkback* or *P.A.* (public address) *system.*

sampling　Taking a great number of samples (voltages) at equally spaced intervals of the analog video or audio signal.

scanning　The movement of the electron beam from left to right and from top to bottom on the television screen.

scene　Event details that form an organic unit, usually in a single place and time. A series of organically related shots that depict these event details.

scenery　Background flats and other pieces (windows, doors, pillars) that simulate a specific environment.

scoop　A scooplike floodlight.

scrim　A heat-resistant spun-glass material that comes in rolls and can be cut with scissors like cloth; it is attached to a scoop to diffuse the light beam.

script　Written document that tells what the audience will see and hear.

sequencing　The control and structuring of a shot sequence.

set light　See *background light.*

shader　See *video operator.*

shot　The video contained between transitions. Also called *take.*

shot sheet　A list of every shot a particular camera has to get. It is attached to the camera to help the camera operator remember a shot sequence.

shotgun microphone　A highly directional mic with a shotgunlike barrel for picking up sounds over a great distance.

signal-to-noise ratio　The relation of the strength of the desired signal to the accompanying electronic interference (the noise). A high signal-to-noise ratio is desirable (strong video or audio signal and weak noise).

site survey　See *remote survey.*

slant track　The video track that is recorded on the videotape in a slanted, diagonal way.

slate　(1) To identify, verbally or visually, each videotaped take. (2) A little blackboard or whiteboard upon which essential production information is written, such as the title of the show, date, and scene and take numbers. It is recorded at the beginning of each videotaped take.

slow lens　A lens that permits a relatively small amount of light to pass through at its largest aperture (relatively high *f*-stop number). Can be used only in well-lighted areas.

SMPTE　Stands for *Society of Motion Picture and Television Engineers.* This time code is officially called SMPTE/EBU (for European Broadcasting Union).

SMPTE time code　A specially generated address code that marks each video frame with a specific number (hour, minute, second, and frame).

sound perspective　People (or other sound-producing sources) sound farther away in long shots than in close-ups.

source VTR　The videotape recorder that supplies the various program segments to be edited by the record VTR.

spotlight　A lighting instrument that produces directional, relatively undiffused light.

Steadicam　A camera mount that allows the operator to walk and run with the camera remaining steady.

storyboard　A series of sketches of the key visualization points of an event, with the corresponding audio information given below each visualization.

strike　To remove certain objects; to remove scenery and equipment from the studio floor after the show.

strip light　Several self-contained lamps arranged in a strip. Used mostly for illumination of the cyclorama. Also called *cyc light.*

studio camera　Heavy, high-quality camera and zoom lens that cannot be maneuvered properly without the aid of a pedestal or some other type of camera mount.

studio control room　A room adjacent to the studio in which the director, producer, various production assistants, TD (technical director), audio engineer, and sometimes the LD (lighting director) perform their various production functions.

studio pedestal   Heavy camera dolly that permits raising and lowering of the camera while on the air.

studio talkback   A public address loudspeaker system from the control room to the studio. Also called *S.A.* (studio address) or *P.A.* (public address) *system.*

summative evaluation   The final evaluation of the finished production.

super   Short for *superimposition.* The simultaneous overlay of two pictures on the same screen.

sweep   Curved piece of scenery, similar to a large pillar cut in half.

sweetening   The manipulation of recorded sound in postproduction.

switcher   (1) Production person who does the video switching (usually the technical director). (2) A panel with rows of buttons that allows the selection and assembly of various video sources through a variety of transition devices, and the creation of electronic special effects.

switching   A change from one video source to another during production with the aid of a switcher. A form of instantaneous editing.

sync   Electronic pulses that synchronize the scanning of various video equipment.

sync generator   Part of the camera chain; produces electronic synchronization pulses.

synthetic environment   Electronically generated settings, either through chroma key or computer.

take   The video contained between transitions. Also called *shot.*

talent   Collective name for all performers and actors who appear regularly in video.

tally light   Red light on the camera and inside the camera viewfinder, indicating when the camera is on the air (switched to the line-out).

tape format   See *videotape format.*

TD   Stands for *technical director.* The TD is usually operating the switcher.

telephoto lens   Gives a close-up view of an event relatively far away from the camera. Also called *long-focal-length,* or *narrow-angle, lens.*

teleprompter   A prompting device that projects moving copy over the lens so that the talent can read it without losing eye contact with the viewer.

threefold   Three flats hinged together.

tilt   To point the camera up or down.

time base corrector (TBC)   An electronic accessory to videotape recorders that helps make videotape playbacks electronically stable. It keeps slightly different scanning cycles in step.

time code system   See *SMPTE time code.*

time line   A production schedule listing the start times of major production events. Also called *production schedule.*

tongue   To move the boom with the camera from left to right or right to left.

track   See *truck.*

triangle lighting   The triangular arrangement of key, back, and fill lights. See *photographic principle.*

triaxial cable   Thin camera cable in which one central wire is surrounded by two concentric shields.

tripod   A three-legged camera mount.

truck   To move the camera laterally by means of a mobile camera mount. Also called *track.*

twofold   Two flats hinged together. Also called a *book.*

two-shot   Framing of two people in a single shot.

unidirectional   Pickup pattern with which the microphone can hear best from the front.

uplink truck   Small truck that sends video and audio signals to a satellite.

variable-focal-length lens   See *zoom lens.*

vector   A directional screen force. There are graphic, index, and motion vectors.

vector line   An imaginary line created by extending converging index vectors, or the direction of a motion vector.

video leader   Visual and auditory material that precedes any color videotape recording. Generally called *academy leader.*

video operator (VO)   In charge of the camera setup and picture control during a production. Also called *shader*.

videotape format   Indicates the width and other characteristics of a videotape that fits a specific videotape recorder.

video track   The area of the videotape used for recording the video information.

viewfinder   A small video monitor on a camera that displays the picture the camera generates.

virtual reality   Computer-simulated environment with which the user can interact and that can change according to the user's commands.

visualization   Mentally converting a scene into a number of key video images. Such visualizations are necessary for drawing a storyboard.

VO   See *video operator*.

volume   The relative intensity of the sound; its relative loudness.

VTR log   A record of each take on the source tapes.

VU meter   A volume-unit meter; measures volume units, the relative loudness of amplified sound.

wedge mount   Device similar to the quick-release plate. Has a wedge-shaped plate.

white balance   The adjustments of the color circuits in the camera to produce a white color in lighting of various color temperatures (relative bluishness or reddishness of white light).

wide-angle lens   A short-focal-length lens that provides a large vista.

window dub   A dub of the source tapes to a lower-quality tape format with the address code keyed into each frame.

windscreen   Acoustic foam rubber that is put over the microphone to cut down wind noise.

windsock   A moplike cloth cover that is put over the windscreen to further reduce wind noise in outdoor use.

wipe   A transition in which one image seems to "wipe off" (replace) the other from the screen.

wireless microphone   A system that sends audio signals over the air, rather than through microphone cables. The mic is attached to a small transmitter and the signals are received by a small receiver connected to the audio console or recording device.

XLR connector   A professional three-wire connector for audio cables.

Y/C component video   A system that keeps the Y (luminance, black-and-white) and C (color, red-green-blue) signals separate. Y and C are combined again when recorded on tape. Often called *Y/C system* or *S-video*.

Y/color difference component video   Analog system in which three signals—the luminance (Y) signal, the red minus its luminance (R–Y) signal, and the blue minus its luminance (B–Y) signal are kept separate. All three signals are recorded separately on videotape. Similar to the RGB system.

z-axis   Indicates screen depth. Extends from camera lens to horizon.

zoom lens   Variable-focal-length lens. All video cameras are equipped with a zoom lens.

zoom range   How much the focal length can be changed from a wide shot to a close-up during a zoom. The zoom range is stated as a ratio, such as 10:1. Also called *zoom ratio*.

zoom ratio   See *zoom range*.

Index

480p, 46, 51
720p, 46, 51
1080i, 46, 51

A-roll, 268
Above-the-line personnel, 26, 30–31, 33, 34
Acting. *See also* Performing
environment and audience, 331
repeating action, 332–333
small screen and close-ups, 332
techniques of, 330–333, 337
Actor, 31, 318, 319
and auditions, 333
and clothing, 333–334
makeup for, 335–336
Actual process message, 4, 7, 16
AD. *See* Associate director
Ad libbing, 331
Adapters for audio cables, 198
Additive color mixing, 147–148, CP-5
Additive primary colors, 51, 138, 147–148
Address code, 234, 270–271, 286
Address code system, 244, 270–271
Aesthetics
of complexity editing, 309–312
of continuity editing, 294–309
control of, 45
framing a shot, 80–95
lighting, 140–147, 160–165
motion, 100–103
of performer's clothing, 333–334
set design, 359–365
sound, 206–208
visual effects, 214–223
AGC. *See* Automatic gain control

Ambient sound, 133, 206, 278, 371
Analog audiocassette machines, 201–202
Analog recording equipment, 200–202, 209
Analog signal, 46
compared with digital, 52–53
Angle of view. *See* Focal length
Animation, 226
Announcer, 31
AP. *See* Associate producer
Aperture, 58, 64
depth of field and, 99
Arc, 108, 111, 112
left, 111, 112
right, 111, 112, 113
Area field of view, 83
Art director, 29, 31
Artifacts, 54, 235, 334
Aspect ratio, 78, 80–81, 104
and moving objects, 102
and wipes, 218
Assemble editing, 254, 272–273, 286
Assistant chief engineer, 33
Associate director (AD), 30, 31, 239
Associate producer (AP), 30, 31
ATR. *See* Audiotape recorder
Attached shadows, 138, 142–145
Audience
acting and, 331
performing and, 320–321
target, 10–11
Audio cables, 176, 197–199
Audio console, 196–197, 208
calibrating, 242
Audio control, 194–200, 351
Audio control booth, 351
Audio control center, 383
Audio cues, 324, 328

Audio engineer, 30, 33, 346, 351
responsibilities of, 35
Audio image, 45
Audio mixer, 194–196, 209
Audio monitor, 349
Audio postproduction, 200
Audio sweetening, 30, 176, 200
Audio synchronization, computer system and, 203
Audio synthesizer, 205
Audio track, 230
Audiocassette machine, 201–202
Audiotape, digital, 200
Audiotape recorder (ATR), 200, 202
multitrack, 201
open reel, 200
operational controls, 202
twenty-four-channel, 201
Auditions, 333
Auto-focus, 101, 127–128
Auto transition button, 259, 264
Auto white balance, 126
Automatic gain control (AGC), 142
Automatic iris, 65, 334

B-roll, 268
Back light, 138, 160–162
Background, 258
and closure, 94–95
shooting outdoors and, 96, 380
Background button, 261, 264
Background light, 138
Backing up videotapes, 246, 276, 279, 282
Barn doors, 151, 153, 159
Base picture, 215
Baselight, 138, 140–141
Battens, studio lighting, 150, 159
Batteries, camera, 132
Battery reconditioner, 132

Beam splitter, 58, 60, 65–67, 76, CP-2
Bean bag mount, 125
Below-the-line personnel, 26, 30, 32, 33, 34
Betacam cassette tab, 241
Betacam VTR, 237, 238, 240, 382
Beyer 500 microphone, 193
Beyer Dynamic microphone, 183
Big remotes, 383–384
Binary digit, 46, 52
Bit, 46, 52
Black button, 256, 263, 264
Blocking, 84, 102–103, 318
acting and, 332
z-axis, 102–103
Blue-screen technique, 217
BNC connector, 71
Books, of flats, 356
Boom, 108, 111, 112
down, 111, 112
perambulator, 188
studio, 188
up, 111, 112
Boom microphone, 188–190
performing with, 322
Boom operator, 188
Brainstorming, 20–23
Broad floodlight, 155
Building a show, 293
Bus
direct switching, 258
effects, 258, 264
key, 259
M/E, 258, 260
mix, 256–257, 258, 261–264
preset, 258, 259
preview, 257–258
program, 256–257, 258, 260–261
Bust shot, 82–83

C-clamp, 159, 356
C signal, 67
Cable guard, 120
Cables, audio, 176, 197–199, 377
  balanced, 198
Calibrating zoom lens, 108,
  127–128
Cam head, 108, 122–123
Camcorders, 58, 68, 72–75, 76,
  109, 377
  checklist for care of, 132–133
  connectors, 133
  consumer, 68, 73–75
  holding, 114–116
  mounting, 123
  and light, 141
  panning, 115
  Steadicam for, 124
  testing, 133
  viewfinder on, 67
  zoom control, 130
  See also ENG/EFP camera
Camera, 58–77
  ENG/EFP. *See* ENG/EFP
    camera
  field, 68, 72–73
  focusing, 127–130
  handheld, 114–116
  HDTV, 71–72
  mount, 100, 114–125, 135, 377
  mounting head, 108,
    117–119, 135
  movement, controlling,
    100–103, 109–113, 135
  performer and, 320–322
  position, vector line and,
    304–308
  power supply, 70
  shoulder-mounted, 114–117
  studio. *See* Studio camera
  tripod-supported, 117, 119
  video. *See* Video camera
  white-balancing, 108, 126,
    133, 135, 148–150, CP-4,
    293, 370
Camera cable, 71, 72–73
Camera chain, 58, 69–70
Camera control unit (CCU), 58,
  70, 351, 352, 383
  gain circuit on, 141
  and white-balancing, 126
Camera head, 70
Camera microphone, 73
Camera operator, 30, 33
  steadying, 114–115
Cant camera, 108, 110, 111
Cardioid pickup pattern, 176,
  180
Cast shadows, 138, 145–146

CCD. *See* Charge-coupled
  device
CCU. *See* Camera control unit
CD-ROMs, 248–249, 250
C.G. *See* Character generator
C.G. operator, 346, 348–349, 350
Character-generated slate, 244,
  278
Character generator (C.G.), 30,
  212, 215, 223–224, 244,
  259, 260, 348–349, 350,
  352, 383
Charge-coupled device (CCD),
  58, 60, 66–67
Chief engineer, 33
Choreographer, 31
Chroma key, 212, 216–218,
  CP-6, 334
Chroma-key drop, 343
Chrominance (C) channel, 67,
  CP-3, CP-10, CP-11, CP-12
Clip light, 153
Clip-on lavaliere microphone,
  183
Clocks in control room, 350
Close-up (CU), 78, 82
  acting and, 332, 333
  depth of field and, 129
  extreme, 82
  framing, 93
  makeup and, 335
  and mental map, 294
  performing and, 321–322,
    333
  and shadows, 144
  and sound, 207
  and zooms, 101
Closure. *See* Psychological
  closure
Clothing, of performers,
  333–334, 337
  color, 334
  texture and detail, 334
Clustering, 20–21, 23
Coaxial cable systems, 250
Collision montage, 311
Color, 147–150
  additive primary, 51, 138,
    147–148, CP-5
  of clothing on-camera, 334
  generated, 148
  of makeup on-camera, 335
  mixing, additive and
    subtractive, 147–148
  temperature, 138, 148–150
Color bar, 143
Color media, 149, 162
Color television receiver, 148,
  CP-1
Combining segments, 292

Compact disc (CD) player,
  203–204
Complexity editing, 290, 309–312
  intensifying the event,
    309–311
  supplying meaning, 311
Component system, 236
Composite system, 235, CP-19
Composite video, 230
Composition, picture, 85–92
  and closure, 92–95
Compression, 46, 54–55
  lossless and lossy, 55, 248
Computer audio recording,
  202–203
Computer disks, 247–248
Computer-generated
  color, 148–150, CP-7
  EDL, 284–285
  graphics, 223–225, CP-7,
    CP-8, CP-9
  image, 45, 223–225
  set, 385–386
Computers, desktop, 249,
  274–275
Condenser microphone, 181
Condensing material, 292–293
Conductor, 31
Connectors, 71, 377
  audio, 197–198
  BNC, 71, 378
  checking, 132–133, 198
  mini plug, 198, 378
  phone plug, 198
  RCA phono plug, 71, 133,
    176, 198, 378
  XLR, 176, 198, 345, 378
Contact person, 368, 374
Content, 11–12
Continuing vectors, 290,
  298–299
Continuity
  of graphic vectors, 298
  of index and motion vectors,
    298–303
  of on- and off-screen
    positions, 294–297,
    303–309
  shooting for, 277
  sound, 207–208
Continuity editing, 290,
  294–309
  and mental map, 294–297
Contrast, 138, 141
Control room. *See* Studio
  control room
Control track, 230, 273, 282
  with sync pulses, 270
Control track system, 270

Converging vectors, 290, 300,
  302, 309–310
Cookie pattern, 152
Copy-bed device, 329
Correcting production
  mistakes, 293
Costume designer, 32
Crane, 108, 111, 112
  down, 111, 112
  up, 111, 112
Crew call, 39
Cross shooting, 306–307, 363,
  364
Crossing the line, 306–308,
  309–310
Cross-shot (X/S), 78, 82–83
CU. *See* Close-up
Cube effect, 222
Cucalorus, 152
Cue cards, 318, 330, 331
Cues
  audio, 324, 328
  directional, 324, 327
  director's, 321, 349
  floor manager's, 324–328
  time, 325–326
Cutaway shots, 278, 290, 309
Cuts-only, 266, 267, 292
  and program bus, 260–261
Cutting, 256, 261–262, 349
Cyc. *See* Cyclorama
Cyc light, 156–157
Cyclorama, 156–157, 340,
  343–344, 357
  hardwall, 343–344

D-1 system, 239
D-2 system, 239
D-3 system, 239
D-5 system, 239
D-6 system, 239
D-7 system, 239
DAT. *See* Digital audiotape
DAW. *See* Digital audio
  workstation
Defined process message, 4, 7,
  8–10
Delegation buttons, 259
Demographic profile, 11
Depth of field, 78, 104, 128–130
  close-ups and, 129
  focusing and, 128–130
  great, 98
  lens and, 97–99
  shallow, 98
Desk microphones, 190–191
  performing with, 322
  setup, 191

Desktop computers, 249, 274–275
Desktop video, 249
Diaphragm, lens, 58, 64
Diffused light, 138, 140
Digital audio workstation (DAW), 203
Digital audiotape (DAT) cassette, 202
Digital audiotape (DAT) recorder, 202
Digital Betacam system, 239
Digital cart system, 204
Digital image manipulation equipment, 220–221
Digital recording, 202–204, 209
Digital-S system, 239
Digital signal, 46
  advantages of, 54–55
  compared with analog, 52–53
Digital television (DTV), 46
  aspect ratio for, 80
  scanning systems for, 51
Digital versatile disc (DVD), 176, 204, 248–249, 250
Digital video, 47–57, 204
Digital video effects (DVE), 55, 212, 221–223
Digital zoom, 63
Digitizing source tapes, 282
Dimmer, 138, 141, 159, 351
Direct switching bus, 258
Directional cues, 324, 327
Directional light, 138, 140
Director, 29, 30, 31, 134, 346, 349, 373
  responsibilities of, 35
Director of photography (DP), 30, 33
Dissolves, 262–264, 269
Diverging vectors, 290, 300–301, 302–303
Docking, 72
Documentary script format, 4, 12–14
Dolly, 101, 108, 111, 112, 118–120, 134
  back, 112
  field, 120
  in, 111, 112
  out, 111, 112
  tripod, 119–120
  zoom versus, 101
Downlinking, 372
Downstream keyer (DSK), 254, 264
DP. *See* Director of photography
Drama script format, 4, 16–17
Drawing software, 224, 225

Drop-shadow mode, 216, 217
Drops, 343
  painted, 357
  seamless, 357
DSK. *See* Downstream keyer
DTV. *See* Digital television
Dub, window, 254, 279–280, 283
DVCAM digital system, 239, 240
DVCPRO digital system, 234, 239, 240
  cassettes for, 241
DVD. *See* Digital versatile disc
DVE. *See* Digital video effects
Dynamic microphone, 176

ECU. *See* Extreme close-up
Edge mode, 216
Edit controller, 254, 266–268, 286
  in single-source system, 267–268
Edit decision list (EDL), 254, 276, 280, 283, 284–285
  computer-generated, 284–285
Editing
  assemble, 254, 272–273, 286
  complexity, 290, 309–311, 312
  continuity, 290, 294–309, 312
  functions, 292–293, 312
  insert, 254, 273, 286
  linear system, 254
  nonlinear system, 254
  off-line, 254, 282–284, 286
  on-line, 254, 284–285, 286
  paper-and-pencil, 283
  postproduction, 265–285, 286
  purpose of, 291–292
  software programs for, 276
Editing control unit. *See* Edit controller
EDL. *See* Edit decision list
Effect-to-cause production model, 4, 6–19, 23
Effects bus, 254, 258
EFP. *See* Electronic field production
EFP floodlight, 157
Electron gun and beam, 48–50
Electronic field production (EFP), 28, 368, 373–382
  equipment checklist for, 377–379
  postproduction for, 382
  remote survey for, 373–376
  scheduling, 40
  shooting indoors, 380–381
  shooting outdoors, 379–380

Electronic keyboard, 205
Electronic news gathering (ENG), 368, 370–372
  and live transmission, 371–372
  placing the reporter, 370–371
  production van for, 371–372
  satellite uplink truck for, 372
Electronic still store (ESS) system, 212, 220, 248, 352
Electro-Voice RE-16 microphone, 193
Electro-Voice RE-50 microphone, 193
Ellipsoidal spotlight, 152
ELS. *See* Extreme long shot
Energy level, of sound, 208
ENG. *See* Electronic news gathering
ENG/EFP camera, 58, 68, 72–73, 76
  checklist for care of, 132–133
  connectors, 133
  conversion to studio camera, 73–74
  gain circuits on, 141
  manual focus, 127
  white-balance control, 126
  zoom mechanism, 130
  See also Camcorder
ENG van, 371–372
Engineering supervisor, 373
Environment
  acting and, 331
  sound recording and, 206
  synthetic, 368, 385–386, 388
Equipment and facilities, 12
ESS system. *See* Electronic still store system
Establishing shot, 78
Evaluation, 7, 16–19
  formative, 18
  summative, 18–19
Event intensification, 309
Executive producer, 31
Extreme close-up (ECU, XCU), 82
  framing, 93–94
Extreme long shot (ELS, XLS), 82
Extreme-wide-angle position, 60
Eye contact, performing and, 320–321

Facilities, 12
Fade to black, 263–264
Fader, 176, 194
Fader bar, 254, 256–257, 262, 263, 264

Falloff, 138, 146–147
  fast, 138, 146–147
  slow, 138, 146–147
Fast lens, 58
FCC. *See* Federal Communications Commission
Federal Communications Commission (FCC), 72
Fiber-optic cable systems, 250
Fiber-optic cables, 71
Field, 46, 48
  depth of, 78, 97–99, 128–129
  of view, 78
Field camera, 68, 72–73
Field dolly, 120
Field lighting, 165–170
Field log, 230, 245–246, 278, 382
Field of view, 63, 78, 82–83, 104
  area, 83
  distance steps, 82
Field producer, 31
Field production, 368
  and audio mixing, 195–196
  electronic. *See* Electronic field production
  equipment checklist for, 377–379
  remote survey, 373–376
  shooting indoors, 375, 380–381
  shooting outdoors, 375, 380–381
  wrap-up, 382
Figure-ground principle, sound and, 206–207
File management, in editing, 274
Fill light, 138, 160–162, 165–166
FireWire (Apple), 282
Fishpole, for shotgun microphone, 188–189
  performing with, 323
Flats, 340, 354–356
  hardwall, 356
  softwall, 355–356
Floodlights, 138, 154–158
  bank of, 156
  broad, 155
  fluorescent bank, 156
  portable, 157–158, 170
  scoop, 154
  small EFP, 157
  softlight, 155
  special-purpose, 156
Floor manager, 29, 30, 32
  cues, 324–328
Floor person, 30, 32

Floor plan, 26, 29, 35, 41, 360–361
  evaluating, 363–366
  and set and hand props, 360–361
  setup and, 362–363
Fluorescent lighting, 149
  bank of, 156
Fly effect, 223
Flying erase head, 233, 273
Focal length, 58, 61
  depth of field and, 97–99
Focus,
  auto, 101, 127–128
  manual, 127
  racking, 99
  selective, 128
  and zooms, 101
Foldback, 35
Foot-candle (ft-c), 138, 140
Foreground, 96–99
  shooting outdoors and, 96, 380
Formative evaluation, 18
Foundation, 318
Foundation makeup, 335–336
Fractal graphic generation, 225, 385, CP-8
Frame, 46, 48
Frame store synchronizer, 220, 238
Framing a shot, 80–95
  golden section, 86
  nonsymmetrical, 86
  proper and improper, 93–95
Fresnel spotlight, 150–151, 160, 162, 165
f-stop, 58, 64–65
  and baselight, 141
  and depth of field, 99

Gain circuits of camera, 141
Gain control, automatic, 242
Gels, 149, 162
Generation, 52–53, 55
Genlock, 75
Golden section framing, 86
Graphic vector, 84, 298
Graphics generator, 221, 224–225, CP-7
Grass Valley 100 switcher, 258–259, 261
Grips, 30
Ground row, 343–344

Hand microphone, 185–188, 193
  performing with, 322
  positioning, 186–187

Hand properties, 358–359
  floor plan and, 360–361
Handheld camera, 114–116
Hardwall cyclorama, 343–344
Hardwall flats, 356
HDTV camera, 71–72
HDTV picture, 46, 51, 354
Headroom, 78, 87–88
Headset microphone, 191
Hi8 system, 234, 237, 279
High-definition television (HDTV), 46, 51, 72
  aspect ratio for, 80–81
  focusing and, 129
  vertical vector for, 90
High-definition television (HDTV) camera, 68, 71–72
HMI spotlight, 152, 166
Horizon line, 91–92, 110
House sync, 75
Hundredeighty, 304
Hypercardioid pickup pattern, 176, 180, 188

i-link (Sony), 282
Idea generation, 19–23
I.F.B. *See* Interruptible foldback/feedback
Illumination, measuring, 170–171
Image
  audio, 45
  computer-generated, 45
  formation, 47–51
  lens-generated, 45
  rotation of, 222
  synthetic, 45, 223–226
  three-dimensional, 224–225
Image control, 45
Image control center, 383
Imaging device, 60, 66, 76
Incandescent lighting, 149
Incident light, 138, 170
Index vector, 84
Input
  audio, 199
  program, 352
  video, 256
Insert editing, 254, 273
Interactive video, 230, 249–250, 252, 386
Intercom, 340, 345–346, 349, 379, 383
Interlaced scanning, 46, 48–50
Internet, and interactive video, 250
Interruptible foldback/feedback (I.F.B.), 318, 324, 345–346, 349, 383

Interview, light plot, 164
Iomega disks, 202, 247
Iris, lens, 58, 64
  automatic, 65, 334

Jack, 71, 176, 194, 355
Jaz disks, 202
Jib arm, 108, 124–125
  short-arm, 125
Jogging, 220, 290, 310
Joint Photographic Experts Group (JPEG), 55
JPEG. *See* Joint Photographic Experts Group
Jump cut, 290, 304, 310

Kelvin degrees (°K), 138, 148–149
Key, 212, 215
  chroma, 216–218
  matte, 212, 215–216
  normal, 215, 216
Key bus, 254, 259, 260
Key light, 138, 160–162
Keying, 259, 260, 264
Knee shot, 82–83
Krylon pancake makeup, 336

Lashline, 354–355
Lavaliere microphone, 176, 183–185, 192, 193
  advantages and disadvantages of, 184
  clip-on, 183
  performing with, 322
  wireless, 192
LCD. *See* Liquid crystal display
LD. *See* Lighting director
Leader numbers, 244
Leadroom, 78, 87, 90–91
Lens, 61–65, 75
  cap, 132
  and depth of field, 97–99
  diaphragm, 58, 64
  fast, 58, 64
  and focal length, 58, 61
  iris, 58, 64, 65
  narrow, angle, 60, 61
  slow, 58, 64
  speed, 64
  variable-focal-length, 61
  wide-angle, 60, 102
  z-axis length and, 97
  z-axis speed and, 99–100
  zoom, 58, 61–63, 108, 127–128
  zoom range, 58, 63
Lens-generated image, 45

Level, taking a, 323
Light
  incident, 138, 170
  intensity, 138, 140–141, 171
  reflected, 138, 141, 170–171
  types of, 140, 171
Light boxes, 157–158
Light meter, 170–171
Light plot, 138, 164
Light tents, 157
Lighting, 138–172
  back, 138, 160–162
  background, 138, 162–163
  batten, studio, 150
  contrast, 170–171
  control, 351
  diffused, 138, 140
  directional, 138, 140
  field, 165–170, 378
  fill, 138, 160–162, 165–166
  fluorescent, 149
  holes, 170
  incandescent, 149
  indoors without windows, 149, 167–168, 381
  interiors with windows, 168–169, 381
  key, 138, 160–162, 166
  measuring, 170–171
  operation of lights, 158–160
  outdoors, 149, 165–167, 379–380
  overcast days and, 165
  performing and, 323
  photographic principle, 138, 160–162, 171
  safety in, 158–160
  set, 162–163
  studio, 160–165, 345
  sunlight and, 165–167
  triangle principle, 138, 160–162, 171
Lighting director (LD), 29, 30, 33, 346
  responsibilities of, 35
Lighting instruments, 150–158, 171
  broad, 155
  clip light, 153
  cyc light, 156–157
  EFP floodlight, 157
  ellipsoidal spotlight, 152
  for field production, 378
  floodlight bank, 156
  fluorescent bank, 156
  Fresnel spotlight, 150–151, 160, 162, 165
  HMI spotlight, 152, 166
  light boxes, 157–158

portable floodlights, 157–158, 170
portable spotlights, 152–154, 170
reflectors, 166–167
scoop, 154
softlight, 155, 161, 378
strip light, 156–157
umbrellas, 168, 378
Line, 304
Line of conversation and action, 304
Line-out signal, 194
Linear editing systems, 254, 265–273, 284–285, 286
  multiple-source, 268–269
  single-source, 265–266
Linear off-line editing, 283–284
Linear on-line editing, 284–285
Liquid crystal display (LCD) viewfinder, 67
Live transmission, 371–372
Location sketch, 374–375
Logging, 280–282
Long-focal-length position, 61
Long shot (LS), 78, 82
  extreme, 82
Lossless and lossy compression, 55, 248
Low tally, 261, 262
Lowel Omni light, 153
Lowel Pro light, 153
Lowel Tota light, 157
LS. *See* Long shot
Luminance (Y) channel, 67, CP-3, CP-10, CP-11, CP-12
Lux, 138, 140

Mac platform, 55
Maintenance engineer, 33
Makeup, 335–336, 337, 354
  close-ups and, 335
  foundation, 335–336
  pancake, 335–336
Makeup artist, 32
Makeup room, 354
Manual focus, 127
Master control, 340, 352–353, 366
Master potentiometer, 194
Matte key, 212, 215–216
M/E bus, 254, 258
Medium requirements, 4, 7, 10–12
Medium shot (MS), 78, 82
Mental map, 290, 294–297, 303–304, 312
Microphones, 179–193, 208–209
  boom, 188–190, 193, 323
  camera, 73

condenser, 176, 181, 193
desk, 190–191, 322
dynamic, 176, 181
for field production, 378
hand, 185–188, 193, 322
headset, 191
lavaliere, 176, 183–185, 192, 193, 322
omnidirectional, 176, 179, 193
performing with, 322–323
ports, 190
radio, 192
ribbon, 176, 181, 182–183, 193
shotgun, 180, 188–190
sound pickup, 45
stand, 190–191, 323
taking a level, 323
unidirectional, 176, 179
wireless, 192
Microphone-generated sound, 45
Middleground, 96–99
Mini disc, 176, 204
Mini plug, 176, 198
Mix bus, 254, 256–257, 258
  operation of, 261–264
Mix button, 259, 261
Mixing, field, 195–196
Moiré effect, 318, 334
Money, as production factor, 11–12
Monitor, 340, 347–349
  audio, 349
  for editing, 274–275
  stack, 347–348
  studio, 346
Monochrome
  TV, 47–48
  viewfinder, 67
Monophonic audio mixer, 194
Montage, 311
  collision, 311
Morphing, 212, 226, CP-9
Mosaic effect, 220–221
Motion vector, 84–85, 280, 309–310
Motion vector line, 308
Mounting head, 108, 117–119, 123
Moving Picture Experts Group (MPEG), 55
MS. *See* Medium shot
Multicore cables, 71
Multifunction switchers, 258–260
Multimedia, 230, 250, 252
Multitrack audiotape recorders, 201, 202
Music director, 31

Narrow-angle lens position, 61–63
  maximum, 63
Narrow-angle view, 60
Narrow-angle z-axis, 97
National Television System Committee (NTSC), 48, 230, 236
  signal, 67, 230, 235, CP-3
Neutral density filters, 378
News gathering, 370–371
News script format, 4, 15–16
Nonlinear editing systems, 254, 274–276, 284–285, 286
Nonlinear storage systems, 230, 247–249, 252
Nonsymmetrical framing, 86
Normal key, 215
Normal lens position, 61
Normaled connections, 200
Noseroom, 78, 89
Notes, time for, 39
NTSC. *See* National Television System Committee
NTSC signal, 67, 230, 235, CP-3

Off-line editing, 254, 282–284
  linear, 283–284
Off-screen positions, 303–309
  mental map of, 294–297, 303
Omnidirectional microphone, 176, 179, 193
Omnidirectional pickup pattern, 176
On-line editing, 254, 284–285
On-screen positions, 303–309
Optical discs, 204, 248
Optical zoom, 63
O/S. *See* Over-the-shoulder shot
Outline mode, 216, 217
Output, audio, 199
Over-the-shoulder shot (O/S), 78, 82–83, 332, 364

PA. *See* Production assistant
P.A. system. *See* Public address system
Page, 224
Painting software, 224, CP-7
PAL system, 235
Pan, 90, 108, 110, 111, 115
  and cam head, 122–123
  left, 110, 111
  right, 110, 111
Pan-and-tilt head, 117–118
Pan and tilt lock, 119
Pancake makeup, 335–336
Paper-and-pencil editing, 283
Par 38 lamp, 153
Parallel steering, 122

Patch panel, 199–200
Patching, 199–200
Pedestal, 108, 111
  robotic, 123
  studio, 108, 121–123
Perambulator boom, 188
Performer, 31, 318, 319
  and auditions, 333
  camera and, 320–322
  and clothing, 333–334
  makeup for, 335–336
Performing. *See also* Acting
  audio and lighting, 322–323
  for close-ups, 321–322
  and eye contact, 320–321
  techniques, 320–330, 337
  timing and prompting, 323–330
Periaktos, 357–358
Personnel
  above-the-line, 26, 30–31, 33, 34
  below-the-line, 26, 30, 32, 33, 34
  production. *See* Production personnel, Technical personnel
Perspective, sound, 207
Phantom power, 181
Phone line (P.L.), 351
Phone plug, 198
Phono plug, RCA, 176, 198
Photographic lighting principle, 138, 160–162, 163–164, 171
Pickup device, 60, 66
Pickup pattern, 176, 179–180
  cardioid, 176, 180
  hypercardioid, 176, 180
  omnidirectional, 176, 179
  ultracardioid, 180
  unidirectional, 176, 179
Pickup shot, 293
Picture balance, 86
Picture composition, 85–92
Picture depth, 104
Picture manipulation, 55
Picture resolution, 66
Pixel, 48, 63, 66, 221
P.L. *See* Phone line, Private line
Platforms, 358
Plugs, 71
  BNC, 71, 378
  mini, 198, 378
  phone, 198
  RCA phono, 71, 133, 176, 198, 378
  XLR, 176, 198, 345, 378
Polar pattern, 176

Pop filter, 181, 186

Ports, microphone, 190

Postproduction, 4, 6, 382, 385
  audio, 200
  recording for, 245

Postproduction editing, 265–285, 286
  assemble editing, 272–273, 286
  correcting errors in, 293
  insert editing, 273, 286
  linear editing systems, 265–273, 286
  nonlinear editing systems, 274–276, 286
  off-line and on-line, 282–285, 286
  preparation for, 276–282

Postproduction team, 26, 30–32, 41

Potentiometer (pot), 194

Power supply, 377
  for camera, 70
  for condenser mic, 181
  for videotape recorder, 240

Preproduction, 4, 6
  remote survey, 368, 373–376

Preproduction team, 26, 28–30, 41

Preread systems, 266

Preroll, 245, 267

Preset bus, 258, 259

Preview bus, 254, 257–258

Primary colors, additive, 51, 138, CP-5

Prism block, 66

Private line (P.L.), 340, 345–346, 383

Process message, 4, 7–19, 283, 359–360
  actual, 4, 7, 16
  defined, 4, 7, 8–10
  persuasion-oriented, 11

Producer, 4, 28, 30, 31, 349, 373
  and postproduction, 30
  responsibilities of, 34–36

Production, 4, 6
  effect-to-cause model, 6–19
  field. *See* Field production

Production assistant (PA), 30, 31

Production personnel, 12
  above-the-line, 26, 30–31, 33, 34
  below-the-line, 26, 30, 32, 33, 34
  nontechnical, 30, 31, 34
  technical, 30, 33, 34

Production process, 5–25

Production schedule, 26, 28, 38–41

Production switcher, 256–258, 286

Production team, 26–42

Program bus, 254, 256, 257, 258
  operation of, 260–261

Program input, 352

Program log, 352

Program retrieval, 352

Progressive scanning, 46, 50

Prompting devices, 324, 328–330, 337

Prop list, 362

Property manager, 29, 32

Props (properties), 340, 366
  hand, 358–359
  set, 358
  set dressings, 359
  storage of, 353

Prosumer camera, 68

Protection copies of tapes, 246–247, 279

Psychographic data, 11

Psychological closure, 78, 92–95, 104
  undesirable, 94–95

Public address (P.A.) system, 346, 349, 383

Pulse-count system, 254, 270

Quantizing, 46, 53

Quartz lamps, 159

Quick-release plate, 119

QuickTime software, 226

Racking focus, 99

Radio microphone, 192

Random access, 224, 247, 248

RCA phono plug, 71, 133, 176, 198, 378

RCU. *See* Remote control unit

Read/write optical discs, 204, 248

Record VTR, 265–266

Recordkeeping during videotaping, 245, 278

Reflected light, 138, 141, 170–171

Reflector, 166–167

Refresh rate, 46, 50

Rehearsal, 40

Remote, 368
  big, 383–384

Remote control unit (RCU), 72–73, 378
  and white-balancing, 126

Remote survey, 368, 373–376

Remote truck, 368, 383–384

Reset break, 27, 39, 40

Resolution, 66

Retakes, 245

RGB, 46, 48, 51, 67, CP-1, CP-2, CP-3
  and white-balancing, 126, 149–150

RGB component system, 230, 236–237, CP-13

Ribbon microphone, 176, 181, 182–183, 193

Riding the gain, 184, 195

Risers, 358

Robotic pedestal, 123

Rotary potentiometer, 194

Rotation effect, 222, 225

Rough-cut, 30, 280, 283

Run-out signal, 245

S.A. system. *See* Studio address system

Safety, field production and, 169–170, 381

Sampler, 205

Sampling rate, 46, 53

Sampling software, 205

Satellite news vehicle (SNV), 372

Satellite uplink truck, 372

Scanning, 46, 48–51
  digital television systems, 51
  interlaced, 46, 48–50
  progressive, 46, 50

Scenery, 354–358
  hardwall flats, 356
  set modules, 356–357
  set pieces, 357–358
  softwall flats, 354–356
  storage of, 353

Scoop, 154

Screen-center placement, 85

Screen-left, 296, 301

Screen-right, 296–297, 301

Scrim, 154, 158

Script, 4
  documentary format, 4, 12–14
  drama format, 4, 16–17
  formats, 4, 12–16
  news format, 4, 15–16
  single-column, 16, 17
  studying, 333
  two-column, 12–14, 15

Seamless drop, 357

SECAM system, 235

SEG. *See* Special-effects generator

Selective focus, 128

Sennheiser MKH-70 microphone, 193

Servo-zoom, 130–131

Set, computer-generated, 385–386

Set design, 359–365

Set dressings, 359

Set modules, 356–357

Set pieces, 357–358

Set properties, 358
  floor plan and, 360–361

Setup
  and camera control unit, 70
  floor plan and, 39, 362

Shadows
  attached, 138, 142–145, 171
  cast, 138, 145–146, 171

Shock mount, 188, 190

Short-arm jib, 125

Short-focal-length position, 60

Shoulder-mounted camera, 114–117

Shoulder-mounted ENG/EFP camcorder, 116–117

Shure SM58 microphone, 193

Shure SM63L microphone, 193

Signal processing, video, 67

Single-column script, 16, 17

Site survey, 368, 373–376

Slate, 278
  character-generated, 244, 278

Slow falloff, 138, 146–147

Slow lens, 58

SMPTE. *See* Society of Motion Picture and Television Engineers

SMPTE/EBU time code, 244, 271

SMPTE time code, 203, 254, 271, 279

SNV. *See* Satellite news vehicle

Society of Motion Picture and Television Engineers/ European Broadcasting Union (SMPTE/EBU), 244, 271

Softlight, 155, 161, 378

Softwall flat, 354–356

Solarization, 220–221

Sony ECM-55 microphone, 193

Sony ECM-77 microphone, 193

Sony ECM-672 microphone, 193

Sound
  aesthetics of, 206–208
  ambient, 133, 206, 278, 371
  computer-generated, 45
  continuity, 207–208
  and environment, 206
  energy level of, 208

for field production, 381
and figure-ground principle, 206–207
microphone-generated, 45
mixing, 30
perspective of, 207
synthesized, 45, 205, 209
volume levels of, 242
Sound bites, 292
Sound control, 194–200, 351
Sound designer, 30, 33
Sound-on-tape (SOT), 15
Sound pickup, 178–193
Sound pickup principle, 178, 208
Sound recording equipment, 200–204, 208–209
analog, 200–202, 209
audio mixer and console, 194–196, 209
audiocassette machines, 201–202
compact disc (CD), 203–204
computer disks, 202–203
digital, 202–204, 209
digital audio workstation (DAW), 203
digital audiotape recorder (DAT), 202
digital cart system, 204
digital versatile disc (DVD), 204
multitrack, 201, 202
open-reel audiotape machines, 200, 202
optical disc, 204
See also Videotape-recording systems
Sound track, 311
Source tapes, digitizing, 282
Source VTR, 265–266
Speakers, studio, 346
Special-effects generator (SEG), 268
Spill, 40
Split screen, 218
Spotlights, 138, 150–153
ellipsoidal, 152
Fresnel, 151–152
HMI, 152
portable, 152–153, 170
Spreader, on tripod, 117, 119
Stand microphone, 190–191
performing with, 323
Standard television (STV), 48
aspect ratio for, 81
focusing and, 129
Standup report, 370
Steadicam, 108, 124
Stereo audio mixer, 194

Stopwatches in control room, 350
Storage systems, nonlinear, 230, 247–249, 252
Storyboard, 277
Stretching effect, 222
Striking, 40
Strip light, 156–157
Studio
makeup room, 354
storage areas, 353
support areas, 353–354, 366
video production. *See* Video production studio
Studio address (S.A.) system, 346, 349, 351
Studio boom, 188
Studio camera, 68–71, 76
checklist for care of, 133–135
converting ENG/EFP camera to, 73–74
gain circuits on, 141
manual focus, 127
zoom control, 130–131
Studio control room, 340, 346–351, 366
image control, 347–351
lighting control, 351
sound control, 349, 351
Studio lighting, 160–165
Studio lighting battens, 150
Studio monitor, 346, 347–349
stacks of, 347–348
Studio pedestal, 108, 121–123
Studio producer, 31
STV. *See* Standard television
Subject placement, 85–86
Subtractive color mixing, 147–148
Summative evaluation, 18–19
Superimposition, 212, 214
Survey team, 373
S-VHS system, 202, 235–236, 237, 240, 279
S-video, 235
See also Y/C component system
Sweetening, 30, 176, 200
Switcher, 256–265, 349
layout, 256–258
multifunction, 258–260
operation of, 260–265
Switching, 256–265, 285, 353
Sync generator, 70
Sync pulses, 234
Synthesized sound, 45, 205, 209
Synthetic environment, 368, 385–386, 388
Synthetic image, 45, 223–225

Take button, 259, 261
Taking a level, 323
Talent, 12, 31, 318, 337
Tally light, 134
Tape counter, 244
Tape formats, 239, 251
Target audience, 10–11
TBC. *See* Time base corrector
TD. *See* Technical director
Technical center, 383
Technical director (TD), 29, 30, 33, 346, 349, 373
responsibilities of, 34, 378
Technical meeting, 39
Technical personnel, below-the-line, 30, 33
Technical supervisor, 33
Telephoto lens position, 61
Teleprompter, 318, 319, 328–330
Three-dimensional images, 224–225
Threefold, 356
Three-shot, 82–83
Tilting the camera, 91–92, 108, 110, 111, 115
Time, as production factor, 11–12
Time base corrector (TBC), 230, 238, 251
Time code, 244, 270–271, 279
SMPTE, 244, 271
Time code system, 270–271
Time code track, 234
Time line, 38–41
interview, 38–39
Titles, keyed, 215
Tongue, 108, 111, 113
Tracking, 112
Tracks, 108, 111, 112, 232–234, 251
audio, 230, 232, 233, 273
control, 230, 232, 233–234, 270, 273, 282
video, 230, 232, 273
Transcribing speech, 282
Transparency, 55
Triangle lighting, 138, 160–162, 171
multiple triangles, 163–164
Triax cables, 71
Tricycle steering, 122
Tripod, 108, 117
benefits of using, 119
with spreader, 117
Tripod dolly, 119–120
Tripod-supported camera, 109, 117–120
Truck, 108, 111, 112
Truck, uplink, 368, 372

Two-column script, 12–14, 15
Twofold, 355–356
Two-shot, 82–83

Ultracardioid pickup pattern, 180
Umbrellas, diffusion, 168, 378
Unidirectional microphone, 176
Uplink truck, 368, 383

Variable-focal-length lens, 61
Vector line, 290, 304–309, 312
camera position and, 305–306
crossing the, 306, 309–310
motion, 308
Vectors, 78, 84–85, 104, 298–303, 312
continuing, 290, 298–299
converging, 290, 300, 302
diverging, 290, 300–301, 302–303
graphic, 84, 298
and horizon line, 91
index, 84, 298–303
motion, 67, 84–85, 298–303, 308, 309–310
reversal of, 299
Velocity microphone, 182
VHS system, 230, 240
cassette for, 241
Video
and color, 51
digital, 47–57
image formation, 47–57
interactive, 249–250, 252
Video camera
functions of, 59–61
lens, 60, 61–65
Videodisc, digital. *See* Digital versatile disc
Video editor, 30
Video effects
animation, 226
cube, 222
digital, 220–226
electronic, 214–220, 226
fly, 223
jogging, 220
key, 215–218
mosaic, 220–221
rotation, 222
solarization, 220–221
stretching, 222
superimposition, 214
synthetic image creation, 223–225
wipe, 218–220

Video engineer, 30

Video inputs, 256

Video leader, 243–244

Video operator, 30, 33, 70

Video production studio, 342–346, 366

installations, 345–346

physical layout, 342–345

Video recording, and operating speed, 245

Video-recording head, 233

Video signal processing, 67

Video slate, 244

Video track, 230, 232

Videotape, 377

cassettes, and tabs, 241, 243

formats, 132, 239, 251

tracks, 108, 111, 112, 230, 232–234, 251

Videotape editor, 33

Videotape operator, 33

Videotape recorder (VTR), 237–238, 251, 265

analog, 237

digital, 239

heads in, 240

one-inch, 237

operating speed of, 245

power supply for, 240

record, 265–266

source, 265–266

and tape formats, 132, 239

types of, 237–239

Videotape-recording process, 240–247

for postproduction, 245

recordkeeping for, 245–246

Videotape-recording systems, 232–239

composite, 230, 235, CP-10

RGB component, 230, 236–237

tape and disk-based, 232

tracks on, 232–234

Y/C component, 230, 235–236, CP-11

Y/color difference, 230, 236–237

Viewfinder, 58, 60, 67–68, 109, 116

and horizon line, 298

tally light, 134

Virtual reality, 368, 386

Visual effects. *See* Video effects

Voice-over (VO), 15

VTR. *See* Videotape recorder

VTR center, 383

VTR log, 280–282

VU (volume unit) meter, 176, 194–195, 293

Wagons, 358

Weather, shooting outdoors and, 379–380

Weathercast, and chroma-key, CP-6

Wedge mount, 119

White-balancing, 108, 126, 133, 135, 148–150, CP-4, 293, 370

auto, 126

Wide-angle position, 63

maximum, 63

and z-axis movement, 102

Wide-angle view, 60

Wide-angle z-axis, 97

Wind jammer, 182

Window dub, 254, 279–280, 283

Windows platform, 55

Windscreen, on mic, 176, 182, 190

Windsock on windscreen, 182

Wipe button, 260, 264

Wipes, 212, 218–219, 264, 269

corner, 218, 219

diamond, 218, 219

horizontal, 218, 219

patterns, 264

soft, 218

split screen, 218

vertical, 218, 219

Wireless microphone, 192

Wrap, 38

Writer, 28–29, 31

X-axis, and microphone, 189

XCU. *See* Extreme close-up

XLR connector, 133, 176, 198

XLS. *See* Extreme long shot

X/S. *See* Cross-shot

Y signal, 67, 235

Y/C component system, 230, 235–236, CP-11

See also S-video

Y/color difference component system, 230, 236–237, CP-12

Z-axis, 78, 95–100

blocking, 102–103

and dollying, 112

lens and, 97–100

and microphone, 189

narrow-angle, 97

position switch, 306–307

speed, 99–100

wide-angle, 97

Z-axis index vector, 302

Zip disks, 202, 247

Zipping, on Windows platform, 55

Zoom, 100–101, 113, 130–131

digital, 63

fast, 101

in, 113, 130

optical, 63

out, 113, 130

versus dolly, 101

and z-axis, 99–100

Zoom lens, 58

calibrating, 108

presetting, 127–128, 135

Zoom range, 58, 63

Zoom ratio. *See* Zoom range

PHOTO CREDITS

360 Systems: 8.34

Edward Aiona: 3.2, 3.3, 4.3, 4.4, 4.5, 4.6, 5.1, 5.2, 5.3, 5.4, 5.8, 5.9, 5.10, 5.11, 5.12, 5.13, 5.14, 5.15, 5.16, 5.19, 5.22, 5.23, 5.24, 5.27, 6.1 (left), 6.2, 6.3, 6.4, 6.5, 6.6, 6.7, 6.8, 6.26, 7.5, 7.12, 7.28, 7.29, 7.30, 7.31, 8.7, 8.9, 8.10, 8.14, 8.15, 8.16, 8.17, 8.29, 9.2, 9.10, 9.12, 9.13, 10.8, 10.9, 11.1, 11.6, 11.7, 11.8, 11.9, 11.10, 12.1, 12.2, 12.3, 12.4, 12.5, 12.6, 12.7, 12.9, 12.10, 12.11, 12.12, 12.13, 13.1, 14.5, 14.7, 14.11, 15.1

AKG Acoustics, Inc.: 8.6

Ampex Corporation: 8.28

beyerdynamic Inc.: 8.8, 8.19

Cinekinetic PYT, Ltd., Australia: 6.22, 6.23

Cinema Products Corporation: 6.19, 6.20

Cooperative Media Group: 9.19, 9.20

Egripment USA: 6.14

Electro-Voice: 8.4, 8.21

Fujinon, Inc., Broadcast and Communications Products Division: 6.24

The Grass Valley Group, Inc.: 9.7, 11.4

Ideas to Images: 4.15, 8.5, 8.25, 8.27, 8.31, 9.18, 14.8, 15.2, 15.7, color plates 7, 8, 9

Ikegami Electronics: 4.16

Lowel-Light Manufacturing, Inc.: 7.16, 7.17, 7.22, 7.25

Larry Mannheimer: 8.35, 12.18, 12.24

Mark IV Pro Audio Group: 8.24

Matthews Studio Equipment: 6.9

Miller Fluid Heads (USA), Inc.: 6.10

Mole-Richardson Co.: 7.14, 7.18, 7.20, 7.21, 7.23, 7.24

Nikon Inc./Ideas to Images: 4.7, 6.27

Panasonic Broadcast & Television Systems Co.: 4.11, 11.11

Professional Sound Corporation: 8.21

Steve Renick: 6.12, 6.13, 6.25, 6.28

Selco Products Company: 8.23

Sennheiser Electronic Corporation: 8.21

Shure Brothers Inc.: 8.21, 8.22

Sony Electronics, Inc.: 4.9, 8.21, 10.6

Stanton Video Services, Inc.: 6.21

Telex Communications, Inc.: 8.20

Vinten, Inc.: 6.11, 6.15, 6.17, 6.18

Alex Zettl: 9.9 (bottom)

Herbert Zettl: 4.2, 4.14, 4.19, 5.5, 5.6 (right), 5.17, 5.18, 5.20, 5.25, 5.26, 5.28, 5.29, 5.31, 5.32, 5.33, 6.1 (right), 7.1, 7.3, 7.4, 7.6, 7.7, 7.8, 7.9, 7.10, 7.11, 7.13, 7.26, 8.11, 8.12, 8.13, 8.30, 9.1, 9.8, 9.9 (top), 9.11, 9.14, 9.15, 9.16, 9.17, 11.5, 11.16, 11.20, 11.22, 12.8, 12.22, 12.26, 13.2, 13.3, 14.1, 14.3, 14.4, 14.6, 14.9, 14.10, 14.12, 14.16, 15.6

The storyboard (11.21) is courtesy of Bob and Sharon Forward